DATE DUE

OCT 27 '71			
DE 1 '71			
MAY 24 '72			
JUN 7 '72			
DE 17 '76			
AP 8 '85			

NORMAL
CHILDREN
AND MOTHERS

NORMAL CHILDREN AND MOTHERS

THEIR EMOTIONAL OPPORTUNITIES AND OBSTACLES

By Irving D. Harris, M. D.

ILLINOIS INSTITUTE FOR JUVENILE RESEARCH

THE FREE PRESS OF GLENCOE, ILLINOIS

To My Mother and Father

ACKNOWLEDGMENTS

THIS study and its report could not have been accomplished without the help of many persons. And for this help I am deeply appreciative.

I would like first to mention my great indebtedness to the four whose contributions and support were unique and indispensable. Mrs. Edith Morales, the social worker on the research team, provided the valuable data on mothers, assisted in setting up rating scales and gave a helpful critical reading of the manuscript. Dr Charlotte Altman, the psychologist on the research team, supplied additional data on the child through test administration and through categorization of the Rorschach responses.

Less directly connected with the study itself but of utmost help were Dr. Raymond Robertson and Mrs. Lilian Davis. Dr. Robertson, as superintendent of the Institute for Juvenile Research, provided the very necessary support and funds during the long period of data evaluation and writing. Mrs. Davis, librarian at the Institute, gave of herself unstintingly in the preparation of the manuscript. Her warmth, optimism, and loyalty were a buffer against the inevitable stresses and discouragements connected with writing a book.

My indebtedness is also keenly felt to the many others who contributed in one way or another. This study could not have been possible without the co-operation of the parents and children, the personnel of the four schools, and the Chicago Board of Education.

I should like also to extend my thanks to the following:

Dr. Sophie Schroeder Sloman, superintendent of the Institute in 1949, who gave initial approval for the study.

Dr. George Perkins a later superintendent, who facilitated certain aspects of the evaluation.

Mrs. Frances Perce, head of the department of psychology at the Institute, who helped considerably in the planning of the study, secured the co-operation of the schools and the Board of Education, and gave a critical reading of the manuscript.

Miss Merrie Anne Newman, who contributed to the readability of the book by her expert copy editing and suggestions.

A number of readers whose reactions and suggestions were quite helpful in the several revisions of the manuscript.

Helen Ross, Harry Kalven, Jr., Jerome Kavka, Maurice Rosenthal, Kirsen and Rita Weinberg, Joseph Kepecs, and Irene Gebauer.

Finally, I wish to express my appreciation to my wife and my children. Not only did they bear patiently with me, but they were my principal instructors as to the nature of mother-child relationships.

CONTENTS

OPPORTUNITIES FOR EMOTIONAL GROWTH

NORMAL
CHILDREN
AND MOTHERS

Children and Mothers

《《-《《-《《-《《-《《-《《-《《-《《-《《-《《-《《-《《-《《

WHAT

IS

NORMALITY?

ORIENTATION

AMONG the several themes and sub-themes running through this book, the reader will find that the most basic theme is that suggested by the *plural* terms in the title. The variety of human nature and the variety of solutions to growth problems are, we have found, too rich for one to speak in such singular, confining, and over-standardized terms as *"The* Normal Child," or *"The* Normal Mother." Full justice can be done to that richness only if we speak—as we will speak—of children and mothers, opportunities and obstacles.

But we have begun the book with a conclusion. To proceed more chronologically—our entry into the entire subject was stimulated by a question that at least intrigues and often torments parents as well as workers in the behavioral sciences—the question of "What is normal?" The nature of this question can perhaps be best appreciated if we view the diagnostic problems frequently encountered in a large child-guidance clinic such as the Illinois Institute for Juvenile Research.

The two following common examples would be helpful as a brief illustration of our work and problems. Mrs. A. applied for help with her son, Johnny, age eight, because she could not handle him. She stated that ever since she could remember he had been very rebellious, had temper tantrums, and had not made friends. The school reported that Johnny appeared isolated and peculiar, and displayed sudden outbursts of temper. The Rorschach test indicated that he had poor contact with reality. The psychiatrist found, in his interview with the boy, that he could not form a relationship with him and that he was quite withdrawn. The social worker characterized the mother as being rejecting, cold, and insensitive.

In the case of Johnny A., the diagnosis had been relatively simple. We definitely could say that he was at least very seriously disturbed if not psychotic. In all areas—home, school, clinical interview—the boy's behavior indicated considerable emotional disturbance. Furthermore, this disturbance was of a chronic nature and had not been stimulated by some recent external stress. Thinking along the lines of causation, we would have suspected that the mother's attitudes and feelings had much to do with his emotional disturbance. Our only problem would have been to determine whether the mother would be motivated and accessible for help or, if the mother could not be influenced toward a change for the better, whether we would have to recommend placement of the boy outside the home. Thus, while the problem of diagnosis had been a comparatively simple one, the therapeutic problem may have been quite difficult.

A contrasting example was the case of Tommy, also age eight. In her application, his mother stated that she could not handle him. She said that he was rebellious and unable to make friends, and that he had always behaved in this way. The school reported that Tommy was doing rather well in his studies but was not working up to full capacity, that he had a tendency to daydream and that he teased and interfered with other children, although for the most part he was capable of friendly relations with them. The interview with the psychiatrist revealed that Tommy was somewhat restless, easily distracted, and unorganized in his play with the toys, but likeable, and reaching out for friendship with the psychiatrist. He told the psychiatrist that he had dreams in which a gorilla was about to eat him. The psychologist found in the Rorschach test that although there was some evidence of anxiety and immaturity there were other evidences of personality strengths. The social worker characterized his mother as capable of warmth but inclined to be impatient and irritable when under stress—and then guilty about her anger. Tommy's mother told the social worker that his father considered him a normal boy, in fact, the father felt that he had been that way himself as a child.

The diagnosis in the case of Tommy was not simple. At the staff discussion of the clinical findings, interpretations probably would have differed. One worker might have maintained that Tommy essentially was not emotionally disturbed; that his behavior was just a reaction to his tense, impatient mother; that no treatment of the boy was necessary; and that all the situation required was some counselling of the mother to help her relieve her tension and correct her handling of the boy. Another worker might have pointed to the boy's daydreaming, his meddling with his classmates at school, his distraction in the psychiatric interview, his dreams of the gorilla, and the signs of anxiety and immaturity revealed on the Rorschach test, as indications of some definite emotional disturbance. This worker also would have felt that unless Tommy was treated immediately he would continue to have difficulties that might be intensified in puberty or adolescence. As a whole, the staff probably would have agreed that if the boy and the mother were treated at once, it would be a relatively simple case to handle, since both Tommy and his mother had a capacity and a desire to relate to others.

For every "open and shut" case such as Johnny's there has been a "neither here nor there" case such as Tommy's. It was the Tommys who stimulated our dissatisfaction with the present knowledge regarding normality and the dynamics of the age-span of six to eleven, since with the present status of this knowledge certain risks were inevitable. If we had erroneously diagnosed Tommy as normal, we had run the risk of failing to give help to a really disturbed boy. However, if we erroneously diagnosed him as definitely disturbed, we had run the risk of expending therapeutic skills on a child who did not need it and, therefore, since there are a limited number of therapists available, we would have deprived other more seriously disturbed children of our help. With a better knowledge of what is normal in the latency period, we could diagnose the child more adequately and prescribe for him and his family.

It was in such a setting of moderate dissatisfaction that a research team, composed of psychiatrist, psychologist, and social worker from the Institute for Juvenile Research, decided to embark on an exploratory study of normal children. In setting up the project there were several considerations. The prime one was the decision on where to obtain normal children. Of all the possible sources for such children, we thought the school would be the most likely and the most feasible. It was our feeling that if the teacher, principal, and adjustment teacher co-operated in selecting children who they thought were rather normal, then we would have a sample, although admittedly a rough one, from which to draw some conclusions and impressions. We were under no illusions that all the children recommended by the school personnel would be normal in the optimum sense of the word. We expected that out of this group some would be optimally adjusted and that possibly others would be maladjusted under a superficial facade of adjustment. Once having secured the children and the mothers, we gave them the same tests and interviews that emotionally disturbed children and their mothers receive at the clinic. The full details of our methodology can be found in Appendix D, *I. Methods of Study*.

The mention of our dissatisfaction with the present knowledge of normality does not mean that we were alone in our dissatisfaction. The relatively unexplored territory of the normal has brought the following questions insistently to the minds of theoreticians, clinicians, educators, and parents: Is there such a thing as normality? If there is, what are the signs of it? What are the causes of it?

Most of the emphasis in the attack on the mental health problem has been in the opposite direction. Such questions as the following have principally occupied us: What is abnormal? How can we diagnose emotional abnormality or disability in its beginning stages so that we can treat it more effectively? What are the causes of abnormality?

In recent years, however, the emphasis has begun to change. Workers in the behavioral sciences are becoming increasingly interested in normality, and the positive aspects of mental health, and in the conclusions that can be drawn for purposes of mental hygiene. Representative of this interest was the mid-century White House Conference of 1950 which included a symposium on the healthy personality.

There is no doubt but that the two emphases, the two directions of investigation are both necessary and intimately related. One cannot determine the extent of an individual's abnormality unless one knows what the normal individual is like. Similarly, one cannot determine the extent of a person's normality unless one has some understanding of the abnormal.

Even the psychoanalysts—investigators principally concerned with the abnormal—have been and are interested in the normality-abnormality question. That this question constituted an enigma for Sigmund Freud was indicated in one of his later writings. After commenting on the interesting question of why some children outgrow their childhood neurotic symptoms whereas others retain their neurosis, he wrote: "In other words, we find ourselves abruptly confronted once again by the oft repeated riddle, 'What is the source of neurosis, what is its ultimate, its specific underlying principle?' After decades of analytic effort this problem arises up before us as untouched as at the beginning."

Much more recently, Ernst Kris, a leading psychoanalytic theoretician, indicated the great value of studying normality.

How soon can we, from observational data, predict that pathology exists in a given child; how soon can we spot it from the child's behavior, from the child's family unit, or the history of mother and child? . . . Our criteria of diagnosis require constant refinements. . . . The self-healing qualities of further development are little known. . . . These and other questions not mentioned here are bound to direct us into an area which, never abandoned, has by necessity been left underdeveloped. This distressed area of psychoanalysis is the study of the normal and we are directed to it by many considerations . . . we are forced to postulate that psychoanalytic child psychology embraces the total field of normal development.

The purpose of this book, then, is to increase our growing understanding of what goes on in normal personality growth. Since comparatively little has been written about the age span of six through eleven—technically known as the latency period—a secondary purpose of this book is to add to the existing information about the emotional growth which occurs during this period.

The evidence and impressions that will be presented here are based primarily on an investigation of 54 boys and girls, ages eight and nine, and their mothers. These subjects were exposed to a variety of diagnostic tests and interviews. (Auxiliary data were provided by follow-up school reports four years later.) The data obtained by these methods were then evaluated by the case-study approach and by some quantitative procedures. Throughout the collection of the data and the subsequent evaluation of them, the predominant theoretical orientation was psychoanalytic. There was no attempt made during the investigation to test any particular hypothesis regarding normality. Rather, the study was conceived and conducted as a fact-finding exploration attempting to add to, and extend the boundaries of, the existing knowledge about normality and latency.

The reader may be puzzled at times by the use of the word "we" throughout the book. The word is used to convey several meanings: at times it refers to the editorial "we," at other times to the reader and the writer, and at still other times to the collaborative atmosphere that existed between the writer and the social worker, particularly during the phases of data collecting and data refinement. (The psychologist, due to other later commitments, was not able to participate fully in the evaluation of the data.) However, with the exception of certain conclusions concerning adjustment, the writer bears sole responsibility for the opinions expressed in this book.

The reader will also find that we occupy a mid-position so far as language, style, and methodology are concerned. A deliberate attempt has been made to keep professional psychiatric terminology at a minimum consistent with proper understanding. This has been done not only because all readers may not be familiar with the professional jargon but also because there is a certain point at which theoretical terminology ceases to be an aid and becomes instead an obstacle to new thinking.

Our methodology—observations of the subjects' behavior and detection of rough quantitative trends—can best be described as that used in naturalistic field observations. Thus, it will be most comfortable for those readers who are not overly predisposed to a deep investigation of a few cases (as occurs in psychoanalytic research) or a rigorous statistical treatment of many cases (as occurs, for example, in experimental psychology). While our original intention was toward a rigorous statistical treatment of the data, the variety and heterogeneity encountered in the children and mothers produced numerous small sub-groups that defied statistical handling.

It must be emphasized that the book deals as much with the mothers as it does with the children. We found it impossible to understand the child's behavior satisfactorily until we also understood *how* the mother handled the child and *why* she handled him in the way she did. The father, despite our title, has not been entirely neglected. Several chapters deal with his emotional contribution to the child (27 fathers were interviewed). However, the reader will find that in these chapters the main emphasis is on how the mother affects the relationship of the father to the child.

FIRST IMPRESSIONS

Once the data had been collected, our search for the manifestations and essences of normality met an intriguing barrier: the barrier of an immense and external variety. As will be shown, the variety extended in almost every possible direction. Not only were the current behavior and early development of one child different from the next; not only were the current mothering functions, adult behavior, and past history of one mother different from another, but also—and this was less expected—the judgments as to whether the child was really well adjusted showed much variation. If we had had to form an opinion about normality based solely on the exterior picture, we would have had to entertain the notion that there is not one kind of normality, but rather, 54 kinds; and if we had examined 73 children, there would be found 73 kinds of normality. Although we had not expected the children and mothers to be an entirely homogeneous group, the amount of heterogeneity we did encounter proved to be a formidable, diverting, and time-consuming obstacle in our search for the basic elements in optimum personality growth.

Some idea of the variety will be gained if we view the several areas more closely. The school personnel's opinion upon whose evaluation we had depended for selecting the children contained descriptions of the children that were quite varied. Although many children were described as being very well adjusted in all areas of school life, some were characterized as showing mild, symptomatic behavior (somewhat interfering with other children, not working up to mental capacity, etc.) and others were described as showing enough symptomatic behavior to be evaluated as only fairly well adjusted.

The psychiatrist found similar variations. Not only was there an expected wide range in their interests, fantasies, dreams, and play behavior, but also a somewhat unexpected variation in how they got along with the psychiatrist. Thus, some children were quite communicative, zestful, friendly, and trustful, while others were less so in these respects, and still others were obviously uncommunicative, inhibited, and uncomfortable with the psychiatrist.

A wide range also was seen in the mothers' descriptions of the children. Most relevant for our purposes was mother's idea about the adjustment of the child. The mothers' descriptions ranged from children presenting problem behavior both in the present and the past (with mother expressing surprise that the child had been selected for the study), to children presenting problem behavior either in the present or in the past, and, finally, to children who never showed any problem behavior.

The variations just described point up what difficulties we had with our first basic question, "What is the normal child like?" Our second basic question, "What made him that way?" met up with similar difficulty. When we looked at his past development as a clue to his present adjustment, we discovered from the mother that some children were fretful rather than contented during infancy; some had trouble in learning bladder, bowel control; while others sailed through this learning phase without any difficulty. Also, some showed considerable sexual activity in the form of sexual curiosity and masturbation, while others showed no sexual activity at all.

Going a step further we again met an impasse. The family life in general and the mother's in particular could not be reduced, at least superficially, to one common pattern. Some families were characterized by affectionate harmony between the parents, by wholesome interest in the children, while others (the minority) could be described as having an atmosphere of chronic moderate strife and alienation with a modicum of sustained interest in the children. The mothers themselves showed a wide range extending from being warm and understanding in their mothering functions, secure and confident in their adult role, having affectionate ties to their own parents, to being cold and controlled in their mothering function, anxious and inadequate in their roles as adults, and having few affectionate feelings for their own parents.

We would like to demonstrate in a more concrete way the range of phenomena that we encountered. In the following pages there are a number of examples taken from the actual case data. The language style is somewhat crude inasmuch as the examples represent observational notes containing the colloquialisms of child and mother. The examples are arranged under several headings—each heading representing a certain segment of the life of the child. Under each heading there are two examples that are calculated to demonstrate the wide range of phenomena. The first examples are the more "normal" ones, although here and there mild symptoms of disturbed behavior can be seen. The second examples are the seemingly "abnormal" ones, the kinds of symptoms one might expect to find in actually disturbed children.

It must be emphasized that each of the child-mother psychological pictures was made up of examples of the first type *and* examples of the second type. In other words, we found no child and mother who in *every* area showed only phenomena of the first type. *What we did find in each case was an admixture of "normal" and "abnormal" phenomena.*

CHILD'S BEHAVIOR
IN THE PSYCHIATRIC INTERVIEW

Example 1.

Susan was a neatly dressed, rather attractive, large, nine-year-old. Upon first meeting the psychiatrist she showed a mild, transitory shyness, but then became quite at ease. Although she was not forward, she was quite free when the situation indicated it. She was quite spontaneous throughout the interview, and would comment to the psychiatrist about things that came to her mind. These comments were never irrelevant, but had some bearing on the discussion of things she saw around the room. Susan's comments were characterized by a well balanced outlook. She had much zest and spontaneity, yet she was not unreasonable in her outlook.

Example 2.

Barbara was an unattractive, mildly plump girl with an adenoidal expression. She was quite devoid of spontaneity and was difficult to arouse to any activity. There was little pep or enthusiasm. Either she was quite serious or she was uneasy with authority. She did not respond to the initial small-talk and although quite co-operative, she rarely amplified her statements. In the middle of the interview, after working with the clay, she had opened up a little and had shown a mild zest. However, when she was asked fantasy questions such as what three wishes she would like, she would pause seriously and say, "I don't know." Even when she had been urged she would say, "I can't think of anything right now."

CHILD'S PLAY

Example 1.

When the toy box was indicated Fred quickly went to it and picked up the gun, then put it down; found the clay and said, "Oh boy," and began to fashion the clay. While doing this he said, "I wonder what mama is doing now. She is probably reading a book." He went to the toy box and picked out a car and said he thought he would make a clay garage for the car. Then he seized the dolls, set up the mother and father dolls, then picked up the brother and sister dolls, put them near the edge of the desk and said, "Oh, they are going over the edge of the cliff." He went back to the clay and after a minute of modeling the clay he returned to the dolls. He gave the sister doll a swat on the rear because she wouldn't sit up straight. He put the brother doll safely to one side and aimed rubber bands at the sister doll. Then he shot the father doll and had the boy doll fall over the edge of the cliff.

Example 2.

When the toy-box was indicated, Harold went over to it eagerly and then told the psychiatrist that he had many trucks like these at home. He kept his hands in his pockets and when asked why he didn't play with the toys, he said the reason was that he liked to have his own little houses with him and that he had a certain box which he used and he didn't like to play with what we had here. Efforts to get Harold to play were unsuccessful.

SCHOOL REPORT

Example 1.

Carl is considered very well adjusted. He is very co-operative with the teacher and the school regulations. He is friendly toward the teacher, mixes well with other children, is usually a follower, and his mood is appropriately serious or carefree depending upon the situation. He has no nervous habits; there have been no complaints from his parents; and his work is up to capacity.

Example 2.

William is considered to be only fairly well adjusted. He is average in his co-operation with the school regulations and with the teachers and authority. He is distant toward the teacher. He mixes well with his classmates. He leads or follows, depending on the situation. He is usually of a serious mood. He has some nervous habits and there have been some complaints from the parents about the child. He is not working up to capacity.

MOTHER'S DESCRIPTION
OF CHILD'S BEHAVIOR AND PROBLEMS

Example 1.

Mother said she was not too surprised that her boy was selected as one of the well-adjusted children, because she thinks Joe is a very normal boy. He likes and does not like school, but mother has noticed that he does his homework studiously without having to be told. Joe does not care for dressing up but likes sports and Boy Scouts. He has a definite dislike for girls and plays with boys of his own age or slightly younger. He behaves well and likes to do things well, sometimes getting upset if things are not perfect. He cries when he is really upset and this is apt to occur when he cannot get the better of his sister. Mother tells him that crying is not man-like, and that is why his sister teases him. When Joe is angry—but this is not often—he is likely to do most anything. According to his mother he will slam things around or burst into tears. He gets angry if anyone is insincere because he likes people to accept their responsibilities. Mother imagines he has been angry with her and his father, but she supposes he gets over this. She would feel uneasy if he did not get angry because she knows everyone has his likes and dislikes, but she would disapprove if he had a complete temper tantrum. He is more calm than his sister, who is more imaginative. His sister lives in a dream world, but Joe is better able to concentrate. A younger brother is more highly strung, sensitive to unusual noises, and has to be handled quite differently. Mother does not think that Joe is a problem now, and she does not think he was much of a problem in his earlier years. She considers him better adjusted than his siblings.

Example 2.

Mother thought that George was not as well adjusted as his siblings. She was surprised at the referral. She knew he got along in school, but when the parents got the letter about the study, they had looked at each other and had said: "Well, maybe he isn't so bad after all." She has had several problems earlier with George. For a couple of months when he was four years old he bit people, including his parents. Mother had handled this by saying a prayer before they went anywhere, but another woman finally cured George by biting him back. Mother could not have done this herself because George knew he could get away with this with her. When he first started school, he had done all right, but when he had a teacher who was rather stern with him he suddenly had not wanted to go back to school and he had become shy and afraid to do things. When he had changed schools, his nervousness had stopped. George still becomes sick, turns white, and faints or wants to throw up, if there is illness or sorrow in the family. He is very sorry if anything sad happens. He will faint at the sight of blood. Mother was not overly concerned about these problems when they occurred, but she did ask the psychiatrist about George being obstinate sometimes with the parents. He will not always listen and acts as though he did not care what they say or do. Mother wondered if he would outgrow this. He is very lively and at home he usually has the house in an uproar, but he is very well behaved when they are out with other people. Other people like George and trust him with their children more than any other child in the neighborhood. He likes to protect others. When he gets angry he shouts at his mother, but not at his father. He never curses but may say, "Boo!" or "Nuts!" and may throw things. He talks over his troubles with his parents and tells his mother everything, and then wants her to tell his father, but his father loves to have George talk to him. (See Appendix D, 2. Other Sample Behaviors of Children and Mothers.)

Because of this variety, we were led to the conclusion that our study group was not homogeneous, that it did not occupy a discrete, narrow band at the upper end of the so-called abnormal-normal continuum. This conclusion was reinforced when we compared our entire study group with emotionally disturbed children and their mothers seen at the Institute for Juvenile Research. In general, it could be said that our study children were not too different from the mildly disturbed "neither here nor there" cases that had originally prompted our investigation. Thus, as did many of our study children, so did many of the mildly disturbed clinic children get along well with the psychiatrist, or were no problem in the school, or had an uneventful early development.

The problems that many of our study mothers complained of in their children were at least in type very similar to, if not identical with, those mentioned by mothers of clinic children. Thus, disobedience, temper display, shyness, thumb-sucking, stubbornness, crying easily, fear of being separated from the mother, reluctance to go to school were some of the problems mentioned as occurring at the ages of eight and nine. The pre-school problems—toilet training difficulties, over-aggressive play, sibling rivalry, etc., were also non-distinguishable from those problems of the clinic children.

Realizing now that our study group was quite heterogeneous, we embarked on the task of separating the better-adjusted children from the less well-adjusted children. Our questions now were: "How well adjusted is the child?" "How well is he getting along?" For answers to these questions we relied on three judges of the child's adjustment. The three judges were the school, the psychiatrist, and the mother, all of whom had first-hand contact with the child. It was possible to devise a 3-point scale so that in the school area, in the psychiatric interview, and in the family life, the appropriate judge could rate the child as being very well adjusted, well adjusted, fairly well adjusted. Those procedures are later described in full in the appendixes.

We had hoped that these rating procedures would produce three discrete groups, ranging down from very well adjusted to fairly well adjusted. This, however, was not to be the case. The three judges varied in their evaluation of the same child—the closest agreement being between the school and the psychiatrist; the greatest disagreement being between the school and the mother, and between the psychiatrist and the mother. Rather than conclude that none of the judges was correct in his evaluation, we felt that each judge was evaluating a particular facet of the child's adjustment. Thus, the school personnel were in a better position to evaluate how the child got along in a group situation in which there was an authority figure and a learning task. The psychiatrist was in a better position to evaluate how the child got along in a one-to-one situation with a strange adult. The mother had the advantage of seeing how the child adjusted to the family life.

It is perhaps better appreciated now to what extent variety (not only as to the case data, but also as to adjustment evaluations) was the keynote of our first impressions as we viewed the exteriors of normality. A final note should be added in this connection. We found the adjustments at ages eight and nine to be quite useful in understanding certain aspects of normality. In fact, the emerging formulations seemed worth while enough that a final report of the study was considered feasible. However, four years later our formulations appeared less neat to us when we received follow-up reports from the schools, the children now being 12 and 13.

While some of the children persisted in the same adjustment evaluation (very well adjusted in latency *and* in puberty, or only fairly well adjusted both in latency *and* in puberty) the majority of children showed variations in adjustment (very well adjusted in latency, and only fairly well adjusted in puberty or only fairly well adjusted in latency and very well adjusted in puberty. Although we were tempted to dismiss these follow-up reports on the basis that there were now different school teachers and that the children and mothers were not directly re-interviewed, our re-examination of the data led us ultimately to the idea that there are different factors influencing latency adjustment as opposed to puberty adjustment.

In spite of the great variety, did the research team eventually arrive at any general conclusions? It is noteworthy that each of the three team members working independently on portions of the same data and using his or her particular techniques was agreed on one point, namely, *the normality or adaptability of the child seems to be intimately related to the emotional maturation of the mother.* The psychiatrist principally focusing on the behavioral adjustment of the child outside the family, the psychologist centering on the child's performance on the Rorschach Test, the social worker focusing mostly on the child's behavior within the family—all were impressed by how the child's adjustability is influenced by the kind of mother and woman the mother is.

This conclusion is of course not new. It has been known to clinicians and theorists for a long time, and also to the general laity as evidenced by the folk adage, "The apple falls, not far from the tree." Although it was worth while for us to confirm this hypothesis by a study of so-called "normal" material, we were still comparatively in the dark about the phenomenon of normality. In a way we had disposed of the child's normality by pointing to the mother's normality or maturity. But how did the mother acquire her maturity? How did she acquire the self-confidence and ability to correct mistakes that the social worker found? What accounted for the general contentment that the psychologist found to be correlated with the child's personality strengths on the Rorschach? How did the child acquire or fail to acquire these assets from the mother? And how was it possible for this elusive inner maturity to manifest itself in such a variety of exterior pictures?

These were the questions that still remained. They provided the basic queries weaving themselves in and out of this book. They have theoretical implications concerning normality, growth, and maturation—implications that influenced the manner in which we collected our data, and the manner in which we tried to understand the data. It is time, perhaps, that we give some attention to the theoretical considerations.

THEORETICAL CONCEPTS

We might first inquire "What sort of research and theorizing have already been done in the area of normality and adjustment?" In general, there have been two types of endeavor—one concerned with the study of normal subjects, the other with the study of abnormal subjects. Thus, psychologists, in standardizing their intelligence and personality tests, have been occupied for some time with normal subjects. However, the carry-over of their test impressions to actual behavior has been only partially successful. Studies by psychologists of actual normal behavior have been of comparatively recent origin. An important contribution of this nature has been made by Jean Macfarlane of California in her book *Study of Personality Development,* which reports a longitudinal study of average children from infancy through adolescence. (Similar types of study are being conducted in Denver by a psychiatrist, John Benjamin, and his co-workers, and by a group at Yale.) Among Macfarlane's contributions to our understanding, is the important one that all children, in their growing up, manifested at some time or other behavior usually categorized as problem behavior. We are also indebted to the workers at Fels Institute for their contribution in research methods in the study of normal behavior in children and mothers.

The other type of effort has been a speculation about, rather than work on, normals. This has been done by those who have made deductions from their study of the abnormal, the psychopathological, and the emotionally disturbed. That they have made deductions from the abnormal material rather than inductions from normal material does not invalidate their work. On the contrary, the most useful and valuable theoretical guiding lines in understanding the normal have been provided by those dealing with the psychopathological.

Although philosophers have for ages been preoccupied with what is the "good" or normal life, we believe we are most indebted for our theoretical understanding of normality to Freud and his pioneer work in psychoanalysis. His heritage to us has been some permanent insights, well tested and validated by his own clinical work and that of some of his successors, and also some theoretical suggestions and concepts that have not attained the same status of validation and that have been springboards for competing schools of thought. At present we need not be concerned with more than a mention of this state of affairs, although later, in the body of the book, pertinent theoretical concepts will be discussed.

Psychoanalytic theory, stripped to its barest essentials, holds that personality growth proceeds from the simple and undifferentiated to the complex and differentiated. Beginning with the unorganized impulses of the infant, there is a gradual acquisition of regulators. It is the regulation of the energy derived from the impulses that enables the growing child to select and carry out appropriate solutions to life's problems. Some of the regulators come from within the child. Thus the ability to co-ordinate walking, talking, and thinking impulses, and his sexual behavior depend on the maturation of internal biologic mechanisms. Other regulators come from outside the child and are later taken over by the child and made his own. Thus such regulating and organizing mechanisms as his conscience, his aspirations, and his ways of doing things and dealing with people are principally derived from his family.

In the course of acquiring regulators, the infant or small child passes through different developmental stages. What is important for our purposes here is the concept that growth from one developmental stage to another is impeded when there is a fixation at an earlier developmental stage. The fixation can result from undue frustration or undue satisfaction of the emotional or psychic needs characteristic of this particular developmental stage or from a confusing alternation of frustration and satisfaction. These undue stresses produce great anxiety in the child that, in turn, forces him rigidly to adopt certain methods like aggression or timidity in coping with all situations.

An example of fixation may be seen in the early dependency stage where the infant's needs are mainly centered around his being fed and being handled lovingly. Undue frustration in the form of an unresponsive, non-feeding coldness on the part of the mother, or undue satisfaction in the form of the clinging mother's reluctance to wean the infant from her at the proper time, can produce a fixation at this oral, dependent stage. Whenever there are such fixations, such inflexibilities, the psychic organism is comparatively held back in its normal growth. Even if the child with such fixations gives an outward appearance of having grown normally, he will go back or regress to a more immature developmental stage if he is confronted with comparatively minor stress.

This concept, that emotional growth takes place by stages and is impeded by fixation points, is generally accepted by all schools of psychoanalysis. However, what goes on in these stages, or what they should be called has long been a subject for inquiry and debate. The particular description and designation appear to depend on what is the primary focus of the theoretician. Thus, the orthodox Freudians following Freud, stress the inner instinctual growth; the neo-Freudians, such as Harry Stack Sullivan, stress the impact of the social environment; others like Erik Erikson take a mid-position and try to account for both types of growth phenomena.

If we now turn to the personality as it is and not to its developmental antecedents, we find that theoreticians as well as clinicians are faced with an exceedingly difficult problem. This problem consists of determining the crucial criteria that will decide whether or not the person functioning before us is normal. The recognition that emotional growth has been temporarily or permanently stunted is more easily accomplished when viewing seriously disturbed persons, especially adults whom we expect to have grown up through the years. It is more difficult to recognize this in adults under stress and adults from different cultures; in adolescents for whom intense and conflicting emotions are almost natural; and in children who typically show transient problem behavior in the fluidity of the growth process.

A major contribution toward this subject was made by Ernest Jones who said that a general definition of normality falls into two classes: (a) the criterion of happiness, and (b) the adaptation to reality. Of the first criterion, happiness, he says that it is valid, but difficult to employ empirically because different philosophies to life make the judgment of happiness quite subjective. Such questions as these might occur: Is it better to be optimistic or pessimistic? Is it better to endure life or enjoy it? He says of the second criterion that this adaptation to reality does not necessarily imply rigid acceptance of the environmental standards, but rather a sensitive perception of them and their social significance when deciding upon a course of conduct, or estimating the impression that the responses of other people will make. His final statement and summary is that: "The psychological problem of normality resides in the capacity to endure and the ability to hold wishes in suspension without either renouncing them or reacting to them in a defensive way. Thus fearlessness is the nearest criterion of normality."

Lawrence Kubie, another psychoanalytic contributor to the problem of normality, has postulated that the essential characteristic of neurotic behavior is its stereotyped inflexibility, with the consequent corollary that normality is characterized by spontaneity and creativity. Kubie attributes the differences between these two types of behavior to the locus of the impulse activating the behavior. If the mainspring of the behavioral act is in the repressed unconscious, that is, in the area of the human psyche which we cannot reach by introspection or confrontation, then the behavior will be stereotyped, repetitive, not subject to the conscious will, in short, neurotic. If the mainspring is in the more conscious realms of the psyche, the behavioral act is more subject to modification, since the motive for the act can be reached through introspection by the person involved or by confrontation by others in relationship to him.

There is one more contribution to be considered—that dealing with the unity of the inner personality, or the absence of inner conflict. Freud put it in terms of a harmonious interaction between the energy providing id and the regulators such as the superego and the ego ideal. Later theoreticians, psychoanalytic and other, have been much attracted to the criterion of absence of inner conflict as distinguishing the emotionally healthy from the emotionally unhealthy. Thus Heinz Hartmann writes of "the growing independence from the outside world, in so far as a process of inner regulation replaces the reaction and actions due to a fear of the social environment." Gardner Murphy emphasizes the subjective feeling achieved by the unity of the personality, ". . . a sense of identity, continuity, distinctiveness." Erik Erikson speaks of this concept in terms of an ego identity, which is ". . . the inner capital accrued from all experiences of each successive [growth] stage . . . . [It] gives the accrued confidence that one's ability to maintain inner sameness and continuity (one's ego in the psychological sense) is matched by the sameness and continuity of one's meaning for others."

These, then, in terms that run the risk of oversimplification are the principal psychoanalytic contribution to the subject of normality. They, together with certain contributions made by workers in psychology, anthropology, sociology, and other branches of the behavioral sciences, provided a theoretical climate for us as we collected and later tried to understand the data. These theoretical concepts will be referred to and amplified in later sections of this book.

Our main working tool, however, was the concept of behavior adjustment. We chose it for several reasons. One was that our later theorizing would have a solid foundation, supplied by observing actual behavior. Also, we believed that, in the sense we used it, adjustment was a creative, dynamic phenomenon rather than a means for merely getting along with the environment at the expense of personal growth. For we had asked our judges to tell us not only how well the child was adapting to the environment, but also how happy, zestful and vigourous he was. As we shall begin to see in the next chapter, the child's adjustment can be lively and dynamic, rather than monotonous and static.

CHAPTER II

THE CHILD
AT EIGHT
AND NINE

This chapter, like the previous one, is somewhat general in nature. We are not yet ready to describe the child in flesh and blood terms. Before doing so, we must address ourselves to theories about this particular age period. Where, in the last chapter, we considered normality in general, here we will attempt to find out what is theoretically normal for the latency period. Furthermore, we shall offer evidence bearing on a most crucial theoretical question, namely, "how civilized should the latency period child be?"

What is a child at eight and nine like, and what is going on within him? He has been described in various ways. Shakespeare, it will be recalled, spoke of the reluctant schoolboy, Freud of the latency child, and Sullivan of the juvenile. Notwithstanding the different descriptions, there is general agreement that the child of this age is predominantly engaged with affairs outside his immediate family; that the growth task confronting him is a successful adjustment to, and a mastery of, things and people in his social environment. The "things" refers mostly to learning and school; the "people" mostly to his peers and his teachers.

There is, however, no general agreement as to what goes on in the child and what enables him to make a successful adjustment. Observers do agree that in many cultures, ours included, a growing child gets over many of his infantile turbulent tendencies by the age of six, then goes through several years in which he appears and acts more or less civilized, and then at the age of twelve or thereabouts, he again enters a phase of turbulence and stress which begins to level off around the ages eighteen to twenty-one. Although there is agreement that the eight- and nine-year-old is comparatively civilized, there is disagreement as to how civilized he is and what accounts for the civilized behavior.

Shakespeare, for example, indicated the thinness of the civilized surface when he pointed up the reluctance of the schoolboy to put away carefree childish pleasures and to address himself to the serious job of learning. The very orthodox Freudian view highlights the immunity of the civilized surface to disintegration. This immunity is accomplished by a decline in the intensity of the biologic-sexual impulses—impulses that, with their tendency to create strong feelings of love and hate, produce emotional turbulence. The quiescence of these impulses—their latency—no longer obtains at the next growth state, puberty.

Illustrating this position is Anna Freud's statement: "The latency period sets in with a physiological decline in the strength of the instincts and a truce is called in the defensive warfare waged by the ego. It now has leisure to devote itself to other tasks . . . . It becomes stronger in relation to the outside world." (Later psychoanalytic writers on the subject, among them E. Sterba, and H. Deutsch believe, however, that the instinctual decline is more relative than absolute.)

The neo-Freudian viewpoint, as upheld by Harry Stack Sullivan, Clara Thompson, and others, is somewhat different. The civilizing, socializing aspect is emphasized and the instinctual pressure is de-emphasized. Sullivan, who calls this age-span the "juvenile era" writes, "It is the actual time for being social. . . . This is the first developmental stage in which the limitations and peculiarities of the home as a socializing influence begins to be open to remedy." Thompson believes that the apparent dormancy and latency of sexual life are a result of the child's sexual interest being disapproved of and of the enlarging world absorbing his interest.

It is, however, one of Erikson's concepts that closely resembled the viewpoint we gained in these matters. He emphasized that each current growth stage contains the integrated elements of the previous growth stage and also the embryonic elements of the next growth stage. The connection of each growth stage with its predecessor and successor provides the continuity necessary for eventual maturation.

The evidence we gathered on the subject appeared to confirm Erikson's concept. We were attracted to the view that, apart from the particular task of this age period (e.g., learning), it had the general task of providing continuity. If the child is father to the man, then the preschooler is father to the latency child, and the latency child is father to the puberty child. Thus, the latency child may be both a thinly disguised preschooler (corresponding with Shakespeare's idea) and an embryonic pubertal child.

Our findings, which will be reported shortly, led us then to the notion that the latency period has two general tasks. The first task is the opening up to and the mastering of the new extra-familial, social, and learning situations. The successful performance of this task we found to be dependent on the child's heritage from his earlier experience, on a psychological readiness of the child to open up, on a tendency not to be an "outcast at life's feast." The second task pertained not to the latency period per se, but rather to the period following—the pubertal phase. This task consists in maintaining sufficient liveliness of the impulses during the latency period so that there is not a sharp break in the continuity between the lively preschooler and the surgent pubertal child.

To understand what is going on in the optimally adjusted latency child, we resorted to our ratings of behavioral adjustment. It will be recalled that from three judges—the school personnel, the psychiatrist, and the mother—ratings were obtained as to the child's adjustment. These were three-point ratings in each adjustment area, the school, the psychiatric interview, and the family. They ranged from very well adjusted through well adjusted to fairly well adjusted. Because there was a rather close agreement between the school personnel and the psychiatrist, a combining of the two ratings was made to indicate adjustment outside the family, and this was designated the "combined social adjustment."

As we indicated earlier, the mother's impressions as to whether or not her child had adjustment problems was frequently at sharp variance with the impressions of the school personnel and the psychiatrist. Her subjectivity, her personal involvement with the child, her need to prove her adequacy as a mother, and her relative lack of opportunity to compare her child with many other children—all these factors combined to prevent her from being as objective an evaluator of adjustment as were the school and the psychiatrist. Not only were the latter more likely to be objective, not only did they agree in 80 per cent of the cases, but also they were in a better position to view the socializing segment of the child's behavior. It is this segment as represented in adjustment outside the family that is quite pertinent to the topic of normal latency.

The combined social adjustment ratings were also placed on a three-point scale: very well adjusted, 25 children; well adjusted, 11 children; fairly well adjusted, 18 children. In our next step we tried to find a clear relationship between these rating groups and any of the 400 odd items that had been gathered from the psychiatric interview, from the child's current behavior or past development as reported by the mother, and from the Rorschach and Despert Fable Tests. We found many relationships of a type which we called non-crucial. By this we mean that there was no straight-line increase or decrease of symptoms or phenomena as we pass from very well adjusted through well adjusted to fairly well adjusted.

It might be of interest to note what was not crucially related: Was there any crucial relationship of adjustment to whether the child played with the toy material offered in the psychiatric interview? No. To whether the child reported anxiety dreams? No. To a high percentage of good form responses on the Rorschach Test? No. To whether there were difficulties in toilet training? No.

However, we did obtain six items that crucially differentiated the fairly well adjusted from the well adjusted and from the very well adjusted (and which held true for girls as well as boys.) (See Appendix E, Table 6.)

The *six crucial items that distinguished the fairly well-adjusted group* were: (1) Mother rarely reported that the child was difficult to wean. (2) Mother rarely reported rivalry in the child with another sibling. (3) On one Despert Fable which involved a question of whether the young calf will, at his mother's request, go out and eat grass (rather than stay close to the pleasurable milk) these children characteristically said that the calf left the mother cow and ate the impersonal grass. (4) On another Despert Fable involving the question of who gets hurt most when the little dog bites others in the family, the characteristic response was, "The little dog himself." (5) In the psychiatric interview these children rarely related the emotional feelings of sadness or worry to the social scene, i.e., they felt sad because they had lost a toy or had seen a sad picture (not because they were lonely); they worried because robbers might come in at night or because their fathers might get hurt in an accident (not because they might lose favor or approval from the school teacher or from the group). (6) In the play during the psychiatric interview, raw hostility was characteristically evident: they knocked down the dolls or they had the father doll strike the mother doll instead of making figures out of clay or arranging a more peaceful domestic scene.

We were somewhat surprised to find that the first four items were of crucial significance. According to an ultra conventional view of latency, the child, in seriously pursuing his task of learning, should resemble a miniature civilized adult. And according to this view, it would be the very well adjusted child rather than the fairly well adjusted child who would be easily weaned, non-rivalrous, conforming to mother's wishes, and realistic enough to know that aggressive biting will boomerang on the biter.

But if we view the latency adjustment as optimal only when it contains evidences of the preceding growth stage, then these four items should not surprise anyone, for there is no evidence of the turbulent, pleasure seeking, preschooler in these items. A vital something is missing—a vigorous aggressiveness has been put down. As to where this aggressiveness has gone, the last two items may yield a clue in their undertones of morbid destructiveness.

In trying speculatively to account for all six items on the basis of one principle, it seemed to us that all these items could be indicative of a certain type of experience during the early dependency of the child, a period in which the mode of relating to the mothers (the first human object) is predominantly by means of oral experiences. The mother can be the source of nutriment and pleasure for the infant as he feeds, but she can also be the source of pain, tension, and frustration. If she is a source of pleasure, then the growing child will look upon other and later humans as gratifiers; if she is a source of pain and tension, the growing child will react to others and to later humans as frustrating.

Thus in accounting for the six diagnostic items we might speculate that due to exposure to a mother who was inwardly inflexible and frustrating, the usual pleasurable feeding experience becomes unpleasant or dangerous and the infant is eager to give up that experience (easily weaned, gives up milk for grass). A clue as to why it is dangerous may be that the infant who was frustrated in feeding gets a natural impulse to bite and he becomes afraid that he himself will be destroyed if he bites (the one hurt most was the little dog that bites). In other words, he avoids the object that gratifies his hunger because he is afraid that his own biting impulse (aroused by being too hungry) will destroy him. This avoidance of a potentially gratifying object probably accounts for the lessened sibling rivalry. The mother, whose affection is usually fought over as desirable, is now regarded as a dangerous object because she might arouse in the child a self-demolishing, destructive, biting impulse.

There are still two more factors in the child for which we have not accounted: the raw, hostile play and the non-socialized feelings. It is possible that in the play the child was trying to ventilate and work through his destructive feelings toward people who are imprisoning and constricting. That his feelings are infrequently stimulated by the possible loss of social companionship or approbation would be understandable according to the following explanation. Any direct human contact where one may obtain pleasure and frustration is dangerous. There are two possible alternatives: (1) a retreat into one's self, where one is sad and worried if one's personal possessions or parts of the self are lost, and (2) a retreat into a lofty altruism where one, by loving all humans, can guard against the frustration entailed in loving and losing a single person. This solution is contained in the well-known description of the crusader who loved humanity but not his fellowman.

Thus, the six diagnostic items concerning the child would appear to be explainable on the basis that the child, from earliest infancy, had been exposed to a rigid, inflexible, anti-growth mother. (Evidence regarding the mothers will be described in later chapters.) It would seem that his early life experience instructed him that full interaction with other human beings carried much more potentiality for pain and frustration that it did for pleasurable gratification. This being the case, an interpersonal situation, carrying the prospect of pleasure, would be dangerous rather than attractive. It would be dangerous because he would be exposed to all the aches and pains attendant upon the frustration of his pleasure wish. Rather than moving forward to taste of pleasure he would be much safer if he withdrew in some way from the expected pain. Consequently, in extreme cases he will withdraw from all interpersonal contacts, or in milder cases he will protect himself while interacting with others. Since a full human object calls into play the dangerous love and hate impulses, it is safer to deal with the partial object, be that partial object the shoe of the beloved person, the genitals of that person, money, humanity or one's own self and body.

The foregoing evidence and speculations represent the basis for our surmise that the child's present orientation to the social scene outside the family is based on his past orientation to the original and earliest "outside" namely, the mother. What accounts for the child not fully participating in and partaking of the outside world is an inner orientation that a pleasurable tasting and mastery of new people and things will be attended by pain and frustration. If our combined social adjustment rating is valid, we can postulate that the most normal latency child is one who is most free and secure about approaching the outside world.

So much for the continuity between the latency child and his previous out-going pre-schooler self . . . and so much for how it helps the child during latency. But how is this child preparing for puberty, the next stage of development. Here, there will not be the protected atmosphere of the latency period where learning is the main task. Instead there will be an unprotected atmosphere—sexual and aggressive impulses will be on the rise—the child will be getting used to the fact that eventually he will become a responsible and mating adult. What equipment should he have during the latency period that will prepare him for the stormy pubertal and adolescent periods?

To shed some light on this matter, we decided to investigate the nature of the sexual and aggressive impulses at ages eight and nine. The child would have to cope with these impulses at twelve and thirteen. Would he have an easier time of it at twelve and thirteen (as indicated by our follow-up reports) if at eight and nine these impulses were very dormant? Or an easier time, if at eight and nine these impulses were lively and somewhat noticeable in his behavior?

To answer this question we used as indicators of erotic and aggressive impulses: sexual curiosity and sibling rivalry. Was the child currently or just recently asking questions about birth or sexual differences? Was he occasionally quarrelsome and jealous toward his brother or sister?

We used these indicators, which were obtained from the mother's report on the child, to arrange the children in an ascending series: (a) neither sexual curiosity nor sibling rivalry was present; (b) sexual curiosity *or* sibling rivalry was present; (c) sexual curiosity *and* sibling rivalry were present. The major trend that we observed through studying these series was that while there was little difference in the adjustment scores of these three groups at eight and nine, there was a steady increase of favorable puberty follow-up reports with an increase of liveliness. Thus, of the children who showed neither of the two lively impulses, only 33 per cent had favorable puberty reports. Of the children who manifested one or the other lively impulse, 58 per cent of them had such reports. And of the children who showed both lively impulses in the behavior at eight and nine, 75 per cent had good reports at twelve and thirteen.

We had mixed reactions to this trend. On the one hand it was enlightening how latent or quiescent the latency period should *not* be, but on the other hand, it did not square with our clinical experience about the possible dangers of over-liveliness. We were enlightened by finding that a really quiescent latency, while not appreciably affecting the current adjustment at eight and nine, would be poor preparation for adjustment at puberty. The trend cast considerable doubt on the validity of a very literal definition of the normal latency period as a period in which nothing is going on in the way of lively impulse behavior. Instead, the best latency period in terms of preparation for adjustment at puberty, would seem to be in the nature of semi-latency, i.e., a time during which the lively impulses were still finding occasional behavioral expression.

The benefits of a semi-latency as opposed to a total latency period could be seen from two viewpoints: one was concerned with energy, the other was concerned with behavioral know-how. If the child's impulse life has been stifled considerably at the age of eight and nine, he cannot readily draw upon it for the quantity of energy needed when he faces his new maturational tasks at twelve and thirteen. The child of eight who has been overly controlled or discouraged regarding behavior that involves sexual curiosity or rivalry will be ill prepared at twelve for situations that stimulate his sexual curiosity and rivalry. If a boy at puberty is uncomfortable about sexual curiosity, he would be ill-at-ease if this impulse impelled him toward an attractive girl. If he is uncomfortable about rivalrous competitive situations, he would be anxious in handling the inevitable rivalry he would encounter from the other boys who may be seeking the same girl.

The essence of our comments regarding the latency and puberty data has been that a continuity between successive growth stages is necessary for good adjustment. *From this concept might issue two criteria for optimum normality in the latency period: (1) a psychological readiness (based on previous experience) to open up to the environment outside the family; and (2) an active impulse life which prepares the child for the impulse storms at puberty.*

Now it is true that the continuity we have been describing is mostly that concerned with the lively, pleasure seeking, aggressive aspects of the psyche. These aspects—derived from the energy providing and pleasure seeking id—are concerned with one half of adjustment: the enjoyment of life. They are aspects that we would like to consolidate along with a need for variety, challenge, spice, etc., under a general category: the *change* factors. But by themselves they do not account for the totality of adjustment. What, we may ask, prevents this lively *change* side from usurping the whole personality and from making these children perpetual, restless, little savages?

It is obvious that so far we have not taken into account the regulative, conservative, anti-change aspects of the child's personality—aspects that we would like to consolidate under a general category: the *permanence* factors.. By considering the mother as we shall do now, the workings of the regulating, *permanence* factors, and their integration with the *change* factors will become more apparent.

CHAPTER III

THE FUNCTIONS
OF THE MOTHER

THE CHILD'S efforts toward integration and continuity are bound to be influenced by the mother inasmuch as she constitutes his first emotional milieu. The effect for better or worse of the mother on the child's adjustment was strikingly indicated in our study group. It was the one conclusion, it will be recalled, that all three members of the research team arrived at separately and independently.

When we speak, however, of the effect of the mother, we need to be quite specific. Do we mean the effect of her mothering functions (the way in which she directly handles the child in terms of care and guidance), or the effect of her adult personality status (whether, for instance, she is happy in and gratified by her marriage), or the effect of her historical past (whether her unresolved childhood conflicts are manifesting themselves)?

Although the mother (or anyone) operates as a whole, with all three levels interacting simultaneously to produce a certain maternal climate for the child, we find it convenient, for descriptive purposes, to separate artificially these three levels. Thus we shall limit ourselves in this chapter primarily to the effect of her mothering functions with some mention of her adult personality status. In the next chapter we shall be primarily interested in the mother's historical past. We shall speak here, for example, of the child being maladjusted because the mother is tense. We may mention that her tension is due to conflict with her husband, but, at this point, we shall not go into the historical reasons for her marital conflict.

Our main instrument for detecting what maternal handling was most crucial was, again, the combined social adjustment rating of the child. In the same manner in which we isolated six crucial items regarding the child in the last chapter, we culled our maternal characteristics, crucially differentiating the mothers of very well-adjusted children from the mothers of only fairly well-adjusted children.

Again, our negative findings, what we did not find crucial, may be of some interest. Was there any clear-cut relation of excellent adjustment of the child to the mother planning or wanting the pregnancy? No. To breast as opposed to bottle feeding? No. To whether mother said she was not nervous? No. To whether mother said she was not depressed at times? No. To whether mother said she released her angry feelings or held them in? No.

What did appear to be positively crucial were maternal characteristics evaluated by the social worker from the actual story that the mother related and the feeling tones that accompanied it (rather than from more concrete specifics). The finding could be stated in these terms. *The child's excellent adjustment was associated with the degree to which the social worker evaluated the mother as being warmly dependable and as being understanding of the child's surgent individuality.* (See Appendix E, Table 8.) Warm dependability represented the degree of mother's interest and reliability that the child could count upon in times of stress. Many mothers were evaluated rather unequivocally as "warmly dependable." Other evaluations included: "dependable warmth is fluctuating in response to socioeconomic stress or difficulties in relation to the husband"; "resentful of the child's dependency needs"; "anxious when confronted by child's dependent needs." Using these evaluations we were able to divide the mothers into those who were warmly dependable and those who showed some fluctuation, coldness, resentment, or anxiousness regarding the child's dependent needs (the division being about fifty-fifty).

The evaluation of mother's capacity to be understanding was derived from three separate evaluations by the social worker of the mother. (1) Was mother sensitive to the individual needs of the child? Many were sensitive, but others were "insensitive," or "competitive with the child," or "identified with the child," or "working out own problems through child." (2) Was mother understanding of the hostile, negative feelings that children occasionally manifest? Again many mothers were understanding, but others were "not understanding nor empathic with the child's negativism," or "anxious when the child shows hostility." (3) Did mother have insight into her own handling of the child? Many mothers did have this insight, while others were "rigid," or "non-aware," or had "no insight." The data revealed that the mother who scored high in one of these three evaluations usually scored high in the other two, and analogously, for those mothers who scored low. In view of this finding we surmised that these three evaluations probably all measured the same thing, that is, mother's capacity for understanding and accepting the lively, individualistic urges of the child. We then were able to divide the mothers into the "understanding" (those with high scores) and the "not understanding" (those with low scores).

Thus we had two evaluative measures of the mother as a mother: one evaluation measured how much security and stability the child could expect from the mother in times of stresses; the other evaluation measured how much self-individuation and lively impulse expression on the child's part the mother was capable of understanding and accepting. The mothers did not always score equally high or low in these two respects. In other words, the capacity to be warmly dependable did not always go hand in hand with the capacity to be understanding. Shortly, the effects of a predominance of one of these two maternal influences over the other will be described. But for our purposes now, it can be said that the child's adjustment score was quite high when the mother was both warmly dependable and understanding, average when the mother was one or the other, and quite low when she was neither.

What did we learn from these findings? Some of our learning consisted only of a corroboration of what we had known from clinical experience and from the many reports in the psychiatric literature. Thus it was not surprising to find that a child is secure and free to grow if he can depend on his mother's interest in him and at the same time also feel that she understands him. Such a mature mothering would enable a child to develop from one stage to the next without encountering the undue stress that causes growth fixation. The comparatively poor mothering in our "fairly well-adjusted" sub-group of study children and the even poorer "mothering" in our emotionally disturbed clinic children lent much support to our conclusions.

We were reminded also that the quality of mothering should not be confused with specific actions in the process of mothering. The evaluations of good mothering made by the social worker were based on mother's feeling tone and the total range of her mothering. It was not based on such specifics as how long the child was on the bottle, age of toilet training, etc. For example, in good mothering some mothers trained their children for sphincter control rather early (at least by one and a half years), others much later (by two and a half years). In poor mothering there was the same variation. The inescapable conclusion was that there was considerable individuality in the manner and modes with which mothers carried out their mothering.

We also gained a partial answer to the question posed at the end of the last chapter, "What prevents the lively impulses from making restless savages out of these children?" In these two maternal factors we see the means for reducing tension in the child and of enabling him gradually to harken to the voice of reason and restraint. Certainly the music of dependability and understanding hath charms for the savage little child.

What was additionally enlightening for us was the notion that the mothering function might consist of two general components and that mothers varied as to whether they excelled in one rather than the other component. The two components "dependability" and "understanding" might gratify two basic but different growth needs for the child. Dependability would gratify the child's need for someone to hang onto, for togetherness, belongingness, and roots, in short, his need to feel he is united to his mother. Understanding would gratify the child's need for the mother to stand under him and support his separating and differentiating himself from her. In other words, it would gratify his need to feel he is his own master in pursuing his own individual life course.

In psychoanalytic theory these two needs would correspond to the first two stages of psychic growth. In the first (oral) stage the helplessness of the infant requires the dependable nearness, interest, and attention of the mother. Varying degrees of impaired maternal dependability would produce in the child degrees of pessimism, non-confidence, and mistrust about the outside world. In the second (anal-muscular) stage the emerging wilfulness of the small child requires an understanding by the mother that these new tendencies are important for the child's eventual autonomy and self-mastery. Varying degrees of impaired maternal understanding would produce varying degrees of doubt in the child about his own powers and capacities or about his right to use them.

We had some evidence from our data that seemed to support the foregoing. The evidence was gained from a study of the imbalance in the maternal qualities. (See Appendix Table 9.) We studied two groups of children: (1) children whose mothers were dependable but not understanding; (2) children whose mothers were understanding but not dependable. In the psychiatric interview the first group showed signs of restless protest against the restrictiveness of the non-understanding yet dependable mother—whereas the second group showed signs of wishing more love and dependency from the non-dependable yet understanding mother. For example, in telling what made them feel angry towards their parents, children of the first group characteristically said, "When mother won't let me go out to play." "When I have to come in from play." We interpret this kind of response as typifying a protest against mother's curtailing the child's autonomous activity. In contrast, the children of the second group characteristically said, "When I get a scolding." "When my feelings are hurt." We believe this response signifies a sensitivity to anything issuing from the mother that makes the child feel unloved or unwanted: a sensitivity to a mother who is or was not dependably interested or giving.

Similarly, in stating their preferred ages, the children of the first group characteristically said they wished to be older than their real age—a response, we believe, reflecting a wish to get out from under mother's restrictive thumb. In contrast, the children of the second group more often expressed a desire to be younger—possibly, we believe, reflecting a wish for more of mother, for a protection and nearness to her that she insufficiently gave.

Thus we believe that our evidence supports the hypothesis that there are two different factors in the mothering functions which gratify or fail to gratify two different basic needs of the child. When maternal dependability gratifies the child's dependent needs, *and* maternal understanding gratifies his autonomous independent needs, he is able to integrate and internalize the gratifying results within his personality and move on to the next growth stage. We believe we saw the end product of such an integration in the excellent behavioral adjustment of children whose mothers were dependable *and* understanding.

Regarding the two maternal factors and the two needs of the child, we found it theoretically useful to assign them to the dual category of permanence and change. Dependability, with its promotion of non-separateness and of a close-rooted union would make for a feeling of "permanence." Understanding, with its promotion of separateness and individual self-expression and expansion would provide for "change." In the imbalance studied we could see indications of the undesirable repercussions of too much permanence and too much change. As we described earlier, the dependable and yet not understanding mother will certainly gratify the child's need for permanence, but her overemphasis may produce some feeling in the child of restless constriction rather than security or belongingness. On the other hand, the understanding mother who is quite undependably *not* there when the child needs her, certainly would gratify the child's need for change, but her overemphasis might produce in him some feeling of restless chaos, rather than freedom.

FLUCTUATION
IN MATERNAL QUALITIES

The impression may have been given so far that dependability and understanding are fixed capacities in the mother. This impression would not be true. Although in a small minority of instances it might appear that the mother has a rather sustained capacity or incapacity to do well in these areas, in the majority of mothers in our study these capacities were subject to fluctuations.

One kind of fluctuation is connected with the growth phase of the child. An example of this could be seen in the difference between the adjustment at eight and nine, and the adjustment at twelve and thirteen. While it is true that maternal dependability and understanding was associated with excellent latency adjustment, the good maternal handling at that particular age period did not guarantee a carry-over of the child's good adjustment at puberty. The lesson we drew was that a mother could be accepting and understanding of the child when he was in a more civilized latency period, and yet not be accepting of him when he began to manifest the sexual and aggressive impulses associated with puberty.

The other kind of fluctuation has less to do with the age period of the child and more to do with the current situation which may affect mother's energy resources. This fluctuation involving the idea of stress on the mother is a matter that we would like to dwell on at some length. Rather than discuss the wide variety of stresses that the mother may encounter (argument with a relative, not being accepted completely by a group of women in the neighborhood, etc.) we prefer to concentrate on stresses within the home. Of these stresses, the raising of the children, and the management of their problems are of primary importance.

We might first ask; "What occasionally makes a problem in the child so stressful and energy draining for the mother?" "What makes such a normal and common phenomenon as a child's problem so difficult at times for the mother?" Macfarlane, it will be recalled, came to the conclusion (after following normal children from birth through adolescence) that every child in his development shows behavior that can be labelled "problem behavior." Our own findings were highly in agreement with Macfarlane's. (See Appendix E, Table 10.) Only 15 per cent of our study mothers stated that their child had not presented a problem, either in the preschool period or after starting school. (These 15 per cent, as a later chapter will show, did not have totally well-adjusted children.) We would surmise from the widespread appearance of problems in behavior, that problem behavior is a wholesome expression of growth tensions; that as a child is growing and learning new things, there inevitably will be at least a transitory phase in which the ability to master new situations does not always keep pace with the impulse and urge to do so. (See Appendix D, 3. *Continuity in Children's Problems.*)

Why, then, if problem behavior is inevitable in growth, are some problems easily encountered and handled by the mother whereas others give her great anxiousness and difficulty? If there is any one statement which could summarize our findings it is simply that the mother does not know what to do. Just as in any problem or task confronting a person, the accumulation of pressure to do the task plus the inability to proceed with constructive action, produces a mounting state of tension, thus making an ordinary problem a heavy burden.

The major factors in producing the state of not knowing what to do are: unfamiliarity (which we shall take up now) and conflict (which we shall discuss in the next chapter).

The role of unfamiliarity is similar to that of conflict. The similarity resides in the fact that in both situations one cannot choose decisively one course of action from among many courses. We saw in these study mothers, as we did in our clinic mothers, evidences of mother's being increasingly perplexed by a problem for which she had little preparation. In clinic cases there was occasionally a physical condition in the child such as brain damage, chronic illness, or the paralytic after effects of poliomyelitis; sometimes there was a nervous mental condition like epilepsy, mental retardation, or psychosis. In our study group, there were milder instances of unfamiliarity such as a slow-moving mother not being accustomed to an active child, or a quick-thinking and active mother not being accustomed to a relatively slow child. Also, after raising two girls, one mother in our study was perplexed for awhile as to how to raise her third child, a boy.

Probably the most frequent manifestation of unfamiliarity is in the situation of having the first baby. It has been common knowledge for ages that the first-born child receives the brunt of mother's inexperience and unfamiliarity with the role of mothering. It has been popularly said that the mother learns on the first child and that the subsequent children benefit from the lessons mother has derived. In our study we obtained additional confirmation of this state of affairs.

There were findings suggesting that first-born children were more adversely affected by "bad" mothering than were children who were second or third born. (See Appendix E, Table 11.) The combined social adjustment rating was lower in first borns whose mothers were lacking in dependability and understanding than in non- first borns with similar mothers. (First borns, however, whose mothers were dependable and understanding scored as high as non-first borns with similarly good mothers.)

It is difficult not to mention in this connection another finding that properly belongs in the next chapter on historical influences concerning mothering. The finding is to the effect that mothers who were themselves first-born appeared less warmly dependable and understanding than mothers who were middle children, and especially less so than mothers who were youngest children in their original families. (See Appendix E, Table 12.)

We gather from these trends that the first-born is the victim principally of mother's unfamiliarity with children, that he is much more susceptible to the toxins of bad maternal handling; the full dosage is discharged completely on him, whereas the non-first born has the advantage of any maternal toxins being diluted in its distribution among several children.

Indeed, the first born has to bear the brunt of the parents learning how to be parents. In infancy these children are sometimes handled gingerly, as if they were a breakable toy; the development of their speech and habit acquisition is watched anxiously by young parents; they are required to share with their younger siblings, to take care of them, and to be a model for them. In adolescence the parents are concerned about sexual promiscuity and impose strict limitations on the adolescent's freedom of movement, only to relax the strictness (as many of our cases showed) with the younger siblings. No wonder, then, that the mothers who were first-born tended to repeat their tense first-born experience with their own children, to repeat maternal handling lacking in warm dependability and understanding.

This unfamiliarity intensifies a problem. Once the problem is underway and has been exacerbated by the factor of conflict and unfamiliarity, another factor also enters to aggravate the situation. This factor is fatigue that is caused by the energy-draining aspects of the problem and that reduces the ability to solve a problem. Frequently at this point, the chances of not being overwhelmed by the situation or the chances of not being in a vicious cycle of irritation and guilt depend upon the intervention of another person who is more resourceful and less conflicted. The mother can lean temporarily or permanently on another person in order to weather the storm. Sometimes that other person is one of the older children, the husband, her mother, a good maid, the family doctor, the clergyman, a public agency, or a therapist.

In our study mothers there were a few examples of mothers who were chronically unable to handle problems entailed in mothering. In two cases the mothers had had nervous breakdowns, and in one of them the daughter was leaned on, causing premature maturity. In another case the mother felt frightened and overwhelmed by the drain on her resourcefulness because her husband was working nights. She began to improve when her husband gave up his night job for her sake, spent more time with her, and helped her organize and perform her duties. In still another case in our study, in spite of the mother having had three breakdowns, the father did not turn toward his wife to help her, but instead complained that his own needs were not being met. We have noticed in our clinic cases an occasional seemingly miraculous improvement in a problem just by virtue of a mother filling out an application for help and receiving an appointment date a month or two hence. We surmised that the mother then felt that there was someone strong and wise who would share her burdens with her, and that this feeling allowed her to become more relaxed with her children.

Another indication of the role played by fatigue can be seen in the type of complaints made by mothers who considered their children to be problems at present. The complaints were of the chronic fatiguing variety: fretfulness in infancy, sleeplessness, and excessive sibling rivalry. These are the kinds of problems that drain the mother's energy, that disturb her while she is trying to get some sleep, or if she is awake, while she is trying to look after the children and the house. These problems challenge her adequacy as a mother. She wonders what she is doing wrong and she approaches the child with the hope that a new handling, or this or that gift, or punishment, will relieve the tension in the child. But when these fail, she is likely to explode internally or externally with anger.

We believe, then, that the mother's capacity to handle her children well, her capacity to be dependable and understanding are not of a fixed nature. The capacity depends, among other things, upon the particular growth phase of the child and upon the amount of energy-draining stress the mother is undergoing. We might say that the point at which a highly stressful problem will arise depends on highly specific factors and conditions in the mother and child, and that the problem may not arise at a different time with the same child, or at the same time with a different child. We have endeavored in this chapter to describe the characteristics of the maternal climate surrounding the child's growth. This climate, which is subject to fluctuation, allows the child to integrate and internalize his needs for dependency and autonomy—allows him to proceed with his own continuity of development.

But so far we have mainly considered mother as a provider of climates. In our focus on her as a climate providing mechanism we have not taken into consideration her deeper psychological needs and her own continuity with her past development. This new focus will be the subject matter of the next chapter.

The Shadows of the Past

《《-《《-《《-《《-《《-《《-《《-《《-《《-《《-《《-《《-

CHAPTER IV

CONTINUITY
BETWEEN
GENERATIONS

THE REPERCUSSIONS of mother's historical past on her mothering functions and hence upon the child constitute the last link in the chain of causation. Of all the experiences in her past, the ones that touch on how she herself was mothered and how she reacted to being so mothered have the greatest pertinence to the way she will mother her own children. This and other historical features comprise an interaction and connection between the older and the newer generations which we shall call "generational continuity." The continuity may be defined as the tendency for the older generation to repeat, in an unmodified or modified way, their past experiences with the new generation and for the newer generation to take over, in an unmodified or modified way, the attitudes of the older generation.

Our findings begin with a consideration of the broad subject of generational continuity. Both the mothers and the fathers in our study invariably showed evidences of using their parenthood to continue or to resolve, through their children, some aspect of their own growing up, and therefore each of their several children might represent a somewhat different aspect of their past. But, at the same time as they were going through their own childhood with their children, they were also experiencing a parenthood as lived by their own parents. In other words, what happened to them as children was happening to their own children; what happened to their parents was happening to them as parents.

Although this dynamic continuity invariably was found, there were four variables or factors distinguishing one mother or father from the next. The first such variable was the degree to which they were conscious of this continuity. In some mothers there was quite a conscious awareness that manifested itself in the description of their children in terms of the kind of child they themselves had been: "My oldest daughter is not at all as I was as a child, but my youngest girl reminds me of myself quite a bit." In other mothers the continuity slipped out in their spontaneous talking without their being aware of, or pleased by, the connection: "My son is quite lazy; I don't know where he got that from." A little later, in describing her own childhood: "My mother used to get after me for daydreaming and not doing the chores." The reliving of the parenthood of their parents usually was not too conscious. For example, they saw no connection between a vague fear of a menopausal depression happening to them and the menopausal depression that occurred to their own mothers. Nor were they usually aware that their modes of dealing with their children were strikingly similar to the descriptions of their parents' manner of dealing with them.

The second variable concerned the experiences they wished to be continued from their own childhood. Some parents looked forward—and quite consciously so—to the enjoyable aspects of their childhood. These mothers eagerly awaited the time when they could put pretty dresses on their daughters, or enjoy with them the taking care of the first doll. The fathers impatiently awaited the time when their sons would be old enough to take fishing or to a baseball game. On the other hand, some parents wished to continue their own childhood pleasures and expectations by themselves, in the first person singular, so to speak, rather than to live out these pleasures through their children. Such parents were not in continuity with their children. The children were more in continuity with their envied siblings who, they claimed, got more than they did. Other parents had a feeling of continuity associated with anxiety; they feared that their children during puberty or adolescence would participate in the kind of sexual delinquency that had strongly tempted them and that they had narrowly averted by some repressive effort.

The third variable was the degree to which these parents were involved in the continuity of their childhood. One mother, who admitted that she had been quite babied as the youngest of her family, said that although she has four children, she wants another because "I feel that something is missing unless there is a small baby around the house." This mother's great need to participate, at least vicariously, in a babied experience was obvious. Other mothers, however, were only partially involved with their children. While deriving enjoyment from their offspring through some sort of a renewal of their own life, they also enjoyed other aspects of adult life: friends, hobbies, organizational affiliations, etc.

The last variable was concerned not so much with the parents' actual childhood experiences as it was with their unmet childhood expectations. Some fathers wished to take their sons to ballgames because their own fathers had taken them; but others wished to do so because their own fathers had never taken them, and they had wished that their fathers had been more like others in the neighborhood who had been "pals" to their sons. The same was true of the mothers. Some were permissive about their children's sexual curiosity because they had been reared in that manner themselves, but more often they were unusually permissive because their own mothers had been excessively prudish and strict.

It is this last variable which has a special connection with how and why mother developed the capacity for dependability and understanding. There is evidence, soon to be described, suggesting that some mothers developed these capacities more through an imitation and following of their own mothers, whereas other mothers developed them more in reaction against alleged deficiencies in their own mothers. It is as though the former mothers, in reliving their pasts with their children, were more influenced by "I shall relive my good childhood by treating my child as I was treated." The latter mothers were influenced more by "I shall give myself a better childhood by being a better mother to my child than my mother was to me."

These findings begin with mother's statements regarding the difference between the way she handled or wished to handle her children and the way her mother handled her when she had been a child. These comparisons were of the following kinds: (1) very little if any difference (one mother said she used her mother as a model and only hoped she could be as good a mother as her own mother had been); (2) some differences and some similarities; (3) markedly different (a few mothers said in a tirade of resentful feelings, "I try to do everything different; my mother was absolutely no good as a mother").

In exploring what mother claimed were mistakes in her own mother's handling, we found, with few exceptions, that the alleged mistakes were either that mother's mother had not shown enough love, interest, and affection, or that she had been too strict, managerial, and possessive. These two types of complaint we felt were quite similar to, if not identical with, the elements in the two mothering capacities: dependability and understanding. In other words, we believed that these mothers were complaining that there had not been enough dependability (love, interest, and affection) forthcoming from their own mothers or that there had not been enough understanding of them as individuals (strict, managerial, and possessive).

We then had a first indication of what went into the formation of maternal capacities. At this stage it appeared that in some instances the mother used her own mother as a model from which to develop her maternal capacities, while in other instances the mother reacted against her own mother in order to develop these capacities. We also saw that there could be a reaction specifically against her own mother's lack of dependability or specifically against a lack of understanding.

So far, however, we have been dealing, not so much with mother's actual capacities, but rather with her claims, intentions, or aspirations regarding them. In other words, the foregoing pertains to the goals or themes of motherhood rather than to whether mother accomplished her goal or realized her theme. Our next step, therefore, was to determine how adequately or successfully mother realized the goal contained in her theme of motherhood. Was she successful in revising the "bad" example set for her by her own mother? Was she successful in imitating the "good" example set for her?

To answer these questions we used the social worker's evaluation of the mother's capacity for dependability and understanding. Using this evaluation we then might be able to ascertain whether the mother was actually handling her own children any differently than she claimed she had been handled. For example, if mother claimed she was trying to be more dependable, interested, and affectionate than her own mother had been, we attempted to determine whether the social worker had found this to be true, or whether mother was being equally as undependable and ungiving as she described her own mother. Similarly, we tried to ascertain whether mother was much more permissive and understanding than she claimed her own mother had been.

In our study of this aspect we found that about half the mothers had actually corrected in some way this alleged mishandling by their own mothers whereas the other half had not made any progress. With the question in mind as to whether progress had been made, we then studied the mothers who claimed their own mothers had made no mistakes. Again we found two groups of about equal number. The one group was composed of mothers trying to emulate their own mothers, and who were, in the social worker's opinion, dependable and understanding of the child's individualism. We considered that this group was an adequate, somewhat progressive group inasmuch as, while no marked progress was evident, the model that mother's mother presented was possibly adequate enough so that there was no great need to change. The other group of mothers were satisfied with their own mother's handling and yet were found by the social worker to be not dependable and understanding. This group, we felt, showed definite lack of progress in so far as they were obviously and obliviously continuing an unwholesome situation.

When we grouped all the adequate mothers (those who corrected their mother's mistakes and those whose mothers were progressive, favorable models) and grouped all the inadequate mothers (those who had not corrected their mother's mistakes and those who were oblivious of or defensive regarding the fact that their mothers were bad mothers), we found that the children of adequate mothers were better adjusted than those of the inadequate ones.

This relationship of maternal adequacy to the child's good adjust-ment was even more crucial than that of maternal capacities to ad-justment. (See Appendix E, Table 13.) The reader may wonder what the difference is between this finding and the finding described in the previous chapter. Now we say that the child's good adjustment is associated with the mother's adequacy, then we said it is associated with mother's capacity for warm dependability and understanding. The difference is subtle but we believe highly important. Adequacy entails more than the mere presence of beneficial maternal capacities. It represents a personal achievement, a culmination of personal growth. It suggests a mother who, originally as a small or young girl, may have been in contact with good or bad mothering models, who not only was able to discriminate and choose between the good and bad models, but also (by virtue of drive, will, or some internal psycho-logical mechanism) was able to put into successful execution her aspiration concerning good mothering.

There is obviously more personal growth, more force of autono-mous character, and less of being controlled by the past, when mother is dependable although her own mother was not so than when mother is dependable because her mother was so. These are the same con-siderations as when we think of a self-taught man receiving a college degree being probably more adequate and forceful than a man who receives the degree after being exposed to good schools and good teachers during his entire youth. The latter may often be quite competent but he, as yet, has not demonstrated whether he can grow beyond his beneficial past. Least adequate, of course, would be someone who was chronically unable to utilize any beneficial aspect of his past.

Thus in our use of the term "adequacy" we are dealing not only with what mother is like at present, but also with what it took on her part to become that way. Again we see that the maternal capacities are not fixed. The historical past, as we have said, is weighty but not necessarily fateful. Not a few mothers have apparently been able to separate themselves from unwholesome aspects of the past and to follow and grow from the more wholesome aspects.

It will be recalled from the previous chapters that those children secure enough to verbalize anger toward their parents had two general types of complaints: (1) feelings of being unappreciated, undervalued, and unloved; (2) feelings of being overly restricted. The first type was related to deficits in mother's dependability, the second to deficits in her understanding. Perhaps it is these secure children—who are quite conscious of some lacks in the way they are being mothered—who will remedy matters for themselves through their own children. It is as though they as children are beginning to formulate their future attitudes as parents, "When I become a mother (or father) I'll spend more time with my children, or I won't interfere with them so much."

Concerning the children's adjustment, we could not help being impressed with the intimate connection between the child's growth potential and the mother's capacity for growth. Her capacity for growth was demonstrated in her ability to individuate herself sufficiently from her own mother that she could remedy with her own children any faulty or anachronistic maternal handling. Mothers with such capacities would obviously be helpful in promoting the child's adjustment at eight and nine, a time when the child must grow to some extent away from his family, must grow to absorb the new and unfamiliar.

With this viewpoint we can again look beneath static exteriors of normality such as adjustment and capacities and find something dynamic, elusive, mysterious, and intangible, such as growth. The ability to grow when there is a necessity to grow, the ability to learn new things and attitudes when the old learned things and attitudes no longer suffice for an adaptive mastery of a situation—these abilities arise from an internal essence as mysterious as life itself.

Since we have been preoccupied with the topic of optimum normality, we might ask: "What kind of relationship between generations is optimum for growth?" "What kind of generational continuity is most desirable?" It would seem that a flexible continuity is most growth promoting.

It will be recalled that in our discussion of the maternal capacities we had suggested that dependability promotes a wholesome feeling of secure permanence in the child, and understanding allows the child to change and expand. It is not unlikely that the same considerations apply to the relationship between generations. There should be enough continuity to gratify the need for permanence, and enough flexibility to gratify the need for change.

The continuity can also be described in terms of an interaction between past and present. We might say that the past can influence the present in three ways: by the present rigidly conforming to the past, by the present using the past as one of the guides of life, or by the present reacting against the past. Put slightly differently, the present may memorize the past, learn from the past, or violently reject the past.

Perhaps in a more traditional and stable society than ours, we might find that the past is more directly influential, that the mothers take over rather completely and without question the methods used by their mothers. There would be no necessity to question or to change things so long as that particular society was thriving through use of of its traditional customs. In our American society, however, class mobility and the desire for self-improvement has so permeated the social climate that mothers are constrained to try to improve on their own mothers. Mores and technology have so changed—at least superficially—from those of grandmother's day that the modern mother may be ill adapted to social reality if she clings to grandmother's methods instead of being alertly sensitive to the modern order. Children whose mothers are old fashioned (this is particularly true of first-generation Americans whose parents emigrated from a more traditional Europe) raise a rebellious outcry against any conformity to older customs that make them seem different from their more emancipated and modern peers.

Thus, while in a traditional society parents hope that their children will carry on the established beliefs, customs, and methods that they have accepted unreservedly from their own parents, in a more mobile society such as ours, parents more often hope that their children will be able to achieve some of the unrealized dreams and expectations that they themselves were not able to accomplish in their own youth.

It can be seen that our concept of generation-continuity takes in not only what a child takes over from a parent, but also what the child brings forward from his own psychological past when he eventually becomes a parent. Accordingly, we may speak of generation-continuity as being composed of an interpersonal social continuity and an intrapersonal individual continuity. Both components have been familiar to us for ages, the interpersonal social one in the folk adage, "The apple falls, not far from the tree," the intrapersonal, individual one in the adage, "The child is father to the man."

In the next section we will concentrate on the relationship between the tree and the falling apple—on what one generation imparts to the other.

The Shadow of the Grandmother

WITH THE additional dimension of time and history a more full-bodied, detailed view of personality and behavior is possible. Many of the aspects and areas we had no more than mapped out in the earlier chapters, will become, we believe, more vivid when we observe the specific workings of continuity. Particularly necessary to be filled in are the different problems arising for mother and child when she is rather inflexibly bound by her continuity to the past, or in desperate conflict with it, and the much less difficult growth problems confronting mother and child when there is a flexible, non-conflicted continuity with the past.

Let us begin with a matter touched on in the previous chapter—the continuity of mother with her own mother. Since mother in adult life is not only to take up her role as mother but also is to re-experience her own childhood, the following questions come to mind: Does she consciously want her second childhood as lived vicariously through her children to be the same as she went through, or does she want it to be different and better? Does she want to be the same kind of mother her mother had been, or does she want to be different, and if so, in what way different?

By using just the criterion of mother's conscious intent or aspiration regarding her role as a child rearer, we were able to divide the children into three large groups. (1) Children of *traditional* mothers, i.e., mothers who consciously were satisfied with their own mother's handling and apparently used this as a reference point in bringing up their own children. (2) Children of *rebellious* mothers, i.e., mothers who were dissatisfied to some degree with the excessive amount of control, strictness, or interference exercised by their own mothers and who aspired to be less controlling. (3) Children of *dependent* mothers, i.e., mothers who were dissatisfied to some degree with the lack of attention, love, or interest coming from their mother, and who aspired to be more attentive, loving, etc. (See Appendix E, Table 14.)

We would expect that all three kinds of mothers would have some subjective ax to grind with and through their children. Their subjectivities might take the form of a reproach of others and/or a guilty reproach of self. Thus, the traditional mother would be expected to have considerable investment in the preservation of the status quo in continuing in her own children a filial loyalty and adherence to the traditional customs, standards, and values that had been inculcated in her. If other people (father, school, neighborhood) should undermine the child's adherence to the traditions, mother would be angry at them and at the child for deviating. If she herself failed to continue the tradition, she would feel guilty or inadequate.

The rebellious mother would tend to see her child as being overly coerced where only ordinary, wholesome limits were present. She might be angry at the school teacher, for instance, if the latter critically suppressed her child's efforts to talk in class when he was not supposed to. She might be angry with herself or guilty if she, like her own strict mother, nipped in the bud any of the child's individualistic activities. She might be disappointed in the child if he did not rebelliously protest about infringements on his individualism.

The dependent mother would tend to see her child deprived of interest and attention in a situation where undivided attention might be impossible. Thus she might be angry at the busy father for not having time that particular evening to answer the child's question or to admire some achievement of the child. She might feel self-reproachful if she herself spent too much time away from her child, since she would feel that she was just as bad as her mother who was "never home." She might be disappointed in the child if he did not carry out the love and interest theme by being devoted or needing devotion.

It can be seen that when there is too much of a discrepancy and conflict between what mother aspires to in her mothering and what actually occurs, she is prone to feel resentful, disappointed, and guilty. In her conflict, she may take out these feelings on the child, the father, or herself. When these feelings reach a certain intensity, they constitute a stressful problem in mothering.

The following example, drawn from a mother and child in treatment at the Institute for Juvenile Research, may serve to illustrate this role of inner conflict. This particular mother happens to be one we would characterize as a "dependent" mother. She brought up the problem of her four-year-old girl who monopolized her attention. The child would not go to bed on time, insisted that her bedroom door remain open so that she could see her mother, and refused to go to the nursery school on time because she did not feel well. As a consequence the mother was not free to pursue her vocational interests.

Investigation of this situation revealed that the mother was conflicted about handling the girl. She was unable to be firm about the child's going to bed on time because in her own childhood she had resented being left alone by her parents at night when they were entertaining grown-ups in the parlor. In order to be a better, more interested and giving mother than her own mother had been she, in her present mothering (or vicarious second childhood) only feebly tried to keep the child within limits.

It can be seen that both the problem in the child and in the mother arose from the mother's past and from her identification of herself with her daughter. The case shows how an increasingly tense situation is created when the mother is pulled two ways, when she is conflicted in her continuity. The mother is in conflict between what she would like to do as an adult woman and what she feels she ought to do as a mother. If she acts solely on her adult leanings, she will feel guilty for fear that she is just as inattentive as her own mother allegedly had been. In other words, she will feel guilty that she is a bad mother and falling short of her ideal of being a good mother. If she acts solely according to her ideal of being a good mother, she will have to neglect her self-expression as an adult; then she would become increasingly irritated with the child for restricting her. This irritation, however, would soon evoke in her a feeling that she is a bad mother and she would continue in this vicious circle. This chain of feelings and events can arise, of course, in the traditional and rebellious mothers as well as in the dependent mother.

Not always, however, does the feeling of being a bad mother—of falling short of one's motherhood-aspiration—lead to a vicious cycle of irritation, guilt, and a deteriorating mother-child relationship. On the contrary, in the more adequate, flexible, mature mothers, it frequently serves as a stimulus to better mothering. Such mothers are more able to reduce the discrepancy between aspiration and achievement—either by reducing the aspiration or by increasing the achievement. Less needful of a vicarious better second childhood for themselves, they are more prepared to revise their motherhood aspirations so as to be more in keeping with the individual needs of the child. In other words, along with their own second childhood gratifications they can allow the child his first childhood gratifications. They are not so deeply involved in their own personal continuity that their traditionalism, rebelliousness, and dependency are not susceptible to some modification.

Furthermore, they are integrated and resourceful enough that they are able to achieve their aspirations. As we found in the adequate mothers, their aspiration becomes an arrived-at personal goal rather than merely a wished-for fantasy. The child is not faced with the contradiction emanating from a mother who aspires to one thing and does another. For it is certainly contradictory for the child if one part of the mother advocates individualistic rebellion while another part of her suppresses and controls such expression; or if one part of the mother stimulates a child's seeking of affection while another part rebuffs and avoids such attempts.

Thus, the motherhood aspirations and themes may have an influence for good or bad. Their useful function is to integrate the mother, to provide a continuity between her present and her past. Her mothering function is consequently less stressful and conflictful; the child benefits accordingly. Their non-useful function consists in binding the mother to an orientation based primarily on her own childhood, an orientation productive of inflexibilities and contradictions. The latter, in turn, make mothering a stressful task with diminishing benefits for the child.

We shall see in the next three chapters certain effects on the child that arise from mother's aspirations. The effects, which we will call imprints, are more or less specific and depend on the particular theme aspiration of the mother. Each motherhood theme type—traditional, rebellious, and dependent—seems to leave a certain characteristic imprint on the child. The wholesome repercussions of the imprints will be seen when we describe children of adequate traditional, rebellious, and dependent mothers; the unwholesome repercussions when we describe children of inadequate traditional, rebellious, and dependent mothers. (See Appendix E, Table 15.)

A final word is in order before we take up the detailed consideration of the theme-aspirations and the imprints. In proposing the three categories of traditional, rebellious, and dependent, we are deliberately, for the sake of better delineation, treating mothers as though they are "pure" types. We are purposely considering the most prominent aspects of the mother as representing all of the mother. This, however, is not the case in actuality. There is considerable overlapping, each mother having some of each of the three themes.

As for the imprints, the kind and degree, of course, would depend on other factors such as the intensity of mother's feelings about the past, and her attachment to it; the susceptibility, by virtue of constitutional endowment and other circumstances, of the child's being influenced by such a mother; the presence of other adult figures (such as father) who might leave a different imprint on the child. Thus, in our description of the trends, we can only point to the types of imprints seen in the child, and we shall not be able to say much about how deeply the child may be affected by this aspect of the mother.

Also, regarding the imprinting impact of these maternal themes, some impacts are rather normal and innocuous, others, if indelibly imprinted on the child would result in severe psychopathology. These "bad" maternal influences, using a medical analogy, can be considered in the nature of micro-organisms like the tubercle bacillus. Although tuberculosis cannot occur without the person being affected by the tubercle bacillus, not every one exposed to or infected by the bacillus develops tuberculosis. While it is true that some persons contract a mortal disease or a chronic disabling disorder, most people develop only a small harmless tubercle that, like vaccination, protects against an overwhelming later infection. Thus the differences in severity of reaction depend, among other things, on the general constitution of the person affected and on the quantity of the infecting micro-organism.

Similarly, with our investigation of the imprinting effects of "bad" maternal influences on the child. Sometimes we shall see no effect, sometimes a trace or nuance, and at other times a truly disabling emotional disturbance. Although for purposes of graphic delineation we may describe some tendencies of the mother and child as though they signify ominous psychopathological states, it should be kept in mind that these mothers and children represent at least an average healthy sample and that certain strengths keep in check a tendency towards marked psychopathology.

CHAPTER VI

THE
TRADITIONAL
MOTHER

IN THIS chapter we shall be interested in the mothers whom we have designated as traditional. If we compare their children with those of rebellious and dependent mothers, we find that they show, characteristically, *an insulation against outside events and stimuli.* (See Appendix E, Table 16.) This characteristic would fit the mothers' wish not to change from what they had been accustomed to in their relationship with their own mothers. If these traditional mothers had been more receptive to events or stimuli from the outside, inevitably they would have made comparisons between their mothers and their aunts, or between their mothers and the mothers of neighbor children. Thus, the children of these mothers appear to bear an imprint of their mothers' insulation from the outside.

How does the insulation of the children manifest itself? In the first place, they have difficulty in relating to persons outside the family. During the psychiatric interview they related slowly, frequently were not able to achieve complete rapport, and often showed inadequate zest or emotion. The school reports, rather than mentioning failure to work up to mental capacity, more frequently described some interpersonal difficulty such as being distant, not being completely cooperative with the teacher, or some difficulty with peers such as interfering with them or isolating from them. This reaction of discomfort apparently did not impair their intellectual functioning since they worked up to mental capacity in school, and in the psychiatric interview they were able adequately to verbalize their feelings, attitudes, dreams, and fantasies. This suggested that they were more comfortable with the impersonal than with the personal.

The second manifestation of this insulation appeared in the fact that they seemed relatively impervious to strong stimuli. These were

[52]

the children who were not frightened by murder or mystery movies. In fact they liked them. Their Rorschach tests revealed the least neurotic shock, i.e., their appreciation of form and reality was not markedly affected by being shown a card that had vivid or disturbing colors. Further evidence that their impulse life was not lively or disturbing was the fact that none of these children spontaneously reported, when asked about their anxiety dreams, that they had dreamt of falling. Although the falling dreams will be discussed later in another connection, it may be said here that it is a dream that occurs when an individual fears that there is some danger of his impulses getting out of control. In these children we surmised that the impulse life was so insulated or under control that outside stimuli did not have the ordinary power of activating the child's erotic or aggressive impulses.

A cause or an effect of this insulation could be seen in the characteristic conformity of the children to the mothers' wishes. It is not surprising that the mother's traditionalism should be associated with conformity in the children. Mother is traditionally conforming to her mother's example and the child is identifying with his mother's conformity. Thus, on the Despert Fables, responses showing antagonism to, or defiance of, the mother were infrequently seen in children of traditional mothers. For example, the mother deer was rarely shot by the hunter, the calf complied with the mother cow's request to go out and eat grass.

Thus we might say that with the traditional mothers and their children there was a relative insulation and imperviousness to the outside stimuli and a relative dependence on built-in traditional systems that react only to the most familiar. We should expect that these characteristics in a mild degree would actually help one's adjustment in the outside world. Not to be thrown by or tempted by what happens outside of them, not to become dissatisfied by the grass appearing greener in someone else's yard, not to have moments of doubt about what one should do in life—all these are certainly useful assets to help one get along in the world. The disadvantage, of course, is a certain lessening of maneuverability when confronted by entirely new situations. For example, it will be recalled that they did not react flexibly to the new situation of meeting a strange adult such as the psychiatrist.

Actual clinical illustrations of the insulated, traditional orientation are not too vivid or dramatic inasmuch as there is usually a quiet rather than a dramatic quality associated with the following of tradition. We saw in our study that traditional mothers, for example, had a tendency toward depreciation of the unfamiliar. This is more noticeable in clinical cases where the conflict arises between a mother who is orthodox in custom or religion and an adolescent child who wants to experiment with new ways of behaving or who wants to mingle with people outside the mother's religion, nationality, or race. An example of this may be seen in the following. A patient, a physician of twenty-eight, was the only child of a mother who exerted considerable influence over him. His mother was insular and provincial, having few friends or interests outside her home and her blood relatives. She would comment, whenever he wanted to do what the other boys in the neighborhood were doing: "What do you want to do that for? It's foolish." So long as he was in the familiar role of student (which he was up to internship and residency), he was not too emotionally disturbed. Perhaps the main reason for his seeking therapy was that his medical residency was soon coming to an end and he would be called upon to leave his familiar role of student and to face the unfamiliar outside world. A dream of his may illustrate his difficulty in deviating from the traditional. He reported a dream in which he was on a horse, going down a beaten path, on both sides of which was snow. When he wanted to go back along the same path he experienced (in the dream) considerable anxiety and discomfort because in turning the horse around the horse would have to step off the beaten path into the snow for a brief moment.

CHILDREN OF THE ADEQUATE TRADITIONAL MOTHERS

So far our focus has been on the motherhood theme of traditionalism and we have not taken into account how, apart from mother's aspiration, she actually had handled the child. In this section we will be concerned with those traditional mothers who were evaluated by the social worker as being warmly dependable and especially understanding of the child. (See Chapter III on good and bad mothering.) The reason for stressing the factor of understanding is that since the traditional mother already has a tendency not to sense objects outside of, or different from, her familiar self, it would seen to be a better indicator of her adequacy and flexibility if she is able to understand and accept the child's separate individuality than if she is able to be warmly dependable.

Now we can investigate what happens with the group characteristic of insulation when the mother is adequately traditional. (See

Appendix E, Table 17.) One phenomenon noted in the children was that their adjustment at twelve and thirteen was better than their adjustment at eight and nine. This may be accounted for by the fact that two different tasks are required of the child at the two age levels. As we have said earlier, the task during latency is to open one's eyes, ears, and psychic pores to the outside in order to learn what is different in the world outside one's family. The task of puberty, however, is to be able to sustain the impact of rising sexual impulses and to begin to formulate the direction one will take as a responsible adult. Certainly our adequate, traditional children, by virtue of their insulation, would be comparatively less open to the outside world at the age of eight and nine. At twelve and thirteen, however, by virtue of their relatively imperviousness to impulse upheaval, they would be able to handle the impact of these new sexual impulses, and would have, by virtue of their built-in traditional system, a better idea of where they are going in life. Their situation would be similar to that of children in a traditional society in which puberty and adolescence are not the periods of turmoil that they are in our more mobile society. In traditional cultures there are set forms, rituals, and ceremonies to guide the beginning adult in his voyage toward mutual responsibility. In these cultures parents would not be indecisive as to how late they should permit their adolescent sons and daughters to stay out; nor would they be indecisive because they do not want to be more stuffy and strict than other parents or do not want to be accused of being old-fashioned for following the traditions of their youth. But rather in these cultures, the decisions are not in the hands of the individual parents inasmuch as the answers are embedded in the traditional mores of the culture.

By their perceptions on the Rorschach Test of a more human movement than of color, the adequate, traditional children showed a tendency to inner living. It is such a tendency that at its optimum, buffers individuals against the strains and stresses of the outside world. The imaginative and contemplative inner life not only offers a respite from outer confusion, but aids in the creative integration of conflicting influences and stresses. However, this imaginative inner life was not just an escape from real life, since the impression obtained from the Rorschach was that these children showed good reality testing. The type of creative personality associated with this tendency is similar to that seen in the research scientist where there is a quiet eccentricity, an absentmindedness which connote inner absorption and insulation from the outside. This is a different creative type than the more unstable, rebellious personality (which will be described shortly) who flaunts his eccentricity and his iconoclasm.

As to the mothers, an indication of the confident manner in which they handled their children was revealed when they were asked at the end of the interview with the psychiatrist whether they had any questions regarding the child. Characteristically they said they had none. While this showed some imperviousness to the possibility that an outsider could have some information valuable to them, on the other hand, this very attitude might be a source of a certain kind of strength: an anxiety-relieving faith to the effect that if one just follows the familiar method of the past, one will have little trouble.

One boy in our study group exhibited this typical inner absorption in one particular interest, an absorption that made him somewhat eccentric. Arthur was small and freckle-faced with a rather serious attitude and outlook. He was one of the few boys who had minded missing school to come in for the study interview although the purpose of it had been explained to him by his mother. During the interview Arthur showed some spontaneity, but all of it was on the serious side. He exhibited an intense curiosity and wanted to know about a great many things. He asked many thoughtful questions about the Institute for Juvenile Research: how many rooms there were, how many people, did we ever have fires, etc. Arthur said that for fun he liked to build huts, and look up things in the encyclopaedia about the sun, moon, and stars, because he liked science. With the toy-box he very experimentally investigated all the toys to see how they moved and worked. For instance, instead of depicting some dramatic interplay with the dolls, he tried to see how high the tallest doll could reach. His wishes reflected his interest in science: first for a new rocket which could go 300 million miles; second for something which could travel underground and underwater and would go around the world in one minute; third for something which could go through the earth to the other side. Even his present dreams reflected his scientific interest. In the dream he was looking through a telescope at Mars and saw a man with "a real round head and a round face and small ears and a fat neck and a moustache." Another, an anxiety dream, showed his father's reaction to his scientific interests. In this dream he was walking around the street in the summer and kept on asking a certain man questions. The man said that if Arthur asked him one more question he would call the police; Arthur asked one more question and ran away from the police, but they caught up with him in a police wagon.

Arthur's mother was described by the social worker as warmly interested in her son. She was evaluated as being understanding of, and somewhat empathic with, his impulses and individualistic strivings. Also she was evaluated as being sensitive to his needs as an individual, and as having insight into some of her own tendencies and foibles. Thus, the mother can be described as dependably interested and also understanding.

Her traditional theme of motherhood was indicated in her description of her own family. She spoke positively and warmly of her own mother, saying that she found little reason to depart from the example she had provided her regarding child rearing. She did not like her father and blamed him for the many quarrels between her mother and himself.

Thus, in the case of Arthur we see a boy with an imaginative and constructive preoccupation with impersonal objects. His preoccupation was rather typical of many of the children who were exposed to a maternal atmosphere of adequate traditionalism.

CHILDREN OF
INADEQUATE TRADITIONAL MOTHERS

The traditional children whose mothers were not understanding, appeared somewhat pathologic. (See Appendix E, Table 18.) One of the prominent characteristics of these children was a marked trend toward what we shall call anti-pleasure. When they had been asked in the psychiatric interview what they would do with a thousand dollars (if that amount were given to them), they had not frequently said, as had other children: "Buy a car." "Buy a house." "Buy a lot of bikes, etc." Rather they said they would put it in the bank and save it. Even after the psychiatrist pressed them with the possibility of spending a few dollars or a large amount, they frequently and inflexibly repeated their previous stand, "Save it." Also, when they were asked if they had pleasant dreams, unlike the majority of other children they had not described dreams in which they had been given a birthday party or in which Santa Claus had given them a toy; but rather they had said either that they had never had such dreams, or that they could not remember them. A deadening of the zestful pleasure life was indicated by the fact that the mothers rarely reported that there was any masturbation or sexual curiosity, or any jealousy reaction upon the birth of a younger sibling.

In addition to this anti-pleasure trend there was a characteristic that we shall call interpersonal isolation. This isolation or lack of closeness appeared to have started in a relationship to the mother. It was suggested by the fact that the children's responses to the Despert Fables rarely indicated that they had any positive or negative feelings toward the mother. Unlike most of the other children, they had not indicated that their mothers were either a source of dependent pleasure or that they had any angry feelings towards them. In other words, the children had not mentioned them either as a source of pleasurable dependency feelings or as an object toward whom they would direct even some hostility.

There were other findings pointing to interpersonal isolation. For example, most of these children did not confide their troubles to their parents, but kept them to themselves. They exhibited, both in the psychiatric interview and in their school situation, a difficulty in relating to other persons. The impressions obtained from the Rorschach were that they scored comparatively low in reality testing.

The two characteristic trends—anti-pleasure and interpersonal isolation—seemed to add up to what is described as a schizoid personality. It is this personality nucleus that is at the center of several kinds of psychopathological individuals: the hermit, the misanthrope, the lone wolf criminal, the sadist, the schizophrenic, the unfeeling opportunist, the lover of totalitarianism, etc. These individuals all seem to have in common a lack of empathy, a lack of feeling for their fellowman. What kind of adolescents and adults these children of inadequate traditional mothers will turn into is highly problematic since much will depend upon the intensity of this schizoid drive. We are only indicating here, however, the direction the adult personality may take.

Some of these trends may be seen in the following examples. Fred was a husky, full-faced, red-headed boy who seemed to be quite apprehensive with a reactive self-sufficiency and withdrawal due to this apprehension. At the beginning of the interview the psychiatrist's small talk brought only monosyllabic responses. After awhile Fred became a little more spontaneous, although he always remained somewhat slow to smile. Throughout the interview there were many shrugs, much guardedness and blankness, and many initial "I don't knows." It required pressing by the psychiatrist in order to obtain any sort of content. When Fred was asked about his activities he said that, although he had lots of friends, when he was inside he preferred to be alone, because it becomes too crowded in the house and things might be messed up. During the time that questions were being asked, Fred took an order book from his pocket and had begun to write in the order book. When he was asked what the orders were for, he replied, "For different things." Fred picked up the toy-box without any hesitation when it was offered to him and said that he could make some funny figures out of the clay. Then, without hesitation or asking permission, he picked up a clay figure that had been made by another child and quite readily pulled off the head and limbs of it in order to use it for his own creation. In reply to a question about his emotional feelings he said that he becomes angry occasionally; however, he denied ever feeling sad or worried. He said that his brother might get him angry, but his parents never did. If Fred has any troubles he keeps them to himself rather than tell them to his father or mother. At first he said he did not dream, but when he was directly questioned about dreams, he recalled a few. One involved a monster that was going to eat him. At this point in the description of the dream, he took the father doll from the toy-box and made him walk home from work. This was followed by doll play in which he had the father doll fall over on his back and placed the mother and brother on the father's feet as the father was still lying on the ground. Then he added the baby doll to the group of brother and mother and had the father get up, go to the dolls who were sitting, and knock them all over. When the interview was terminated Fred did not respond to the good bye offered by the psychiatrist.

The school report on this child described him as only fairly well adjusted, not working up to capacity, stubborn with the teacher, distant with his fellow classmates, and rather solitary. The follow-up report at puberty described him as being better adjusted, now working up to mental capacity, but as still distant with his teacher and solitary with his classmates.

Fred's mother was a tense, anxious person who lacked warmth and described Fred as a good boy who had many good points, although mischievous. Fred was a sensitive child, very thoughtful and gentle, a dreamy type who would never think of talking back. Spiritually he was good, in fact he brought tears to her eyes because of the things he said that most little boys never think of. The mother impressed the social worker as being without understanding of the boy and having no empathy for any aggressive behavior. Her lack of feeling was exhibited when she laughed at Freddy's anxiety when he injured his hand in their washing-machine, and when she seemed to show no understanding of Freddy's jealous feeling about the next sibling. In regard to her family background mother gave a pollyannish, idealized picture especially of her own mother. She said her childhood was very happy, her parents got along "marvelously" and her mother was just "wonderful." Although not critical of her father she seemed somewhat detached in speaking to him.

We believe that Freddy illustrates the schizoid, withdrawn repercussions of exposure to an imperceptive, unfeeling mother who clings rigidly to an emulation of her own mother. In her idealization of her own mother, Freddy's mother is certainly repressing much hostility. The hostile lack of warmth is evident in her treatment of Freddy. Freddy, in contrast with Arthur who showed a lively zest in impersonal things like science, seemed to have no constructive outlets. His main solution appeared to be to keep away from potentially hostile people.

Our other example shows the effects of inadequate traditionalism in a girl. Irene was a sad, winsome girl with a faint smile on her lips. Although she was pleasant and co-operative and responded to small talk she seemed to be lacking in zest. When she was asked what she liked to do for fun, she gave the very unusual response that she liked to wash the bathtub and the sink. Further questions about what else she liked to do elicited the response that she liked to wash the floor and that outdoors she liked to sprinkle the lawn. She did say that she liked to play tag and Red Light when she was out with other children. However, when she was asked what she would most like to do if she had a free hour, i.e., play tag or wash the tub, she said: "Well if the tub was dirty, I would rather wash the tub." Irene enjoys reading books about older people, but doesn't like children's books too well. Her face did not light up when the toy-box was indicated. Even after considerable persuasion and reassurance, Irene maintained that she did not want to play with the toys. When asked what she did with her toys at home, she said: "We play like we are mothers and we have certain rooms to take care of; each of us has three rooms to take care of. We straighten out the furniture and do the dusting. We have dishes and food and we have our children play in the basement." Although she could not remember any pleasant dreams when she was asked about them, she did remember some unpleasant ones such as a mad animal being after her or someone trying to break into the house.

The school report on Irene described her as only fairly well adjusted, and that she was working up to mental capacity. However, she was stubborn toward the teacher, sought attention from other children, had a tendency to be carefree, and had some nervous mannerisms. The school report at puberty, however, still showed her only fairly well adjusted; she was no longer working up to mental capacity; she not only sought attention from the group but also interferred with them. She was a follower as she had been in latency.

Irene's mother was described by the social worker as quite warmly interested in her daughter. However, she was also described as controlling and not too sensitive to Irene's individual needs inasmuch as she saw the child almost completely as an extension of herself. Thus mother could be described as warmly dependable but not understanding. Regarding her own background, she spoke fondly and admiringly of her dominant mother and detachedly about her father.

It would seem that Irene had the advantage which Freddy did not have of a mother who was warmly interested. Irene did not show the severe and somewhat bizarre withdrawal that Freddy showed. However, the inhibition and avoidance of pleasure and self-individuation was prominent in Irene and had continued on to the age of twelve and thirteen.

In this chapter we have followed the central repercussion of traditionalism in the mother. This repercussion, an insulation of the psyche against stimuli may be of several varieties. When the insulation is alleviated by maternal understanding, there appears to be a zestful expansion along impersonal, abstract lines. When the insulation is aggravated by maternal non-understanding, there appears to be a non-productive, non-expansive withdrawal from outer stimuli.

CHAPTER VII

THE
REBELLIOUS
MOTHER

The rebellious mother, the type who wishes to be less strict and interfering than her own mother presents a sharp contrast to the traditional mother. Instead of the aspiration of traditionally observing the rules, this mother aspires to break with tradition. Rules for herself and her children are to be rebelled against. The degree of the rebellion, of course, was not as marked in our study mothers and children as it would be in families seeking help at a guidance clinic. It should be remembered that our study families were drawn from the conventional middle class and that one would not expect to see rebelliousness take the marked form of lawlessness or anarchy. Instead, the revolt appeared in certain nuances of the child's personality and in certain features of his development. (See Appendix E Table 19.)

The rebellious features are most apparent in those areas in which restrictions are usually placed on the child's behavior. For example, sexual curiosity, asking the parents questions regarding the origin of babies and why boys are different from girls, very frequently was present in these children, at least as reported by the mother. Ordinarily there are some taboos against this curiosity, but these mothers who had complained of their own mother's sexual prudery seemed intent on removing for their children the traditional barriers blocking the obtaining of sexual knowledge.

Another area of rebellion in the children's behavior was that of so-called oedipal feelings. It was in these children that we found the highest frequency of the son's preferring the mother to the father and the daughter's preferring the father to the mother. In other words, what Freud described as the classical oedipal situation—the love of the child for the opposite sexed parent—was most prominent in this group. This characteristic, we feel, is in keeping with the leitmotiv of the group; the rebellion against any rules interfering with pleasure. It is as though the mother, having been deprived in her own childhood by the silly rule that father belonged to mother, in her second childhood, as lived through her children, will see to it that her children will get what she feels is their due: the right to the opposite sexed parent.

Another area especially suited to rule breaking is that of learning bowel and bladder control. Certainly there is a restriction of a child's freedom of movement if he is taught that excretory functions are not to be performed at will, but rather are to be regulated by learning that the excretions are deposited in the lavatory. Typical of the rebellion against rules and interference with pleasure, the children of the rebellious mothers were most frequently reported to have difficulties in achieving and maintaining control of the bowel and bladder. We feel that while the more conscious part of mother is motivated to train the child in these habits, the less conscious and rebellious side is actually encouraging the child to rebel against these infringements on its autonomy.

Still another area where rule breaking can enter is in the intellectual functioning. Whereas the followers of tradition would become uncomfortable about a new idea, the rebellious minded would become uncomfortable about an old, traditional idea. It is almost incumbent upon the rebels to break with tradition, to become idol smashers. Thus it was not surprising that the Rorschach Test impression was that this group of children had the highest percentage of original responses in their perceptions of the cards. These children, also, most often used play material in a creative manner; they fashioned clay into figures or they enacted dramatic stories in their play with dolls.

As the originality represents the desirable repercussions of the rebellion theme, there are, of course, the undesirable repercussions. With no strong matrix of rules to live by and with almost a compulsion to break any established rules, these persons, if their rebelliousness is extreme, would be subject to marked instability. The Rorschach Test impression was that these children scored lowest in emotional stability. Also, by their own admission they were not able to tolerate frightening movies. The mothers themselves showed their instability by being frequently subject to depressions and moods.

What would seem to be present here is a rebellion in the child encouraged by the mother against her own weakly postulated rules. There is some striking evidence that she is working out her own rebellion to her own mother through her children. Antagonism by the child to the mother (as seen in the Despert Fable responses) appeared most frequently when the mother is rebellious to her own mother's strictness. While this hostile rebellion of the child to her is somewhat disconcerting and undesirable on a conscious level, it is quite satisfying on a deeper level inasmuch as it means that through her child she is able to attack a maternal authority figure.

It was easier in the rebellious than in the traditional study group to see vivid, concrete indications of the rule-breaking orientation. The rebellious, rule-breaking, authority attacking tendency was noted both against the mother and against the outside world. In our study cases, for example, we saw one boy whose mother had reported that when he had been three years old she could not cure his tendency to bite his playmates, his younger brother, and herself (although not the father). Mother had been rather helpless in this situation and said that the father gradually brought about a cessation of the biting by being firm about it. Her own mother was described as being very domineering and strict. She would frequently rebel and criticize her mother. We felt that the boy's biting had been really incited and abetted by his mother's own rebellious, attacking attitude to a maternal authority.

In examples apart from our study, an eight-year-old girl was referred to the Institute for Juvenile Research for unruly behavior in school. The mother reported that her daughter, at the age of four, would kick her in the stomach. At the time this occurred the mother was pregnant. This mother quite easily admitted considerable anger at her own mother's strictness and interference in her life.

An illustration of sexual misbehavior was the case of a boy, fifteen, referred because of sexual misconduct with younger girls. He described his father as being strict but his mother as being easy going and permissive. The mother, who was quite protective of her son, said of herself: "I was too obedient as a child; I had to help so much at home; my mother made me. I didn't have any time to get into mischief." In this case the rebellion of the mother against her own mother was somewhat masked than in others, but there was a decided hint that only the rules laid down by her mother prevented her from getting into the same kind of mischief as her indulged son was getting into.

Finally, concerning rule-breaking in the area of excretory functions, a mother seen in private psychiatric practice mentioned as one of her concerns the fact that her five-year-old son would soil himself in the kindergarten room, the back yard, the living room, but seldom in the lavatory. Since she was the oldest in her family she identified herself closely with this son who was the older of her two boys. At the age of thirty-three, she was still bitterly rebellious toward her mother, describing her as hopelessly middle-class, conventional, and lacking in understanding of her daughter's needs for freedom of thought and artistic leanings.

Perhaps the most clear-cut example of how the mother's rebelliousness to her own mother manifested itself in her children was seen in those cases where the resented, domineering grandmother was living in the household. One such striking example of this was a three-year-old girl referred to the Institute by her mother for "convulsions." It was revealed that the maternal grandmother had been living with the family since the child's birth. During this time the mother had been trying unsuccessfully to stop grandmother from interfering with the way the household was being managed. Mother had become increasingly bitter and angry about the situation. The child had been free of these convulsions during only one period: when the grandmother had been away for a month visiting another daughter. The rebellious, attacking component in the girl became apparent when it was learned that her grandmother was more upset by the convulsions than was her mother. On two occasions the grandmother had fainted when the child had had a convulsion. It seemed possible that the mother's rage at her own mother was being communicated to the child and that she was attacking her own mother through her child's seizures.

CHILDREN OF ADEQUATE
REBELLIOUS MOTHERS

When we divided the total group of rebellious mothers on the basis of whether they had accomplished their aspiration, a group emerged which was understanding and accepting of the child's individuality. We have designated these mothers as the adequate rebellious group. On the basis of various diagnostic items their children showed a personality characterized by buoyancy, flexibility, and an aggressiveness of a constructive nature. (See Appendix E. Table 20.) For example, these children were much more frequently described by the school as leaders. Whereas they were reported by the mothers as having shown open jealousy reactions on the birth of a younger sibling, the present relationship to the sibling contained only mild rivalry.

Reflective of the buoyant, flexible personality was the school's description of their moods. Many of the children in the study had been described by the school as having some fixity of mood: the child was mainly serious or mainly carefree. These children, however, were described as having an emotional response appropriate to the situation. Thus, whereas the mainly carefree child would be appropriately carefree at recess but inappropriately so during recitation, and the mainly serious child would be appropriately serious during recitation and inappropriately serious during recess, the children we are now discussing were appropriately carefree during recess and appropriately serious during study.

On the liability side, these children showed a few trends that may indicate repercussions of undue individualism and undue tradition-breaking tendencies promoted by the mother. One such liability may be reflected in the Rorschach Test impression of their being comparatively low in reality testing and in acceptance of the code of the group. This would be a mild repercussion of their rule-breaking tendencies. In general, these children might be said to face the problem of not having enough limits or controls. Their growth was not tied either to a matrix of tradition or suppressive control. They could not rest in the arms of either a benevolent or malevolent authority figure. Their plight might be that represented in the story of a child who was attending a progressive nursery school where individuality was stressed. One day she was found in tears by the teacher and when asked what the trouble was the child plaintively responded: "Do I always have to do what I want to do?"

An example of this aggressive personality in our study group was Peter, a small, blond, nine-year-old, very well dressed in a blue serge suit. Although at the beginning of the interview he was somewhat uneasy and polite, he soon opened up. In the interview room, he was about to push a big chair up to the desk when the psychiatrist said that he himself would do it. Pete then said that he was used to doing work and that he liked it. He was asked what kind of work he did: "Anything my father does—shovel coal, sweep sidewalks." By this time Peter was beginning to relax and when he was asked to describe the kind of fun he liked to have he reported that he liked to play with guns, Indians and Robbers, and that he plays with his boy friends and his 50 cousins. "When I come home from the show my sister and

50 cousins are home and have taken toys out. I like to play guns with my seventeen-month-old brother." In reply to the psychiatrist's astonishment that the brother could play with guns, Pete said: "Oh, yeah, he can shoot a gun now. Once I pointed a gun at him and my father leveled the water hose at me and got me full force." Pete revealed some anxiety beneath the aggressiveness when he animatedly said: "Oh, boy, when I go near a hospital I am ready to keel over. I can't see a dead person." One of his three wishes was that he get ahead in school. When he was asked if he was not ahead in school, he replied: "Oh, no, I want to be 'way ahead.'" Pete's answer to what was his preferred age was to be younger, and he admitted that he would rather be four years old again so he would not have to go to school, and in fact, would not have to do anything. As an older age he would prefer thirteen so that he could graduate: "You see, my mother wants me to go to high school and college." At this point he gave a sigh and continued, "and I want to get through with it as soon as possible so I can relax."

The school report at the age of eight and nine described Pete as well adjusted, working up to mental capacity, very co-operative with the teacher and the school program, friendly with his classmates, mixed well with them, a leader in his group, and that his moods were appropriately serious and carefree, depending on the situation. The school report at twelve and thirteen described him as very well adjusted, very co-operative with the school program, and still working up to mental capacity.

Pete's mother was described by the social worker as being rather warmly interested in her son but as having a tendency to become anxious if too much dependency and support were required of her. On the other hand, she was quite sensitive to her son's needs, empathic and understanding of his aggressive and negativistic tendencies, and had insight into herself. Thus, according to our method of designation, she would be termed "understanding but not dependable."

Pete's mother described her father as wonderfully kind and understanding. However, she had considerably mixed feelings about her mother who, she said, was the dominant parent. Her particular grievance was that her mother had not allowed her to pursue her favorite hobbies in grade or high school. Her resolve had been not to interfere with her children's interests the way her mother had with hers.

Thus Pete illustrates the boy with aggressive qualities resulting from an adequate rebelliousness in the mother. One detected that Pete was on the go, that he had more understanding than he had dependence satisfactions from his mother. One also saw that his mother was attempting to relive her balked interests through her children. Although the pace of her children's growth may not be leisurely, she was not confusing them by placing contradictory obstacles in their path.

CHILDREN OF INADEQUATE
REBELLIOUS MOTHERS

We have designated as inadequate rebellious mothers that group whose aspirations it was to be less controlling and interfering than their own mothers and yet who were found by the social worker to be insensitive, controlling, and interfering. The children of such mothers seemed to have personalities characterized by passive resistance. It had appeared as though the rebelliousness, which had been the characteristic of the whole group, had become intertwined with the trait of conformity, so that superficially the child may not have appeared rebellious, but inwardly he was being quite so. (See Appendix E, Table 21.)

The psychological maneuver that these children seemed to use was to abide so strictly by the letter of the law that they easily were able to obstruct and oppose the wishes of others without appearing to be rebellious. If the child had been instructed to wash his hands before dinner, and he wanted to delay the dinner in order to revenge himself on his parents, all he had to do was to engage in a prolonged washing of his hands. If he was reprimanded for this he could explain: "But you told me to get my hands clean before I ate." This is the same maneuver as that used by the bureaucrat who wants to use his power without seeming to be openly dictatorial. By a strict adherence to each letter of the law he is able to tie the other person into knots and still claim that he is only doing his right and proper duty. In other words, he is actually using the rules in a hostile, aggressive way.

The origin of this maneuver might be seen in the behavior of the mothers. These mothers were not only controlling, but characteristically they were open, harsh disciplinarians who were admittedly frequently angry and who released their anger rather than holding it back. (The inadequate traditional mother was infrequently angry and she held her anger back.) The children were thus afraid to be openly rebellious (even though one aspect of the mothers encouraged them to be so) and the only recourse they had was to be latently rebellious under a facade of conformity. Their position was not unlike that of servants of a harsh, disliked, master who, under polite "Yes sir's," "No, sir's" and "I really do not know, sir's" quietly obstruct and sabotage the wishes of the master by just not doing rather than refusing to do it.

This maneuver and the general personality characteristics were well described by Freud in his description of the anal character who was stubborn, meticulous, and parsimonious. He felt that this type of character resulted from trauma such as a child suffers when undergoing bowel training. Many writers have extended the causation to mean too much interference by the mother in the child's autonomy at that time. For a long time it has been known that at the age of two or three the most frequent word on the child's lips is "No." Therefore, fixation of the child's personality around the negativistic oppositional maturational level is influenced by mother's interference with the child's surgent individuality. (Bowel and bladder training disturbances were high in the entire rebellious group.)

Perhaps the more striking evidence of this personality trend is that the mothers described their problems with the child in terms of passive opposition. In other words, the mother would say that the child just got on her nerves with his dawdling, or that sending the child to school in the morning was an ordeal because he claimed he had a stomach-ache and couldn't find his shoes. (The adequate rebellious mothers described their children in terms of active opposition. The mother would say, "Peter, run this errand for me," and the child would reply, "Why don't you ask Johnny?") The other evidences of conforming perfectionism used to defend against criticism and also to control others were seen in the Rorschach Test responses, in which perceptions of form were very good, but only the most correct form perceptions were seen. One child protected himself by giving only three responses, all of which were very good form, but he also succeeded in frustrating the psychologist who desired more responses. Their adherence to the letter of the law might be reflected in the Rorschach finding of a comparatively high degree of acceptance of the code of the group.

In general, most of the diagnostic items seen in this group spoke of a pseudo-conforming, passively resistant character. The causative factor seemed to stem from the behavior of the mother with the child. On the one hand, either by example or by encouragement, she incited the child to rebel, while on the other hand, in being angrily controlling, she squelched the child's active rebellious impulses. The solution for the child, if he was to be in rapport with such a contradictory mother, was to rebel *and* to conform, and this he did by a literal adherence to rules; an adherence which protected him from criticism and yet allowed him to thwart others.

What showed up mostly in the interview behavior of these children was a certain evasiveness and difficulty in getting any clear-cut statement. It would seem as though the child were aware of the examiner's wish to get at some material and, out of both a fear and a desire to thwart, could not give the examiner what was wanted. An example of this was Mary, a slender eight-year-old who showed a shy, jerking nervousness. Frequently she did not finish her sentences leaving the psychiatrist in doubt as to what she really meant. She gave, or attempted to give the impression that she was hesitant and doubtful of her own abilities. She avoided much talk about herself, was very evasive about her feelings and preferences, and preferred instead to concentrate on the clay doll. She picked out the dolls when the toybox was indicated and began rolling the clay. When she was asked whether she liked clay, she said: "Yes, if I can get it to be round, but I don't know if I can." Later when she was asked if she liked to draw, she replied: "I don't know if I can do it well." Mary was asked about her emotional feelings, to which she said that she did get angry. However, when she was asked what she would become angry about, she said, "I don't exactly know, I just get angry." At that point she turned to the clay saying, "I think I'll make a snowman." She was asked specifically whether she got mad at the other children. To this she responded, "Yes, when they play something I don't want to play." About anger toward her teacher she said: "I don't think so, except that teacher screams at the other kids and it sounds so horrible." She did not think that she got angry at her mother or her father—at least she could not remember exactly. And again at that point she turned back to the clay doll. It seemed that throughout the interview, whenever she was asked a question, there was an immediate denial in turning to the clay which she had been offered and with which she could legitimately be occupied.

In the history given by her mother Mary was reported as having been constipated since birth. Toilet training had begun at six months but because of Mary's constipation it had been very difficult to regulate her. Mary still had a special time in the evening when she must go to the toilet. The school report described her as very well adjusted, co-operative, friendly, and working up to mental capacity. At twelve or thirteen the school reported a drop in adjustment in that she was now distant with her schoolmates rather than friendly.

The social worker evaluated Mary's mother as lacking in understanding as well as in dependability. The mother would become anxious and uneasy of any negativistic or aggressive aspects appearing in Mary's behavior and to reduce her anxiety she would be controlling of Mary. Furthermore, mother had excessive need for Mary to achieve. (Her dependability was impaired also inasmuch as it decreased whenever there was socio-economic stress.)

Mary's mother described her own background in rather negative terms. She was detached about her father who had not taken much interest in the family. More important, though, for our purposes, she resented her dominant mother's need to run her life. She had resolved not to interfere that much in her own child's life.

We see in Mary the typical passive resistance which is a repercussion of inadequate rebelliousness in mother. Although mother was perceptive of the defects in her own mother's mothering, for some reason she was not able to act much differently with her own child. The child then faced a contradiction: an incitement to rebel and a squelching of the rebellion.

Another example was Carl, a pale, blond boy, soft and frail looking. Although he seemed to relate quickly and could talk easily at first, as the interview progressed he showed more and more a certain slow deliberation which, of course, slowed up the interview. When he was asked whether he knew why he was here, he said: "Yes, to find out why good boys are good." Later he said that he becomes awfully mad at his sisters sometimes when he makes something like a vase and colors it, and they break it. He tried to get back at them in some way, but he was careful to let the psychiatrist know that *he* did not break things. An example of his caginess and worry lest the authority figure criticize him was revealed in his play. When the play-box was indicated, Carl said he had been looking at it all the time. When the psychiatrist indicated that he could play with anything he wanted to, Carl looked at the box, then looked at the psychiatrist, and then said: "Oh, I see what you mean. If I pick up the guns, you think my ambition is to be a cowboy and movie actor." Finally, Carl picked up the clay and began to fashion it. He spent about five minutes very meticulously making a bird, which turned out to be very good. An indication of how he was attempting to control his aggressiveness was shown in a dream. "I dreamt I was in the circus and I was a lion-tamer. One of the lions sprang at me and I woke up." An example of his fear that his hostile, destructive impulses will emerge and get him into trouble was indicated by his unusual answer when he was asked about his worries. He said that he worried sometimes that the nice dishes his aunt brought back from Scotland might be broken by someone. These dishes were not metal and so special care had to be exercised in using them. He worries that someone might accidentally break one of these nice dishes.

The school report described Carl as only fairly well adjusted, serious, and not working up to mental capacity, average in co-operation with authorities, distant with the children, although he mixed with them. The follow-up at twelve or thirteen was not forthcoming. On the Rorschach Test he gave 16 responses and all of them were of very good form.

Carl's mother was evaluated as not sensitive to the boy's needs nor accepting of his negativism. Regarding her own family, in addition to being detached about her dominant father, she had bitter feelings against her mother. Her mother, she felt, controlled her through martyrdom and clinging. Whenever she tried to take an aggressive step or would talk up to her mother, the latter would become uneasy or cry. Carl's mother seemed to have a similar uneasy reaction when Carl became openly aggressive. Thus, as we noted in the case of Mary, the aspiration to be less controlling failed in its accomplishment.

We have in this chapter explored in some detail the repercussions of a rebellious attitude in the mother. The personality nuances or fixed pattern imprinted on the child seems to have a greater potentiality for social good or evil than those resulting from traditional or dependent mothers, inasmuch as rule-breaking is unique in its capacity to improve or disrupt social order. Thus, from the rebellious component of our society, with its assets of freedom and its liability of instability, will issue forth the stimulus for change which is counterbalanced by the more corrective and binding features of the traditional and dependent orientations.

CHAPTER VIII

THE
DEPENDENT
MOTHER

In this last chapter on the motherhood themes we will be concerned with the dependent mother. These are the mothers whose complaints about their own mothers had been to the effect that they had not been affectionate or interested enough in them. Their aspirations with their own children were to be more loving and interested. The children of such mothers seemed to be characterized by a *quest for pleasure—a seeking for interpersonal warmth.* (See Appendix E, Table 22.) This quest for pleasure is different from the necessity to break rules as seen in the children of the rebellious mothers. The pleasure oriented children were more interested in the pleasure rewards and satisfactions than in attacking the barriers that stood between them and the pleasure. The differences might be represented in the following hypothetical situation: A pleasure-seeking boy and a rebellious boy approach a pool of water in front of which is a sign, "No swimming allowed." If the pleasure-seeking boy really felt like having an enjoyable swim, he might disregard the sign and go swimming. The rebellious boy would not be activated by the pleasure of swimming, but would go into the water if he were in a mood to challenge any limitations on his freedom of action such as would be implied in the sign, "No swimming allowed."

There were several evidences of this pleasure trend. In the psychiatric interview these children almost invariably reported pleasant wishfulfilment dreams. Their responses on the Despert Fables concerning the young calf who was told to leave his mother's milk and go and eat grass were seldom that the calf should go out and eat grass, but rather that in one form or another the calf should stay close to the source of milk: the mother cow. Their orientation toward interpersonal warmth and interchange of emotional affect was evidenced by the finding that not one of these dependent children failed to give a color response on the Rorschach Test.

The one liability of this group, as would be expected, was a comparative low frustration tolerance as revealed by the Rorschach Test. The desire of these children for pleasure probably made them more susceptible to frustration than children who were more accustomed to doing without. It was as though there was an immediacy to their pleasure wishes, as though they had become habituated to the satisfactions and pleasures and underwent a sort of withdrawal tension when gratification was not forthcoming.

Both the pleasure-seeking tendencies and the susceptibility to frustration can be accounted for by the fact that the mothers were mostly interested in the question of affection and interest. To make up for the real or alleged deprivations of their own childhood, they were more or less compelled not to deprive the child just as the rebellious mothers were compelled not to require the child to obey the rules. If these mothers exposed their children to even normal disinterest their guilty uncomfortableness forced them to make it up to them in the form of indulgence. Thus the children became habituated to an abnormal amount of pleasurable indulgence and felt frustrated if they received less than they were accustomed to.

We did not find an abundance of case material either in our study or in clinical cases which would illustrate this pleasure-seeking orientation. What we saw in the study cases were examples of mothers and children seeking interpersonal warmth rather than sheer pleasure. For instance, one mother who complained of cold disinterest on the part of her own mother found considerable gratification in being included in her husband's family which she described as affectionate and warm. One girl whose mother was critical of her own mother's lack of affection made the interesting statement that she had never wanted to have a vacation from school because she was teacher's pet. It was so nice being the pet of the teacher that being away from school was actually a punishment to this child. Some of the dependent mothers made the characteristic statement that it would be very lonesome around the house if there were no small babies and children whom one could love and be loved by. We saw also in this study some indirect effects of the boy receiving too much warmth from a dependent mother. These mothers, who required much interpersonal attention and warmth, would sometimes take their sons to bed with them if the father was out of town. In the psychiatric examination a few of these boys showed a fearful, nervous, startle reaction as though they had been apprehended in the act of looking into the jam pot. Thus, we felt we saw some guilt and anxiety in these boys who had been utilized by the warmth-seeking mothers.

In the clinical cases referred to the Institute, the complaint by mother of coldness from her own mother was frequently associated with the presenting problem in the child of stealing. One child was reported as stealing from his mother's pocketbook or from the teacher's desk and then treating all the other children with the proceeds. This was not a destructive kind of stealing accompanied by breaking and entering or stealing with a gang, but was rather a solitary attempt to gain a symbol of love, the proceeds were then given to other children in order to win their affection and interest. We feel that the mother's feeling of deprivation is transmitted to the child and that, in a way, he has mother's permission to obtain the wherewithal to make him feel loved. That stealing was not reported by the study mothers who were dependent, we believe, points to the conclusion that stealing is associated not only with the child's feeling of deprivation, but also with a certain standard of conduct which is not usually seen in stable families such as we had in our study group. In the clinic cases in which stealing was reported there was not only the complaint of deprivation but also the mode of conduct (how one should solve the problem of lack of affection) was often in the direction of delinquency or criminality. We believe this was due to the greater number of broken homes in the clinic cases.

CHILDREN OF ADEQUATE
DEPENDENT MOTHERS

Following the procedures used in the other motherhood theme groups, we divided the entire dependent group on the basis of whether the social worker found the mothers to be actually dependable. If the mother was actually warmly dependable, we designated her as adequate inasmuch as she had accomplished her aspiration. The children of adequate dependent mothers seemed to be characterized by a high degree of interpersonal responsiveness. This trend was evident not so much in their relation to social institutions as it was in their relation to people in social situations. They presented a picture of the very likeable individuals who primarily wish to be with people, enjoy them, and perhaps feel at a loss without them. They look upon interpersonal situations as an area where they give and receive affection and warmth. (See Appendix E, Table 23.)

As to our evidence, in the psychiatric interview these children had what might be called "bubbling" affect. Whereas other children on meeting the psychiatrist showed ordinary interest or enthusiasm, or a dampening of zest, or even a hostile disinterest, these children much more often showed a bubbling enthusiasm, as though they had met a new friend and were going to have a good time with him. In telling about their sad feelings they almost always placed them in a social interpersonal context. Whereas many of the other children said they felt sad because they had lost their favorite gun, or because they had seen their little brother get a spanking, these children put their sadness in terms of social lonesomeness, i.e., "because there was no one around to play with."

On the Rorschach Test color responses were invariably reported and were predominant over reports of human movement. This is an indication of the extratensive, the outer direction of living, which is in contrast with the good, traditional child who had a tendency toward imaginative inner living.

The origins of this flair, this need for enjoyment of people, appeared to be traceable to the mother-child relationship. It was in these children that there was reported the highest frequency of contentment in infancy. It is in infancy that contentment depends on the attentiveness of the interested mother to the needs of the child. From such an enjoyable experience with one person the child had apparently developed the ability and the need to repeat similar enjoyable experiences later with other people. We saw other evidences in these affectionate, dependent mothers of their own ability and need to be interested in the next person. Of all the mothers studied they related extremely well to the psychiatrist and to the social worker, being pleasant, spontaneous, and co-operative to the extent of sometimes being anxious to please. The other evidence was that at the end of the interview with the psychiatrist characteristically they showed an interest in their child by asking questions about what we found in our examination of him. All in all, we got the impression that these affectionate, dependent mothers were somewhat anxiously concerned that the next person was getting enough from them, as though their peace of mind depended on the other person being well fed and happy. The following are examples of these trends.

Stephen was an alert, friendly, small, eight-year-old, who arose to greet the psychiatrist in the waiting-room. He was full of zest, yet respectful, and talkative when given the green light. He was moderately restless and there was some nail-biting during the hour. His interests and what he does for fun were of the active type, although not as aggressive as the boys described under the heading of rebellious personality. He said he liked other things than school, for instance the game of Goldfinch. The game about birds was played about 60 times a week with his brother and father. He liked to play baseball and football, too, but he did not emphasize gun shooting and gangs. For example, his three wishes did not include guns or shooting anyone. They were to be the captain of a baseball team, a train engineer, and to own a ranch. Sometimes he felt sad when he had to stay in the house while he saw the other boys enjoying the game of baseball. Stephen reported that he had to be outside also when there was a group playing because his mother would never let him stay in on a good day. (His mother in describing her complaints about her own mother said that she was too disinterested in getting her children out to play with other children.) The school report described Stephen as very well adjusted, co-operative, friendly, and working up to mental capacity.

Steve's mother was evaluated as being very warmly interested in her son and dependable. In addition, she was evaluated as "understanding." She was enthusiastically positive about her father, but detached concerning her mother. She described her mother as quite passive, as never being sufficiently interested in her or her siblings to prompt, urge, or interest them in any pleasurable activities with other people. Steve's mother, according to our evaluation, succeeded in her aspiration to be more interested than her own mother had been. Her child showed the repercussions of this resolve in the form of a strong trend to be with people and to be liked by them.

Caroline was a very pleasant, obliging girl, who was soft but still had zest. She seemed to make a point of getting along with people. There was an anticipatory smile constantly playing around her face. However, when she talked seriously, as about some abuse, she stopped smiling. She had a comfortable, trusting relationship with the psychiatrist, and was not defensive. There was enough animation so that when she became involved in telling about her dream, she in a way acted it out. Regarding fun, she said that she liked to dance, does toe dancing, and that in fact she was to dance in school that day. When she was asked whether she has any fun with her mother, she said:"Oh, yes. We go shopping together and she takes me practically every place." Her socializing needs were revealed in one of her three wishes, which was to have a whole lot of friends. She has felt sad at times such as when her girl friend, Barbara, went away to California, and Caroline missed her. Her concern about how well liked she was came out while she was drawing. She asked many questions of the psychiatrist such as whether he thought a classmate, another girl interviewed in the study, was very nice, and did he think she was nicer than Caroline. She looked at the psychiatrist frequently during the examination to see what effect she was having on him.

The school report on Caroline described her as very well adjusted, working up to mental capacity, co-operative with the authorities, friendly and mixing well with her peers. The school report at twelve to thirteen showed that the very good adjustment had continued in all ways.

Caroline's mother was evaluated as being warmly interested in her daughter. (However, there was an impairment of understanding in that she was over-identified with her daughter and would not tolerate any negativistic behavior.) She was very fond of her own father, but had resentful feelings toward her mother. She said her mother was more interested in other people's values than in her own children. It bothered her considerably that her mother had never built up her children's self-confidence with praise, but rather took the teacher's side against the mother. In her vicarious second childhood, she is pro-herself as well as pro-Caroline. Although there is unmistakable pressure on Caroline to realize mother's aspirations, there seemed to be few contradictions placed in Caroline's path.

CHILDREN OF INADEQUATE
DEPENDENT MOTHERS

When we turned to our last sub-grouping, dependent mothers who were not warmly dependable to their children, we obtained a somewhat less distinct diagnostic item profile. (See Appendix E, Table 24.) However, what we did see was in essence the picture of an overly mature child, a child who had sacrificed his own needs to be taken care of in order to cater to the needs of a dependent mother. Whereas the affectionate, adequate, dependent mother gave to the child possibly in order to enjoy vicariously a second childhood, the non-affectionate dependent mother took from the child as though she were in her first childhood, and the child was her original mother. Probably the clearest indication of this was the response of the children to one

Despert Fable. In this fable there was a little bird in a tree while the father bird was in another tree and the mother bird was in still another. A wind comes up and the little bird has to leave his tree. Where does he fly? Most of the other children responded: To the tree in which mother was, or (illogically) the tree in which there was both mother and father. But of these children, not even one responded that he would fly to a tree containing one or both parents. The response was: "Fly to another tree." This kind of a response indicated, we believe, how futile it appeared to the child to wish for or expect any help from the mother figure. Instead of relying on this kind of help, he becomes prematurely self-reliant.

The Rorschach Test impressions indicated that these children were comparatively low in frustration tolerance and intellectual vigor. This could be accounted for by the fact that very little had been put into the child by the mother. In other words, the idea emerged of a child pulling himself up by his own bootstraps. There was a constant drain on his energy in sustaining the mother. Consequently, with the world on his shoulders, he became frustrated easily and did not have enough energy to sustain vigorous effort.

In the mother-child relationship the children differed distinctly from the affectionate adequate dependent group. Instead of a contented infancy, a fretful one was more often reported. This would be consistent with the hypothesis that the mother would be more attentive to her own needs than to those of the child. The more the child would cry, the more mother would feel he was a drain on her easily exhausted resources. Further evidence of mother's needful dependency was that more frequently than in any of the other sub-groupings of mothers, she described herself as quite prone to worry. When a mother worries she becomes the object of therapeutic attention and it is encumbent on those around her to leave their own tasks and shelve their own needs and desires in order to give succor to the worrying, needful mother.

An example of this trend was Harriet, who was an unattractive, bespectacled girl with an adenoidal expression, and quite devoid of any spontaneity. It was difficult to arouse her to any activity since she evidenced little pep or enthusiasm. She was quite co-operative but rarely emphasized her statements. At times the psychiatrist would catch her looking at him in a shy, speculative manner, but when he met her eye, Harriet would quickly look away. When the toy-box was indicated to her, she showed her lack of zest by saying, "What am I supposed to do with it?" When the psychiatrist told her she could do anything she liked with it, she exhibited the first spontaneity as she told the psychiatrist she was going to take a course in art and that she liked to make things at home. Then she began, in a very lackadasical manner, to fashion the clay. Her skepticism about expecting any pleasure was revealed when she was asked to describe three wishes. Instead of the anticipatory smile that was usually seen in the other children, she seriously considered the prospect of getting three wishes, and then said: "I don't know." Even after pressure, she said: "I can't think of anything right now." When she was asked whether she had everything she needed, she said she had about everything.

Harriet's mother, who had complained that her own mother was very cold and unaffectionate, revealed in her interviews both with the social worker and the psychiatrist, that she required much courtesy from her children and consideration of her feelings. She had not been surprised to receive a letter of invitation to the study because Harriet had been no trouble since the day she was born, except for some fretfulness around the age of six months. She has been a very sweet child to rear, has gone out of her way to please people, and has been very respectful toward adults. Mother reported that she had felt very good during pregnancy because she received so much attention. Her father had always babied her and his men friends had complained that he spoiled her for other men. Later she revealed that about every month or so she goes through a nervous crisis with irritability and depression and that her two children (boy and girl) as well as her husband hover around her and attend to her for three or four days until she comes out of it.

The school report on Harriet revealed that she was not working up to mental capacity, had some nervous habits, was only average in relation to the teacher, but that she got along well with her schoolmates. At twelve to thirteen there was no follow-up report available.

The following case of Judith again illustrates this over-maturity. Judith was a pretty, dark-haired girl of eight, who seemed quite composed for her age and had a maturity that was out of keeping with her young years. She did not appear shy, and yet she was not forward. She gave the impression of quiet competence and was quite feminine. Her tendency to look out for others rather than to be looked out for herself was revealed in her statement when she was offered the toy-box that she was too old to play with dolls, and that she would rather be older than she was so that she could baby sit. She said that she never had done baby-sitting but she did like to take babies for walks.

The mother in this case was an attractive brunette who was quite cooperative, warm, and sensitive. However, she did not seem too competent, in fact, she appeared much less competent than her daughter. It was revealed that mother had had a nervous breakdown two years previously and that even before then she had been rather shaky in her competence as a mother. Judith had been thrown on her own and had become the manager of the house, along with father, while mother had been recovering from these nervous crises.

The school report on Judith disclosed that she was only fairly well adjusted. The main difficulty was that she was overly serious and not working up to mental capacity. However, the school report four years later, at the age of thirteen, showed her to be very well adjusted, friendly with her teacher and classmates, working up to mental capacity, and having a less serious mood.

A very unusual repercussion of the mother being an inadequate dependent type was seen in a fourteen-year-old girl referred to the Institute. The cause for referral was bizarre enough that the possibility of an incipient psychosis was strongly entertained. The complaint by the mother and by the school was that the girl talked to an imaginary companion and had little to do with her classmates or other children in the neighborhood. What differentiated this girl from the typical pre-psychotic personality was that she was not hallucinating, she knew it was an imaginary companion, the conversation was animated and zestful, and she did her school work diligently. The teacher thought it rather pitiful to see this attractive girl walking to school, carrying on an interested animated conversation with an imaginary companion.

In the psychiatric interview she seemed sober and over-mature. She said that since she was quite small she has talked with this imaginary girl companion and found the conversations interesting and relaxing. The Rorschach Test showed no evidence of faulty appreciation of reality. In the interview with the mother she complained of unhappiness in her childhood because her own mother had been so busy and interested in other things that she never would talk with her. The mother revealed that she could not get her own daughter to talk with her because she was always preoccupied with this imaginary companion. The mother told of feeling lonesome and neglected by friends, relatives, and her husband.

It was our opinion that this inadequate dependent mother tried to make a conversing mother out of her daughter. In other words, she wanted to reverse their roles, making herself the needful daughter and making her daughter the giving, interested mother. In line with our impression of the group of inadequate dependent mothers, we surmised that the daughter felt drained by her mother's dependency needs, felt that other people would similarly drain her, and in protection had erected a barricade. Behind the barricade she carried on interesting conversations with an imaginary person, whom she could summon or dismiss at will—in short a type of person who made no demands on her.

All three of these excerpts illustrate, we believe, the failure on the mother's part to remedy a defect from her past. The mother craved dependent attention, resented not receiving it from her own mother, and yet could not give it to her own child. As we have said, the mother made a mother out of her own child. The child had its own dependent needs stimulated by identification with such a mother, and yet could not obtain gratification for those needs. The only solution seemed to be withdrawal from emotional contact with people. During this withdrawal, the child went through the external motions of accommodating and not being a burden to others.

The Shadow of the Grandfather

CHAPTER IX

EFFECTS ON MOTHER'S SEXUALITY

Up to this point we have been primarily concerned with mother and her mother. We have been interested in how mother's feeelings about how she was mothered influenced the way she mothered her own children and how the children were affected by this chain of events. Now, however, our attention returns to the relationship of mother to her father. Although we shall find in the last of the ensuing four chapters that this relationship is in part an outgrowth or by-product of mother's relationship to her mother, it is more convenient for descriptive purposes to consider mother's feelings toward her father as though they stand alone.

The importance of mother's feelings toward her father was most strikingly driven home for us when we obtained the follow-up reports at puberty. No other diagnostic item was as crucially related to the reported pubertal adjustment as was the nature of these feelings. In essence, the finding was that *good pubertal adjustment of the child was highly associated with a positive affectionate feeling of mother toward her own father, whereas only fair pubertal adjustment was associated with a negative feeling.* (See Appendix E, Table 25.)

Although we had not anticipated this finding, we should not have been overly surprised by it. According to psychoanalytic theory, a positive father-daughter relationship represents the final point in the daughter's psycho-sexual maturation. In the final phase of maturation

[83]

(around the age of five), the daughter represses her frankly sexual feelings toward her father, and develops a positive, affectionate feeling toward him which is later transferred to another male at the time of dating, courtship, and marriage.

Thus, it was not surprising that such a positive feeling of mother for her father would be associated with her child adjusting well at puberty. As the child is encountering the problems of puberty, he is emotionally supported in continuity with a mother who has had a satisfying experience in these matters. She has lived through the experiencing of her own erotic and aggressive impulses so that she is not overly intrigued by the child's erotic needs, nor rivalrous because the child is going to get something she did not get, nor ashamed, guilty, and anxious because the child is about to embark upon the forbidden, "dirty" area of adult sexuality.

Long before puberty (even as early as the ages of two and three) the mother has been in a position to communicate to the child her attitudes about adult sexuality, and the child long has been in a position to be affected by her attitudes. However, it is at puberty that everything becomes real for mother and child. The child is pressured by his individual drives and by the social situation. The mother cannot be oblivious to the sexual budding of the child, to the emergence of the secondary sex characteristics.

The child's psychological equipment for handling the new pressures is what he has previously taken over from the mother. The mother's equipment is a memory of how she went through the pubertal phase. A pleasant memory would make her confident about the child's negotiating this phase successfully; and unpleasant memory would tend to make her feel anxious or pessimistic. Her reactions to her memories would be transmitted to the child and thus would affect his adjustment. The sequence of mother's own past being reactivated by a growth step in the child and the reactivation having a resulting effect on the child, has been aptly designated by Hilgard as an "anniversary" reaction.

From this finding again we saw evidence of how intimately the child's growth potential is linked with the mother's capacity for growth. Previously we had commented to the effect that the child's successful latency growth was highly associated with mother's ability to grow away from her own mother. Thus the best adjusted latency children had mothers who were seemingly able to perceive what deficiencies were present in their own mothers and were able to remedy them with their children. In other words, they were not hopelessly attached to or identified with their own mothers. Similarly, the presence of positive feelings toward their fathers indicated that they could move away sufficiently from their mothers to be positively attached to their fathers.

It appeared that both kinds of growth steps away from mother's mother were necessary for the child's sustained adjustment. A corrected mothering (if correction was necessary) was associated with a good latency adjustment, but did not guarantee a good pubertal adjustment. A positive step from mother's mother to mother's father was associated with good puberty adjustment, but did not guarantee a good latency. However, *only when both growth steps were present —corrected mothering and a comfortable moving to mother's father —were the children well-adjusted both during latency and at puberty.* As would be expected, *when neither growth step had been accomplished by mother, the children had unfavorable adjustments both during latency and at puberty.* (See Appendix E, Table 26.)

With this finding we were better able to understand some trends that we discussed in an earlier chapter. It will be recalled that we had noted that the child's good puberty adjustment was associated with the presence during the latency period of such lively behavior as sexual curiosity and sibling rivalry. We suggested then that one task of the latency period was to retain the impulses and sufficient liveliness so that the child would be prepared for the surgent pubertal period. We had wondered then what prevented these impulses from running rampant and interfering with the learning process, what regulating mechanism kept them lively but in check.

It was when we took into account mother's positive feelings for her father that we saw more clearly the regulatory framework holding the erotic aggressive impulses safely in suspension. The finding itself was: The child's sexual curiosity *did not* interfere with good latency adjustment when the mother had an affectionate feeling toward her father. However, this erotic, aggressive behavior did interfere with latency adjustment when mother was not fond of her father. (See Appendix E, Table 27.)

We gathered from this finding a corroboration of our clinical experience. As much psychopathology can result from lively impulses being rampant as can result from their being dormant. If the impulses are not channelized by a mature, structuring matrix such as mother's capacity for an affectionate relationship with her father, then they will flood the child's psyche and interfere with his handling of daily problems.

The characteristic maladjustment problem in children who showed lively impulse behavior and whose mothers disliked their own fathers was "not working up to mental capacity" in the school. This lack of intellectual application was frequently combined with poor social adjustment at school. These mothers, in addition to disliking their fathers, were rebellious to their mothers. Characteristically, they were also highly nervous, irritable, and given to depressions. They seemed to be of the excitable, hysterical type with an ungratified and probably ungratifiable sexuality that might in some way stimulate and over-excite the child.

Whereas we had been a bit nonplussed theoretically somewhat earlier to find that open sexual curiosity at eight and nine was conducive to good adjustment, now we were back on familiar theoretical terra firma. Psychoanalytic theorists have postulated that overt sexual curiosity during latency would interfere by its distractive nature with one of the principal tasks of latency: the beginning of intellectual and ego mastery of the outside world, as one would find in the learning process. However, in the light of our findings, we would tend to re-phrase this postulate along the following lines: If the child's lively erotic impulses do not find a supportive matrix in the sexually mature mother, then the child's impulses will not become integrated or tied into a larger psychic scheme or goal; rather, they will float around loose, as it were, distracting the child from the concentration necessary to apply himself diligently and constructively to a task.

Some other findings indicated to us that it also was *beneficial for the child if the mother's own crude erotic impulses find a supportive, mature matrix in her positive relationship to her own father.* (See Appendix E, Table 28.) In investigating this matter we used mother's feelings toward her father as an indicator of her more sublimated sexuality and her statements about orgastic satisfaction as an indicator of her unsublimated sexuality.

Regarding the lively unsublimated sexuality, we found five types of statements made by mothers when asked about orgastic gratification: (1) "Always have orgasms because I use will power" (11 per cent). (Such a mother would frequently add that if she were not in the mood she would put herself in the mood.) (2) "Usually have orgasms. Sometimes when I am not in the mood I will allow my husband to have his satisfaction" (50 per cent). (3) "Once enjoyed sexual inter-course, but not in the past few years" (15 per cent). (Reasons given were fear of pregnancy, too tired, no interest, "intercourse just to please my husband.") (4) "I don't know—I don't think so" (11 per cent). (These mothers blocked considerably on this question and were quite embarrassed.) (5) "No, I never have enjoyed sexual intercourse. I never have been highly sexed" (13 per cent). We grouped types 1 and 2 as having lively sexuality, and types 3, 4, and 5 as having some block or inhibition about their direct sexual impulses.

As for the effects on the child, *the best adjusted children during latency and particularly at puberty were those whose mothers had both an affectionate feeling for their fathers and orgastic gratification.* We judged from this that mother's own impulse economy was in good order. Her direct lively sexuality had found a mature channelizing matrix in her affectionate feelings toward her father, and had found a place in the larger affectionate scheme. The child would obtain the necessary support for his own sexual maturation without being endangered by crude, erotic impulses spilling over from the mother.

The outstanding maladjustment both in latency and puberty was seen in children whose mothers disliked their fathers, but still had orgastic satisfaction. Here, we believe, was the situation in which mother's crude, raw sexuality overflowed into the child's life with a disrupting effect. Since these mothers were rebellious and unaffectionate toward their own mothers (in addition to having no affection for their fathers), we surmised that their sexuality and their orgasms have a large hostile component. Instead of sexuality being used to unite two people in a harmonious fashion it is probably used in an aggressive, immature way (in a pre-genital way, according to psychoanalytic terminology). The purpose of this sexuality could vary at times from wishing to possess or drain the partner to wishing to harm him or to be harmed by him, etc. (It is of interest that in the group where mother has seemingly sworn off or repressed all heterosexual impulses (dislikes own father, no orgasm) the adverse effect on the children seems to be only mild or moderate. These mothers, had, of course, a very positive, idealized traditional tie to their own mothers, a tie that the severely maladjusted group did not possess, either to the mother or to the father. Similarly, the other remaining group had a positive tie to their fathers in spite of the lack of orgastic satisfaction, and their children, also, were only mildly affected in an adverse way.)

An example of the flooding over from mother to son that occurs when mother dislikes her father and yet has orgastic gratification may be seen in the following excerpt. A mother sought psychiatric help because of headaches and because her ten-year-old son was disobedient and uncontrollable at home, in the neighborhood, and in the school. She had no difficulties in achieving orgasm, her only complaint being that her husband was frequently indifferent to her overtures. She had a deep grudge against him, and she wished to punish him not only for this indifference, but also for an extramarital affair she had had. In the occasional acts of sexual intercourse in which she and her husband participated, she would achieve orgastic gratification by sometimes thinking of another man as her partner or by thinking entirely of her own sexual satisfaction, or by bringing her husband almost to the point of exhaustion in his efforts to gratify her. She had ambivalent feelings about her father, recalling some affection for him before the age of twelve, but since then feeling ashamed and critical of his crude manners and passivity. The son was so uncontrollable and destructive at school that he was on the point of being expelled. (See Appendix D. 5. *On Sexual Curiosity.*)

The several findings we have described serve as evidence for our belief that personality growth both in latency and in puberty consists of a mastery over inner, lively sexual impulses that is gained through some overt behavioral expression of these impulses within the matrix of an emotionally mature mother. (See Appendix E, Table 29.) As we have said, if the mother has known, in her own life experience, what it was to be sexually curious, to be rivalrous with her siblings, to want to achieve her own identity, and if she has come out of all this with a mature, affectionate feeling for her father, then she will be able to be supportive of her child in his growth steps and help him in integrating his impulses toward socially acceptable goals.

The child's mastery of his impulses did not appear to be the result of a massive repression of impulses so that one half of him would be guarding the other half of him, nor the result of a riotous expression of unintegrated inner impulses. On the contrary, the mastery seems to be in the nature of an integration of conscious impulses and feelings of both an erotic and aggressive nature. It appears as though this maternal matrix forms a scaffolding by which the lively, instinctual energy of the child, with its wishes and drives, was being held in suspension, neither renounced either as too frustrating, too humiliating, or too guilt producing, not impulsively acted out with all the repercussions of anti-social conduct.

The major role in all this played by mother's feelings toward her father would naturally make us curious about the fate in store for the man who will inherit these feelings. In the following chapter our attention will be devoted to this inheritor who will play the double role of being mother's husband and the father of her children.

CHAPTER X

EFFECTS ON MOTHER'S MARRIAGE

OUR PREDOMINANT emphasis here will be on the child's father as seen through the mother's eyes. He will not be considered so much as a person in his own right but as one who has to fit in with mother's continuity with her past, particularly with her feelings toward her father. By introducing the child's father into the picture, even in this subjective way, we will be helped to see the child as being influenced by the *family* atmosphere rather than just by the *maternal* atmosphere.

In accordance with our expectations of the husband's fate or fortune, we found that mother's feeling for her husband was intimately related to her feeling for her father. In essence, the finding was: If the mother was fond of her father she tended to have a positive, affectionate feeling for her husband. If, for some reason, she was not fond of her father, she tended to have a varying degree of dissatisfaction with some aspects of her husband. (See Appendix E, Table 30.) (The feelings toward her father and toward her husband were evaluated by the psychiatrist and ranged from very affectionate, through ambivalent and detached, to hostile.)

Although the details may vary from situation to situation, the main impression we received was that both the companionate and the sexual relationship to the husband were associated with mother's feelings to her father. Thus mothers who liked their fathers (in comparison with mothers who did not) spoke more positively of their husbands as persons and more often told of a satisfying sexual life with them. Probably because the 54 children constituted a group of more or less adjusted children and were picked from intact families, there were only a few instances of marked marital discord. The minor latent discord had to be picked up from occasional negatives in the mother's description of her husband and from her expression of some degree of dissatisfaction with the sexual relationship.

The shadow of the past father figure on the present husband was quite noticeable. In mild, almost normal distortion of the present reality by the past, the mother saw all the aspects of her husband but reacted, because of her past, to certain ones rather than others. However, in most severe distortion of the present, she either saw things in her husband which were not actually present, or did not see things that were really there.

On the positive side and in a milder degree, we saw many instances of wives (who liked their fathers) who saw their husbands rather realistically, but who emphasized the positives and philosophically accepted some of the failings. These were frequently the wives who reported that the first two or three years of marriage were somewhat rocky, but that since then the mutual affection between them and their husbands had deepened. Undoubtedly this favorable predisposition toward the husband would bring out the best in him. In our competitive society where men may be uncertain about their achievements and may easily become discouraged, a supportive optimistic attitude on the part of the wife who sees her husband's positives rather than his liabilities would be encouraging to him and help him weather the storms.

One of the cases in our study, Mrs. B., illustrates the fortification the mother has received from her relationship with her own father which enables her to live comfortably with a rather critical, irritable husband. Mrs. B., a small, well-groomed, brunette woman, said that her childhood, for the most part, had been happy. She described her father as being very good hearted and quiet. He was a tailor who had always worked. He spent time with the children and was fond of them. He was a devoted father to whom the children were also devoted. Mrs. B. spoke rather fondly of her husband, but admitted that at times he seems too strict in his attitudes toward the children. She described him as a very good husband and father with a strong personality, who was a little bit on the domineering side, but who was also very intelligent and had good qualities. She said the marriage was pretty good now although there had been some friction at the beginning. She described her husband as a person who does not carry a grudge too long and said that he was more tolerant now.

During the interview with Mr. B., he was quite aggressive, direct, and forceful and disagreed with almost every statement made by the psychiatrist. His oppositional tendencies appeared quite early in the interview when he stated that the Institute for Juvenile Research has made a mistake in calling his son adjusted, and that if his son was adjusted he felt sorry for the maladjusted. His description of his marriage was highly critical: "My wife and I live well together from the standpoint of getting along well in front of people, and although we don't fight, we don't enjoy each other because we don't enjoy the same things." Then Mr. B. gave an example of this incompatibility: "I like Mexico because of the foreign, exotic flavor, while my wife complains of the food and the flies. My wife is extremely average in her dislikes, while I am much more critical." "I can recognize chisellers so I don't get along so well. But my wife can't, therefore she is happier. As for this letter from the school saying that our boy is well-adjusted, my wife is more gullible and sees the brighter side, whereas I can see the boy is not adjusted."

This case illustrates the optimistic, supportive attitude on the part of the wife that maintains the marital ties in spite of her husband's fault-finding and critical personality. Mrs. B. apparently had built up this fortification from her feelings toward her own father, which had accustomed her to seeing the best side of a man.

Still on a positive side, but showing an intense repetition of the past, were a few cases in which the wife actually did not see certain unfavorable aspects or attitudes of her husband. In the case to be reported the wish to repeat the past good relationship with her father, or her ideal fantasy of what that relationship had been, was so strong that she seemed to be actually deluded about her husband.

Mrs. R. was a large, heavy woman who was very jovial and laughed a great deal in a manner that was at times almost giggling. In describing her childhood Mrs. R. said: "I think we had a real good time. We had a chauffeur to take us to the circus and to the best places." When she was asked about her father, she responded: "Gosh, everybody worshipped him. He was the envy of all the ladies, he did so much for Mom. He made breakfast and did the dishes so we girls wouldn't have to. He was a lot of fun. He took us out picnicking and he took us fishing." When she was asked about any faults in her father, she replied, with tears in her eyes: "No, he didn't believe in punishing. To me he was the most perfect man. He was calm and easy going." She described her husband as: "He is a perfect man except that he should stay at home a bit more." When she was questioned further about his habits, she admitted that if he had time he would spend more of it with the children. Alhough he always was reading a magazine, Mrs. R. saw his point—he was just tired from working and wanted to relax. Mrs. R. then added, rather parenthetically, that her two girls think that Mr. R. has a temper, but that she cannot see it at all. Her girls always say that their daddy is "sore," however mother says, "But I can't see it."

Mr. R., when interviewed, turned out to be a mildly irritable man who deliberated before each answer. He presented the picture of a shy, gruff man with a good heart, who seemed at times subdued and depressed, but at other times he exhibited a very warm smile. Gradually, during the interview, Mr. R.'s resentment and irritation toward his wife had become quite open and marked. In response to a question about his angry feelings he said: "Well, this is off the record. I'm angry no place except at home with my wife who tries to dominate. I get angry with her." He gave as an example: "My wife monopolizes the front seat of the car and won't let the kids sit in front." He reported that he does not verbalize his anger but usually permits it to boil inside of him. One time he had gone to a psychiatrist and had asked his wife to go too, but "she was suspicious of being railroaded because I had had her mother committed to an insane asylum." He continued to describe his marriage as: "It's been growing worse lately. If I could separate the children from my wife everything would be OK. As the girls grow older there is much more friction." At the end of the interview the psychiatrist asked if he had any problems. Mr. R. then asked if the psychiatrist was going to see his wife, and said, "Don't bring up any of the things I mentioned about her or I'll catch hell."

We see in the case of Mrs. R. a form of denial of real negatives in the relationship, and an assertion of imaginary positives that are necessary to this unstable mother in order for her to repeat her past relationship with her father. This same sort of mechanism may be observed in children who have been placed in orphanages and foster homes by their parents. In spite of having received neglect and cruelty at the hands of their real parents, in order magically to preserve their psychic balance, they describe their real parents as kind, interested, etc. Although theoretically this phenomenon amounts to a delusion, it is rather a benign delusion inasmuch as it usually encourages positive feelings in other people. Of course, in the case just quoted, when this occurs in a very intimate relationship, it can be a source of considerable irritation. However, when this delusion is spread around among many people, it usually encourages them to feel positively. In clinical psychiatric practice, not too many of this type are encountered since they are overtly promoters of the principles of harmony rather than that of hate.

We shall consider next the shadow of the past on the present when mother's negative feelings to her own father more or less force her to emphasize and create negatives in her husband. The more severe instances of this negative attitude will be described in a later chapter. In mild degrees, the depreciation of the husband sometimes moves him to greater achievement and effort. If the wife's depreciation of her own father was based on his actual or comparative lack of drive and lack of responsibility, then the husband's actual and greater achievements were found in some cases to bring about in the wife a more favorable, realistic appraisal of him. Sometimes the wife's pessimism about her husband's achievements resulted not in a back-seat nagging and depreciation, but in a form of protective activity. One mother in our study, whose own father allegedly was quite improvident, was pessimistic about her husband's money earning abilities. Therefore, she delayed having children until she herself had worked on a job after marriage and saved enough money to provide for the first child. Her husband, who was also interviewed, was revealed to be a quite adequate man who had been earning a good living since marriage, who wanted to start a family early, and who was against his wife's working. Most of the husbands of this study tried to resolve their wives' mild negative feelings toward them by a greater absorption in work, in hobbies, or in the children. In the cases we see at the child guidance clinics the husbands more often, as a result of the wife's depreciation, turns to another woman or to alcohol.

Now we can consider how mother's feelings toward her own father determined her children's estimate of her husband, their father. We are not underestimating how the husband, in his own right, might make a certain impression on the children, for certainly he plays an important part in their lives. The husband may be naturally fatherly or unfatherly or, as we have said earlier, he may increase or decrease his fatherliness or family centeredness in reaction to his wife's negative feelings to him. But, instead of considering this aspect (for which we have insufficient data in this study), we turn now to the slight or strong nuances introduced into the child-father relationship by virtue of the mother's repeating through her children her past relationship to her own father.

In general, we found that in order for the children to prevent an emotional discontinuity or separation from their mother, they took over some of her attitudes about her husband as a father figure. These attitudes could be phrased in the form of questions: Is father a person to be admired or not? Is it safe or not to get emotionally close to father? We found that if mother liked her own father, the children usually admired their father and drew emotionally close to him. If mother disliked her own father, we found that the children tended to depreciate the father and not draw close to him. One of the principal evidences of closeness was whether or not the children chose their father as a confidante for their problems and troubles. *No child whose mother disliked her own father used his father as the exclusive confidante.* We feel that this can be accounted for by means of the continuity principle: The mother who liked her father feels continuous with or identified with the child who seeks out his father. This mother does not feel that the child is being disloyal to her. Also, the child is free of anxiety about drawing close to the father, because the child still maintains a continuity with the mother. In several cases it was obvious that the mother re-enjoyed a closeness to her own father through her vicarious participation in her daughter's emotional closeness to her husband.

The following two case excerpts from our study illustrate this point.

Mrs. A. described her childhood as having been very happy until her mother died when she had been thirteen. After that, life was "pretty rugged." Although she and her sister had a great deal of freedom, they never took advantage of it. In order to take care of his daughters her father refrained from remarrying until she and her sister were married. When Mrs. A. was asked to describe her father, she said: "To me he was just wonderful. Although he is an ordinary man, I think he is just wonderful. He is a maintenance man now. He could never do enough for my sister and myself." In response to a query about her husband, Mrs. A. replied: "He is a swell person—very understanding and lots of fun. He has so many friends. In fact, it is through my husband that I have been able to make so many friends, because I am more on the quiet side, and he takes my part in any friction with the in-laws." When she was asked if her husband had any faults, she answered: "Well, he can't stand to have me boss him. I can get anything I want out of him if I go about it in the right way." Mrs. A. revealed that she had done some dating before marriage and had thought she was in love several times. At the time of her marriage she was in love with her husband, and after a few minor frictions during the first year of marriage this love has grown stronger. She described her daughter: "Well, she is a sweet, lovable child, just a normal girl. She wants to do things for other people, she likes to work in the kitchen and as soon as I start to do the dishes, she will pick up the towel. She loves her daddy. She likes to tell him jokes and to dance with him, and I get a great kick out of seeing her with him."

When Mrs. C., another study mother was asked about her father, she said that she had had a wonderful home; her father had played with her and had been a great pal. "My mother, also, was very understanding. It was such a wonderful house that we couldn't see why people rushed to get married." In response to a request for additional information about her father she said: "He gave us a wonderful feeling of a father's relationship with his children. I was so naive I thought all fathers were like him—so devoted. When I got married I was simply amazed that my husband would object to doing anything for the kids." Mrs. C. revealed the typical affectionate, realistic attitude seen in wives who have had a good relationship with their father. Her husband was described as liking attention and wanting frequent changes. "I'm the only one he hasn't changed. He changes work, and the furniture in the apartment; he will change the furniture in the apartment once a week if I will let him." At this point Mrs. C. asked somewhat plaintively: "Do people outgrow that? I waited for him to settle down, but he has wonderful ideals that cannot be broken down. I think he has a softer disposition now. He doesn't want to be the way he is, but he has intense likes and dislikes. I might feel that way, but I try to see the other side of the problem." She summarized her marriage in general: "It isn't dull, but marriage is quite difficult. I must crave some excitement to stick it out, because it is very exciting. We have had some very happy times. When my husband is contented, I feel so much better and I am very happy to see him happy." When she was asked about her daughter, Barbara, she said that the girl was very close to her mother but that she respected and admired her father. Also, that Barbara has a terrific crush on her father right now, she calls him handsome and cute, and she remarks on how well mother and father dance together. Barbara was reported as having said father doesn't really mean it when he said things that irritate mother; also Barbara attempts to find excuses for any of his actions.

In both these cases there appears to be a continuation on the daughter's part of mother's attitude toward her husband, which was originally derived from mother's positive relationship with her own father. In the first case the husband was actually warm to the children and the daughter's fondness for him was more realistically based. In the second case the husband was on the irritable, demanding, somewhat infantile side, but still the daughter went along with her mother's attitudes toward him.

By way of contrast, the following case from our study is a striking example of depreciation of the father figure—a depreciation handed down over three generations from mother to daughter. Mrs. G., a somewhat irritable person, described her childhood by saying: "Well, I wasn't raised under ideal conditions. My parents continually bickered and argued. My father was a happy-go-lucky type, but wasn't very ambitious. My mother used to argue with him about his lack of drive and his not earning enough money." Mrs. G. revealed that at the beginning of her marriage she had been quite worried about whether her husband was going to be able to earn a living, however, she has become less pessimistic. Mrs. G. had done some dating before marriage, but she attempted to keep the dates at a low emotional pitch so that neither of them would become involved. She had not obtained sex information from her mother, menses came as an upsetting surprise. "Mother frightened me. She said that the birth of a baby would be difficult and sordid." Mrs. G. felt that her mother's influence had a bearing on her sexual adjustment, and that her mother caused her to distrust men by instilling in her the idea that all men were wolves. At first Mrs. G. couldn't give her husband her full confidence, but his lighter touch regarding sex helped her gradually to change. Mrs. G. says that she likes her husband, but she could not see how he was able always to be so optimistic and happy-go-lucky, because the world's realities demanded that a man be on his toes all the time.

Anne, the daughter, was a talkative, lively, zestful eight-year-old, with a bright smile and laugh. She conceived of the interview as a chance to display her brightness. During the interview Anne's behavior and attitudes indicated: overexcitement, much personal curiosity, a strong competitive drive, and some exhibitionistic behavior toward the male psychiatrist. At one point she had moved close to the desk where he was writing and wanted to know what he was writing. At another point, Anne noticed that he had some notes on the table and asked: "Is that all that my father said?" When the psychiatrist indicated to her that this was so, she said: "Well, I want to do more than my father. He thinks he's so smart, and I think I am so smart." Then she had become a little pouty in a provocative manner and said: "Is that all you've got written on me? I just want to get ahead of my father for once. Of course I realize that parents can do more than a child can, but I want to get ahead of him just once." Later she picked up the dolls and remarked: "I'll talk for them." And, in brief, the doll play was as follows. Mother to dad: "You go to work and make money for the family." Daughter to mother: "Don't yell at dad." Mother to daughter: "Stop interrupting me. You study." Mother to baby: "Poor baby." Mother rocks baby and mother and baby go to sleep. Daughter: "I'm through studying." Mother: "Don't butt in and interrupt. You are a bad girl, making me slave for you by cooking all day." Then the mother doll is cooking clay and makes a toy snake. Anne looks at the snake she has just made and says, "No, I think it is a dog." Then the father doll returns to the play activity and the mother doll says to him: "Didn't you make any money today?"

The psychiatrist felt after his interview with Mr. G. that it was the good fortune of the famliy to have someone who was very pleasant, obliging, and deferential. In the interview Mr. G. was somewhat unsure about his status and attempted to use "big" words at times incorrectly. He seemed to regard the psychiatrist with some awe and deference as though he were a father figure. He admitted that his wife was more intelligent than he and laughed comfortably about this. "In regard to the disciplining of the children, I always let my wife have her say, because she is with the children all day and she knows."

This case illustrates many of the points we have been making. First, the depreciation and distrust of men instilled in mother by her own mother. Secondly, the carrying out of this depreciation very dramatically by the daughter in her actual interview behavior and in her play. The impact of all this depreciation on a more irritable husband would be considerable and would give rise to many quarrels in the household. However, this particular father by virtue of his personality, was deferential, easy going, and actually felt that his wife was stronger than he and he took comfort from this very fact.

Thus we see that the mother can encourage or discourage in the child a closeness to or admiration for the father. We should also find some repercussions in the father from this state of affairs. All other things being equal, a father will be drawn to a child who seeks him out since his vanity and his wish to love and be loved are satisfied by such a child. An example of this may be seen in a situation that occurred after World War II when fathers returned home expecting to find a little son or daughter who would happily shout: "Oh, our daddy has come home." Instead, in frequent cases, the little children, not accustomed to the father, reacted to him in a blank way that at least temporarily estranged or hurt him. We did see a few cases in our study, and many more among child guidance cases and in adult therapy, in which the mother's favoritism toward and possessiveness of one son not only made it difficult for him to get emotionally close to the father, but also caused the father to turn away from this unresponsive son, and give his affection to another son who was not so possessed by the mother.

The psychological importance of the father to his children is well known from common experience and from theory. Not only does he represent emotional and material security to them when they are young, but he represents also their first experience with an adult male. The son has to use his father as a model for his own masculinity. What he sees in his father probably depends on what the father really is, but it also depends partly on what the mother sees in the father and partly on what the father becomes in response to the mother's feelings toward him. The father who has the affectionate support of his wife will be seen as admirable to his son. For the son there will be no conflict in his using his father as a masculine model and when he matures he will feel confident about making his way in the world and about winning a loving girl just like his mother. However, the father who is depreciated by his wife will cause some conflict for the son in the boy's attempts at masculine identification. For example, if the father appears unyielding to and rebellious against his wife's criticism, his son who happens to be dependently attached to his mother may resolve not to grow up to be a man like his father. We saw a few hints of this in the boys of eight and nine (e.g., not using father as a confidante) but the boys at this age are not as articulate about resentment toward the father as they are in adolescence. However, a private psychiatric case may illustrate this situation.

The patient, forty-eight years old, had been doing quite well in a subordinate executive position by virtue of his meek affability. He sought psychotherapy because of chronic colitis and moderate marital unhappiness. If his wife seemed misunderstanding, he would go into sulky, cold silences, but he could not raise his voice to her without feeling guilt or shame. The patient's history revealed that he had been the oldest child in his family and that he had been close to his mother and that his father seemed to him hard and merciless in dealing with his mother who was quite aggressive and demanding in her own right. He recalled that it had been due to his dislike and fear of his father that he had resolved to be a nicer person than his father had been. Although he did succeed in becoming a "nicer" person, it was at the later cost of aggression tension being discharged into his gastrointestinal tract or at the cost of assuming a facade of submissive affability which was taken advantage of by others and caused rage in him.

Though many other examples could be given in illustration, the main point is that mother's hostile feelings toward her own father can affect the son's masculinity strivings. The same applies to the daughter with the exception that she is not looking for a model for identification in her relationship to her father, but instead, for a suitable love object.

A few observations are in order about the 27 fathers we did interview. The small number that were seen and the fact that they were interviewed only by the psychiatrist militate against stating anything more than superficial impressions. However, one impression was that they all appeared to have a sense of responsibility of being the head of a household. (This impression also applied to the 27 fathers who were not interviewed and about whose attitudes we had to rely upon the wife's report.) By this we do not mean that they dominated the household (more often the wife had charge of that area) but rather that they were responsible as providers and citizens. They accepted the fact consciously and in their behavior that the responsibility for material provision was theirs. They were interested in their children's growth, although the time spent with the children varied considerably. We cannot generalize about their interest in their children inasmuch as the 27 fathers who did participate in the study were of course more actively interested in their children.

Another general impression was that these fathers, apart from their sense of responsibility, and their interest in the family, did not show the textbook picture of wise, settled maturity. Many were rather lively and boyish, anxious and aggressive in the interview with the psychiatrist, as though they felt "on the spot." Others were on the passive side and quite accommodating. Their personality adjustment on the whole was rather good despite the fact that several mentioned such symptoms as tension, fatigue, headaches, and ulcers.

In summary, we have endeavored in this chapter to show how mother's feelings to her husband might originate, and how they might affect the present family integration. Our findings indicated that mother's feelings toward her own father influenced her feelings toward her husband. Carried over in a continuity from the past might be a trustful, friendly, affectionate feeling which gives an affectionate cohesion to the entire family. Or, carried over might be a suspicious, depreciating, pessimistic feeling about father figures which tends to split up the family.

Husbands and Wives

CHAPTER XI

𝕶𝕶-𝕶𝕶-𝕶𝕶-𝕶𝕶-𝕶𝕶-𝕶𝕶-𝕶𝕶-𝕶𝕶-𝕶𝕶-𝕶𝕶-𝕶𝕶

AGREEMENT
AND
DISAGREEMENT

OF THE many ways in which the family can be viewed, a most important one is contained in the question: How divided or unified, how disharmonious or harmonious is the relationship between mother and father? Leading from this question is another question which will occupy us in this chapter: What are the effects on the child of parental agreement and disagreement?

Disunity being the more obvious pathogenic factor may be considered first. It can be open and easily observed by the child, or subtle and less discernible, or non-discernible because it is deliberately hidden from the child. The subject matter can vary from such relatively innocuous areas as where to go for a vacation to increasingly less innocuous areas where it is seen as dissension over in-laws, or incompatibility in sexual relations, or disagreement over how the children should be raised.

The kind of disunity and disagreement we shall be most interested in is of the open variety and involves the raising of children. The growth problem posed by this disunity for the child is obvious. Just as conflict and contradiction were introduced to the child when the mother was conflicted within herself, so they are introduced when the mother is in conflict with the father. Just as the child does not know what to do when one part of the conflicted mother incites rebellion while the other part punishes rebellion, so is the child confused when mother's "do's" and "dont's" are at sharp variance with the father's.

[101]

Although there can be no doubt that severe open parental disagreement works a hardship on the child, the question may be asked: "Is any disagreement between the parents always pathologic?" According to the line of argument we have advanced regarding generational continuity, we would think not. It is inevitable that both parents entering parenthood will seek to relive their pasts, to experience through their children a vicarious second childhood. Since no two individual pasts can ever be identical, it is inevitable that there will be some disagreement. If, then, some disagreement is "normal," should we not ask: "Is total agreement between parents wholesome for the child?" According to our line of reasoning, again we would have to answer in the negative. We should be as suspicious of too much parental agreement on the specifics of child-rearing as we are of too much disagreement.

Apart from the foregoing theoretical expectations, our attention was turned to this matter because of some empirical findings. These findings suggested that there was an adjustment imbalance (rather than outright maladjustment) when the child was exposed to an overly agreed solid parental front and when the child was exposed to an overly disagreed divided front. It is this adjustment imbalance— the child doing much better in the school situation than in the psychiatric interview and vice versa—that is our main concern here.

It will be recalled that the school and the psychiatrist, the two evaluators of outside-the-family adjustment, agreed so frequently (80 per cent of the cases) that we had to utilize both of them in forming the combined social adjustment score. However, it is the 20 per cent of cases in which they disagreed that now engage our attention.

There were 13 children out of the 54 about whom the psychiatrist's and the school's evaluation differed appreciably. Of the 13, there were six children in whom the psychiatric interview adjustment was very good and their school adjustment was only fair. There were seven children whose psychiatric adjustment was only fair, but whose school adjustment was very good. For the sake of brevity we shall call the former children who got along well when alone with the psychiatrist, the one-to-one relators, and the latter children who got along well with the many in the school, the group relators. (See Appendix E, Table 31.)

The common principle underlying the crucial differences between the two groups appeared to be a comparative lack of family organization in the one-to-one relators and a comparative excess of family organization in the group relators. Whereas with the former there was an increase of those elements placing individual rights and wishes ahead of family group welfare, with the group relators there was an increase in those elements which place family group welfare far ahead of individual wishes.

As for the particular diagnostic items, the most striking one in the family atmosphere was the factor of whether or not the parents agreed on the discipline of the child. Here the two groups differed most markedly: the one-to-one relators having a very high percentage of parents disagreeing, the group relators having a very high percentage of parents agreeing. It is obvious that a child exposed to open parental disagreement over how he should behave will be confused as to how he should conduct himself. There will be a marked tendency to pit one parent against the other to get what he wants, with the result that he has difficulty learning that there are limits to the amount of self-expression and self-gratification he can normally expect to achieve. When such a child enters the structured school situation, he is ill prepared for observing the limits and for curbing his self-gratification.

On the other hand, the child who has been exposed to consistent and possibly excessive parental agreement, who has always been confronted by a solid parental front, will know fully well the limits. He knows what he cannot do, because there is no appeal from one parent to another. But the probable drawback with such ideal parental consistency is that the child may not realize what he *can* do. There is a conformity to authority, a tendency not even to feel consciously an impulse to go beyond what authority has indicated is permissible. Thus, though this child is well prepared for the structured school situation which has familiar limits, well defined, he is ill prepared for the one-to-one situation with the psychiatrist where he is stimulated to be free in expression or play. The idea of "doing anything he wants" is quite unfamiliar and threatening to him.

The two other diagnostic items that differentiated the mothers in the two groups appeared to have the same repercussions as the factors of agreement on discipline. One was the question of whether mother tended to release or hold back her angry feelings, the other was whether or not mother was given to orderly perfectionistic attitudes. In the group relators the mothers tended to hold back angry feelings and to be quite orderly; whereas in the one-to-one relators the mothers tended to be openly angry and not orderly. In the former, there was an atmosphere of calm law and order and an example provided by mother of containing rather than expressing turbulent feelings. The atmosphere and the example helped the child to learn that there were certain limits to individualistic expression. In the latter, however, there was an atmosphere of stormy anarchy and an example provided by mother of expressing rather than containing turbulent feelings. Both of these certainly do not help the child to learn limits.

As to the children in the two groups, not surprisingly the crucial difference was found to be in the sibling relationships. Open rivalry with the brother or sister was excessive in the case of the one-to-one relators, while it was unusually minimal with the group relators. In line with what we have just been discussing, an individualistic, non-limiting atmosphere of the family would stimulate in the child either an excessive jealousy of what the other siblings possessed, or an excessive tendency to act out behaviorally a normal amount of jealousy. Unaccustomed to an atmosphere of law and order, this child could not easily distinguish what was *meum* and *tuum*. When he got into the structured school situation in which he had to share and to take his proper turn with his classmates, he would not be prepared for this task. His jealous reactions, carried over from the excessive sibling rivalry at home would disturb the harmony of the classroom and incur the displeasure of the overtired or inexperienced teacher. The child then would react to her displeasure and tend to intensify and prolong the displeasure by his misconduct or by a lack of application to learning. In the one-to-one situation with the friendly, permissive psychiatrist, this child would not be bothered by rivalry with other children and would be able to relate quite engagingly.

Illustrative of the differences between these two groups are the following excerpts taken from the records of two boys in our study. Arthur, the group relator, was a nice looking, soft featured, nine-year-old boy who appeared ill at ease not knowing what was expected of him. There was an uneven spontaneity and evasiveness regarding his emotions and dreams, and a tendency to say: "I don't know." Although an occasional warm smile came over his face, there was present a certain apathy and languidness and a general preoccupation. When he was asked about his interests he said that although he had more fun with other kids than just by himself, yet he tended to play their games rather than they to play his. Arthur fingered the dolls, the clay, and the gun when the play materials were offered to him, but he did not play with them. He used only one of the three wishes when offered to him. When he was offered, in fantasy, a thousand dollars, all he could think of was to buy his brother a confirmation gift. His most unpleasant dream involved his being caught between a rattlesnake and a tiger and not knowing which way to run.

The school report at the age of nine evaluated him as very well-adjusted, very co-operative with the teacher and with the school program, friendly with teacher and classmates, no nervous symptoms, and working up to intellectual capacity. The school report at thirteen again was to the effect that he was very well adjusted.

In her interview, Arthur's mother presented a mixture of co-operativeness and defensiveness. She seemed on the systematic controlling side. She described Arthur as a good-natured, sensitive boy, quite helpful, easily managed and that other adults have commented to her on these characteristics in him. When she was asked about what faults he had, she said: "Well, he will try to insist on his wishes, but all my three children have that tendency to some extent. But we can explain things until he sees that he's wrong. We are trying to get him to learn a sense of right and wrong." "He acts as a monitor in school when the teacher is away and reports when the other children talk." Then later: "We all work for another as a group in the house. We try not to be too independent and individualistic; we don't have rivalry between the children. . . . He is very appreciative of what is done for him and is easily satisfied." In describing herself she said she had patterned herself closely after her own mother. She was angry infrequently because she was able to see the other person's side of things. She rarely was angry with her husband because they are able to discuss things and they "sit shoulder to shoulder about things." If the children do not pitch in and help her household run smoothly, she has become a little annoyed with them. She decidedly liked neatness and orderliness. Her house was neat and livable, but she would prefer Arthur to go out to other houses to play rather than to invite the gang over to his house. Since she could not stay idle she always liked to construct things with her hands like sewing or knitting.

Father, in the interview, although externally affable, seemed to have rigid attitudes about children being helpful rather than selfish. "I like to make things easier for my wife by helping out just as I learned to do for my sainted grandmother." Speaking of the boy, he used such phrases as: "He tries to have his own way, but he generally succumbs to prohibition." "Though we have some disagreements, we iron them out."

In the case of Arthur (the group relator) we are able to see some of the wholesome and unwholesome effects of curbing one's individualistic expression. There was an insistent pressure by the parents, a type of iron hand in velvet glove technique, which made the child feel anxious, inadequate, or guilty if he became too insistent about his own wishes. He was made to feel lucky and obligated if he obtained anything for himself from his "kind" parents. (In the case of a forty-year-old salesman with a similar background, he felt he was undeserving of commissions he earned in selling because his employer "cried the blues" about how he was making less money than the patient.) Arthur, caught between the solid pressures exerted by his parents and his own desires (possibly reflected in the dream of "caught" between the rattlesnake and the tiger), seemed to have solved the dilemma by aligning himself with authority; he became, in fact, a "company" man by acting as monitor for the teacher to report on misbehaving children.

George, also nine years old, illustrates the one-to-one relator. George, a very engaging, handsome boy, immediately became involved in a friendly and even familiar relationship with the psychiatrist, although he was always respectful and considerate. He acted as if the psychiatrist were a member of his family or someone he had known for years. He was quite talkative and expressed all his feelings. He had a bubbling good humor, full of zest, hummed when he drew, and asked many questions. Some of his curiosity about the psychiatrist was personal, but some of it was to satisfy his own curiosity about the themes of killing or sex. He went to the toy-box eagerly and picked up everything including the gun. George played with the truck, rolled it back and forth until it turned over and crashed, and then the oil truck crashed and he said that it caught afire. Then he asked the psychiatrist whether he had ever seen people killed in an accident or in war. He used his three wishes easily: he wanted five horses, to win a lot of animals, and for his dad to be a lion tamer. With the thousand dollars he said he would buy a nice house, get a dog, and own a farm. He later expressed anger toward his five-year-old brother who would not let him play with the brother's toys. He asked the psychiatrist whether he ever "took babies." The most unpleasant dream he recalled was of a poisonous snake being after him.

The school report at nine years indicated that he was only fairly well adjusted. Although he co-operated with the teacher and with the rules, he had trouble in that he incessantly sought attention from the teacher and was not working up to intellectual capacity. The school report when he was thirteen was not much different. He still was not working up to mental capacity. Instead of seeking attention from the teacher, his co-operation with the teacher has decreased somewhat and he had some nervous mannerisms.

George's mother was a small brunette who seemed shy and at times uncertain. Essentially she gave credit to her husband for whatever good behavior her children exhibited, because she and her husband had been on the opposite side of the fence regarding limits and indulgence. Her husband tended to be rather firm and insistent upon good behavior, while she was inclined to be indulgent. They have had some open battles on this point. She described George: "He has an excessive amount of nervous energy, and he is all boy. He needs affection more than the other child and this might account for some of his outbursts, saying, 'You blame me all the time.' He rebels at certain duties." She said she was doubtful as to how to handle the boy and sometimes she felt that she should show him more affection. Even though she wanted to, she was so busy with the four kids that she hadn't had the time. Mother had felt very close and devoted to her good hearted father; but she felt neglected and ignored by her cold, older sister, and by her busy, dominant mother. She envied other children who had young mothers. She becomes angry when: "I'm being neglected by my family not paying attention, or my husband working out of town." (The father was not interviewed in this study.)

In the case of George we saw a boy whose great need for attention handicapped him in the school situation, but made him engaging and captivating in a one-to-one situation. The carry-over of his rivalry to his five-year-old brother was quite apparent in the school situation. In this case, instead of a solid parental front there was a divided one. George's father seemed similar to Arthur's, however, their mothers were different. Whereas Arthur's mother was firmly and traditionally entrenched in child rearing techniques, and sided with her husband in his approach to limitations, George's mother was not secure in her own mothering and, furthermore she battled her husband about the extent of limitations to which the child should be subjected. It was rather clear that this mother, having felt ignored in her own childhood, and still feeling neglected, would empathize keenly with George's feeling of neglect and would make it more difficult for him to accept the fact that his halcyon days of infancy were over.

Although the two cases described appear to indicate that the traditional mother was associated with the better group relator and the rebellious or dependent mother with the better one-to-one relator, this was not strictly the case since the motherhood themes had no direct bearing on differentiating these groups. The differentiation appeared to be more related to the question of harmony or disharmony between the child's parents. Although we did not have enough data for a study of this, it was possible that there may have been a conflict between the motherhood themes of the mother and the fatherhood themes of the father.

These two case excerpts also illustrated the risk involved in using only one diagnostic procedure to obtain an evaluation of adjustment. According to the school the first boy, Arthur, was well adjusted. It was necessary to view him in a free, one-to-one situation to find out his limitations. According to the psychiatric interview alone, the second boy, George, appeared rather well adjusted. It was necessary to learn how he got along in the structured, long-term situation in order to appreciate his limitations. In our clinic children we saw many examples of individuality restrictions associated with a good school report and an unsatisfying psychiatric interview, and also many examples of impulsive, wild behavior problems associated with a bad school report and a very comfortable psychiatric interview.

In general, the observations suggest that the total capacity for behavioral adjustment can be divided into capacity for a one-to-one relationship, and a capacity for group relationship. In the 54 children a good capacity in one was usually associated with a good capacity in the other, and an incapacity in one with an incapacity in the other. The factors commonly entering into both capacities would seem to be an attitude toward human relationships that they are gratifying, predictable, and not dangerous. If the capacity for group relationship far exceeds that of a one-to-one relationship, we can expect to find a child whose aggressive individualistic impulses have been held to a minimum. In some way he would be soft pedalling his original individuality in the benefit of group harmony. The extremes of such subjugation of individual expression are found in the social structure of the bee colony and in the authoritarian states. More wholesome and less extreme examples are seen in many organizations which are populated by group minded persons whose lives seem to them incomplete unless they are working with others toward a common goal.

On the other hand, we have the child whose need for individual expression or individual attention outweighs his interest in group solidarity. Brought up in a family in which the parents do not hold certain concepts in common, e.g., the way in which a child should be reared, where excessive sibling rivalry is not only tolerated, but by example probably encouraged, in other words, where the family is really a collection of individuals rather than a group, the interests of the child are toward attaining individual prominence. The quickness of rapport noted by the psychiatrist suggests a hunger for individual attention, a desire to win this new adult, to be the favorite. In later extremes we might find such persons espousing anarchic states, as having laws unto themselves, prima donnas rather than team players. In politics a good example would be the many partied and unstable

French parliament. A more wholesome outcome might be a creative person who is more interested in self-realization than he is in group harmony.

What we have been discussing is the balance between the individualistic and the group minded orientation. As to what is desirable, we cannot say without going into the question of values.

There is little doubt but that a vote of desirability would be given by most persons to those who combine in a harmonious way a capacity for individual creativeness and a capacity for loyal spontaneous ties with the group in its common goal, and a vote of undesirability to those who have neither capacity. However, when it comes to which emphasis is more desirable there is a sharp difference of opinion depending on what values are emphasized. When social adjustment is positively emphasized by some, the opponents of this viewpoint describe the resulting person as a Babbit, a robot, etc. When individualistic expression is advocated by others, the opponents of this viewpoint give labels such as "egg-head," "brain trusters," "Bohemian," to the end product. Without attaching any value judgments, we can safely say that the population contains many of each orientation and that each has a function to perform in society.

The imbalance toward a strong group orientation or toward a strong individualistic orientation was associated, it appears, with the relationship between the parents. Too much solidarity between mother and father seemed to give rise to the group orientation; too little solidarity to the individualistic orientation. We would speculate, then, that the proper amount of solidarity between the parents would enable the child to have both orientations, that a flexible solidarity would be the most useful for the child's total growth.

These speculations bring us back to our notion of "permanence" and "change." The parental over-solidarity and the resulting tendency for the child to preserve group values are certainly in the category of permanence and status quo. The parental undersolidarity and the resulting tendency for the child to promote his individualistic needs are obviously in the category of change and expansion. The optimum solidarity, a flexible one, would make for an optimum blending of permanence and change.

The considerations of permanence and change apply also to the motherhood themes. The followers of tradition, the emulators and imitators of the past generation, promote the permanence factors; whereas the revisionists, especially the rebellious, promote the change factors. In general, we might say that the flexible interaction between old and new elements, between permanence and change, are necessary, not only for the individual, but also for society. Without the conflict between old and new, without the Hegelian thesis and antithesis, a growing integration or synthesis is not possible. Thus, conflict, in itself, is not unwholesome, too little producing as much of an obstacle to growth as too much.

How do these general considerations apply to the child and his parents? What would a flexible parental solidarity consist of? It would seem that the solidarity should be based on the mutual recognition and acceptance of the fact that differences in opinion about child rearing are inevitable because they arise out of different historical continuities. Once the parents agree that there will be legitimate disagreements, that the other's historical continuity is as legitimate as his own, a favorable atmosphere will result for the child.

The family atmosphere of minimal friction and minimal suppression, an atmosphere in which parents appear to the child as equal to each other, would certainly be the most wholesome one. It would afford the child a chance to utilize freely the personalities and continuities of each parent—a utilization free from the fear of being alienated from or oppressed by one of his parents. Why the parents do not always treat each other as deserving of equal entitlement and the effects of this on the child will be the topics of interest in the next chapter.

CHAPTER XII

THE CHILD
CHOOSES
SIDES

In any relationship, be it between parent and parent, parent and child, friend and friend, the basic cause for excessive friction or domination of the weaker by the stronger is perhaps the inability of one person to take the other person's viewpoint in an empathic way. Instead of the flexible solidarity and unity created by mutual respect and understanding of each other, there is either a standoff between two equal and opinionated antagonists, or a crushing of one antagonist by the other. Instead of a predominance of "we," "us," and "our" feelings, there is an overemphasis on "I," "me," and "mine" feelings. How these latter feelings affect the relationship between parents and how they affect the child will be our main interest in this chapter.

A basic premise (in fact, almost a truism) underlying much of what follows here can be stated in the following terms: It is advantageous for the child to be on good terms with the mother. If he is not on good terms it will require much more effort and strength on his part to combat the stress he will suffer if mother withdraws her dependability and her understanding. Depending on what the mother requires, "good terms" can be obtained by the child by just being himself, by the child achieving something for the mother, by not being a bother, by the child being loyal to her, etc.

It is this last way of attaining a "good-terms status," being loyal, which is particularly important when there is an open or hidden conflict between parents. We had commented in an earlier chapter that the way the mother regards her husband will influence the way the children regard their father. All other things being equal, it is safer for the dependent child to identify and side with the parent he is most dependent on. Thus if the mother is anti-husband, it is safer for the child to be anti-father.

We may ask: "If mother's negative feelings toward her husband are in large part a carry-over of negative feelings toward her father, how did these latter negative feelings arise?" We found evidence suggesting that the same loyalty considerations were present in the older generation. In other words, just as we found that the child in the present generation tended to follow his mother's cue in attitudes toward his father, so in the older generation did mother follow her own mother's cue in her feelings toward her own father. *Thus, mother's negative feelings toward her father were highly associated with mother's description of open incompatibility or alienation existing between her mother and father.* (See Appendix E, Table 32.)

We discovered, however, a seeming paradox in this area of grandparent incompatibility. This paradox was essentially that the most intense dislike and hatred by mother of her father was not seen in those situations where grandmother and grandfather had severe clashes, but rather in those situations where mother's parents had at least a superficially harmonious relationship. Furthermore, these particular mothers, in addition to having a violent dislike of their fathers, showed obvious and marked psychopathology—three having had psychotic breakdowns. They spoke easily of their fathers as being domineering and selfish. Almost all of them had not corrected any mishandling they received from their own mothers, and most of them claimed that their mothers were very satisfactory models to emulate in motherhood. The children of these mothers related most inadequately in the psychiatric interview, were the least well adjusted in school, and were not any better adjusted at twelve and thirteen.

At this point we collected our thoughts along the following lines: compatibility between parents was the most conducive atmosphere or situation for the development of mother's affection for her father. It was from such a situation that there emerged a mother who felt most positively to her husband and who was able to provide a similar situation in which her children were free to admire and love their father. Somewhat less conducive was the situation in which mother had reservations about her father because her parents had some open incompatibility. Mother's attitude toward her husband also contained some reservations and the children did not feel entirely at ease in using their father as a loved or admired figure. However, this carry-over from the past seemed to be in the nature of a somewhat superficial prejudice, which would bring mother to her marriage with the doubtful expectancy of: "You can't expect too much of men." If the husband were indeed quite adequate, mother's doubts in time would be dispelled or minimized. The least benign, for reasons which we had not yet understood, was the situation in which mother disliked her father in spite of the reported fact that there was little or no open incompatibility between her parents.

For a while we were quite puzzled as to why these mothers, whose parents apparently got along well, should be emotionally disturbed and have more maladjusted children than mothers whose parents openly did not get along. Whereas both groups had a lack of affection for their fathers, the parental compatibility seemed to make for more psychopathology. Several alternative explanations came to mind: Was there a particular something between the mother and her father, a particular something such as the father being not warm enough, or too warm to this particular daughter? A hint that this might be the case was seen in one mother who said that while she had always disliked her domineering father, her hate for him increased at the age of twelve when she learned about sexual intercourse and hated him more for his participation in the act. Or was it that father was dictatorial only to his children but not to his wife? Or that mother did not mind the domineering, but for some strange reason the children did? None of these possible explanations of course, could be proved or disproved because we had no first-hand data regarding mother's original family.

Through the use of our second-hand data, i.e., mother's recollection of what went on between her mother and father, we began to be impressed with a certain pattern which seemed to indicate that the compatibility that mother described was a rather peculiar one. Instead of a healthy, mutually respectful compatibility between grandmother and grandfather, the relationship very frequently described was one in which grandfather had been stubborn and rigidly domineering, whereas grandmother had been a sweetly submissive saintly spouse. Our mothers could not see how their mothers had tolerated such a restrictive, humiliating and self-effacing situation. They made such remarks as: "If he were my husband, I'd give him his walking papers in a minute." "If I were my mother, I'd shoot him or at least tell him off." Some of them revealed that they would purposely visit their parents' home in order to argue with their father and "tell him off." In short, these mothers were infuriated at the high handed methods of their fathers and protectively puzzled, rather than overtly angry, at their mothers for accepting all this abuse without rebellion.

We were puzzled as to why these grandmothers did not rebel angrily. Such questions as these arose: Was the grandmother so secure and stable that she did not mind her husband's domineering tendencies? Was she so attracted to suffering in a masochistic way or so weak that she enjoyed being domineered? Out of fear that her husband would leave her, was she so intimidated that she could not afford to rebel and this resentment would have to go underground?

It was this last possibility—the resentment going underground—which appeared to have some confirmation in the operations of the present family. Not only did the resentment go underground, but it was picked up and acted out by the child. In investigating this possibility in the present family operations, our procedure was to select for intensive probing all the cases in which mother had a lack of affection for her own father. According to the principle of continuity, these mothers should have at least some mixed feelings about their husbands. We found that although the majority of them did have openly stated mixed feelings, there was a sizeable minority who spoke of their husbands only in positive terms. Before our intensive examination of the data in these cases, we had merely assumed that these mothers had flexibility and strength to rise above their past ill-feelings for their fathers. But, on closer examination of their children's play and fantasy life, we found that mothers' dislike of their fathers had probably not died out, that though openly they got along with their husbands, the sons and daughters seemingly carried the seed of hate toward their present fathers. (See Appendix E, Table 33.)

This striking trend which applied both to boys and girls was revealed through the expression of hostile, aggressive feelings toward the parents in their response to certain of the Despert fables. One particular fable dealt with a family who had just so much food which had begun to run out. One of the family had to be sent away. The question was: Who shall be sent away? There were three main categories into which the answers fell: (1) the father; (2) the children; (3) the mother. In the group of which we speak (mother dislikes her father but has only positive attitudes to her husband) 90 per cent of the children sent their father away, whereas in the other groups only about 45 per cent gave this response. We could account for this trend only on the basis that the children were voicing and feeling their mothers' deeper attitudes about the father figures. In other words, mother in her adult role as wife was trying to maintain harmonious relations with her husband; however, on an emotional level, in reliving her childhood through her children, she would have to relive her father-hates. This she does through her children.

The other finding which was detected in their play behavior applied only to the girls in this group. Routinely each child had been invited to play with the same toys which included a family of dolls, clay, gun, scissors and paper. The majority of boys picked up the gun and at least pointed it even if they did not click it, and the majority of the girls were not interested in the gun, but played with the dolls and the clay. However, the girls in the group we are considering, usually selected the gun. (See Appendix E, Table 34.) We felt that the selection of the gun by the girls indicated an attitude of: "I will not be of a weaker dominated sex; I shall be strong and dominating as men are." In trying to account for this trend we were aware that this type of attitude had all the ear marks of that familiar phenomenon variously called "masculine protest," "masculine identification," "penis envy." We are also aware that, according to psychoanalytic theory, every girl is supposed to have a nucleus of penis envy which has been stimulated by the first discovery that the boy has a penis and she does not; and that she would blame her mother for not endowing her with one. Finally, we were conversant with the concept that this normal penis envy could be stimulated or exaggerated by such things as the mother having shown a marked preference for the penis-endowed male, or the daughter having suffered a defeat in her attempts to win affection from her father, and then having developed hostility along the lines of "Hell hath no fury like a woman scorned." However, none of these explanations accounted satisfactorily for the finding that the mother and father were openly compatible.

Instead of our thinking proceeding along more traditional lines, we became aware that a picture was beginning to emerge for us. This picture was one in which a mother suppressed or repressed her hate for her father in her actual relationship with her husband, while she passed on her hate for men to her son and daughter, who possessed this hate for their father probably on a less conscious level. After studying other cases the picture enlarged for us to disclose that when the mother openly took responsibility for her disaffection with her husband and was openly contesting with him or defending herself against him, the child might be troubled with a conscious loyalty conflict, and he may have wished that his parents would love each other instead of arguing, but he was not faced with the heavy burden of having to fight his mother's battle while she maintained a superficially compatible relationship with her husband.

The question of the psychic details of this transfer of hate from mother to child still remains. In other words, what was there in the mother-child relationship that allowed mother to subcontract her father hate to her child? The evidence we had gathered from the individuals in our study and from our clinical cases, seemed to point strongly, especially in the girls, to a very close and strong identification between mother and child. This loyalty identification bond had its more wholesome origins in a rather common and understandable phenomenon—the tendency of parents to perpetuate themselves in their children. Although animals perpetuate the species through their offspring, human beings with their acute awareness of personal mortality, tend to perpetuate and continue their actual selves. This "I" or "me" component ranges from a mild degree, such as a person feeling more comfortable with the people who think similarly to him, or more in rapport with the child who looks or acts like him, to a severe degree as implied in such statements as "Thou shalt have no other gods before me," or "Whoever is not for me is against me." (See Appendix D, 6. *Egocentrism.*)

In our study one indicator of the "I" or "me" component was contained in mother's response to the question: "Whom does the child remind you of in his personality or behavior?" The responses ranged from mother having been reminded only of herself or of herself and her husband, or only the husband or a relative, or no one in particular. As would be expected, more often mother was reminded of herself by the daughter (62 per cent) than by the son (36 per cent). That there was some stabilizing security involved in this personality continuity between mother and daughter, was indicated by the finding that among the emotionally disturbed girls seen at the child guidance clinic, only about 14 per cent reminded mothers of themselves. However, the personality continuation of a mother in her son—the intrusion of the feminine orientation into the masculine personality—had, as would be expected, a less wholesome effect, particularly at puberty.

Although this phenomenon of mother seeing herself in her child was fairly common, and not pathologic in a mild degree, it did have rather specific personality correlates both for the mother and her child. The mothers who in any way saw themselves in their children manifested in other behavior a goodly quantity of the "I" or "me" component. Particularly they called attention in subtle and non-subtle ways to the amount of suffering and hardship they had undergone in their tasks as mother and wife. Much more frequently these mothers complained of much nausea during pregnancy, having been torn badly at the birth of a child, fatigability, feeling frequently angry, but not showing their anger. (See Appendix E, Table 35.) (The effects of this martyr-like attitude will soon be discussed.)

The children of such mothers tended to avoid, or were uncomfortable with any activity or person that had not been mother-endorsed, that did not bear the chauvinistic label, as it were "part of mother." This difficulty in going outside of mother-territory was revealed in the finding that: There were only six children out of the 54 who, as small children, had shown their discomfort with unfamiliar persons by not going easily to strangers, *and* later also by relating very slowly to the psychiatrist. All of the mothers of these six children saw themselves in the child.

After we had examined the mother-daughter interplay in both our study and clinic cases, we found that the mother bound the child (especially the daughter) to her as an ally by means of the identification and by means of her martyr-like suffering. The identification acted as a sort of constricting shadow on the child's personality. It was often of this nature: Mother says, "I'm sure that you, as a person of good sense, wouldn't like this book either. It makes me ill and I think it would make you ill, too." A tactic such as this would be much more entangling than, "I forbid you to read this book." The former tactic would intrigue the child by the flattering offer of membership in the maternal camp, especially if the child felt unloved on another basis. When the child's individualistic zestful attitudes are squelched by "you wouldn't like this book either," there might have been a momentary glimmer of protest from the child. However, the more the mother behaved in this manner (taking for granted that the child will not differ from her) the more difficult it would become for the child to break away from the mother's attitude without having given her an unexpected slap in the face when she discovered that the child had come to an independent opinion. When to this flattering membership invitation there was added a forceful reminder that mother has been ill treated by life and by males, certainly the invitee member would not take the inhuman side of the issue by joining the abusers of mother. The result would be that the child would join mother's camp and would receive interest and dependency so long as he would remain loyal to his mother in her woes.

In other words, the interplay between mother and child, and mother and her husband, was not the more healthy one in which mother, openly dominant, gave her child or husband a direct order, and he rebelled with the sparks flying. On the contrary it was that mother, if crossed, would act hurt, develop some tears, or a droop to the lips, or become ill, or act depressed. The effect of this behavior on the daughter would be that the child would consider herself a beast if she had been the cause of it, or she would consider her father a beast if he had committed the injurious action. These particular mothers in our study had frequently described their own mothers as "saints." It is obvious that the more a person sweetly smiles without retaliating, the more saintly that person becomes. This is well known in political circles where it is dangerous to attack the mild, kindly figure for fear of creating anger toward the attacker. The assassination of political figures always carries the danger of creating sympathy and outrage for the martyred victim.

The final note on this interplay is the effort made by the child (again especially the daughter) to maintain the fantasy, fiction, or delusion that mother is perfect and unattackable and that father is bad and mean, stingy and attackable. In order to preserve this extreme polarity of mother idealization and father disparagement, and to avoid the painful guilt attached to disliking her all-giving, well-meaning, martyred mother, the daughter will sometimes switch negative feelings really belonging to the mother onto the father and also switch positive feelings that belong to the father onto the mother.

We might also ask what is going on in the mother who controls by acting like the pitiful, martyred friend. Her operations bear all the earmarks of an expert political manipulation, Machiavellian in intent and in craftmanship. There is a distinct resemblance between her methods and those used in setting up a totalitarian state, or in preparing a nation for war. First, there is internal unrest tending to rebellion or anarchy. The central figure, in order to retain power, creates the propaganda that there is an external enemy who is intent on doing harm to the innocent, benign, well-wishing, mother state or fatherland. A border incident is created which enables the citizens to direct all their hate toward the external enemy and to experience a feeling of self-righteousness inasmuch as they are defending the innocent and helpless. Some evidence from clinical cases had given indications that the mother was so interested in obtaining the supreme power over the family that she embarked on a policy of divide and conquer. A few cases demonstrated that the mother, in her marked egocentricity, becomes threatened if two people with whom she was in a relationship came together, found rapport between themselves, and seemingly excluded her. As in love and war such a mother will use every means, fair or foul to meet this threat, every means to divide these two who might be enjoying mutual warmth without her.

So far we have concentrated on the daughters of mothers who have disliked their own fathers, but what of the sons of such mothers? We had not found the same clear-cut picture here that we found with the daughters. Though there were evidences of antagonism, they had not emerged as readily recognizable configurations. We saw much more clearly what these mothers were attempting to do to their sons than we saw a particular counter-reaction by the sons to the mother's attitudes. The counter-reaction, to be sure, was present but in a rather broad, ill-defined fashion. For example, the sons had not adjusted well either at eight or nine, or twelve and thirteen. We can surmise that the difficulty with the mother and the estrangement from the father would produce an insecure masculinity but we could not find clear-cut data indicating this.

As for the mothers, most of them evidenced a lack of acceptance of the boy's aggressive surgent masculinity. They were not sympathetic to him when he expressed stubbornness or aggressive protest, nor were they sensitive to his needs as a person. They also exhibited very little insight about themselves. These attitudes were in sharp contrast to the situation in which the sons' mothers liked their fathers. Here there was almost uniform acceptance of the son's aggressive masculinity. The mothers seemed to like to have a growing man in the house, whereas those mothers who disliked their fathers coupled their non-acceptance of masculinity in their sons with the almost explicit feeling that: "He shall pay for what I have suffered at the hands of men." How these sons did pay might be surmised from the interview personalities of the mothers who intensely disliked their own domineering fathers. One personality type appeared gruff, opinionated, domineering in relationship to the psychiatrist, as though she were saying: "I'd like to see any man get the best of me. I'm a better man than you." The other type, apparently believing that as many flies are caught by sugar, offered the Trojan horse gambit to the psychiatrist by being very seductive. Inevitably the male offspring would feel weakened in his masculinity if he were exposed to a barrage of "I can do it better than you"; or he would feel woefully inadequate if he were teased sexually by the hostile seductive mother.

In this chapter we have traced, step by step, the means by which we finally reached our impressions concerning mother's intense dislike of her father. These impressions were essentially that the more pathological form of this dislike arises out of an intense loyalty identification bond which in its extreme degrees tends to distort reality. It appeared that the mother figure (mother's mother in the older generation, or mother in the present generation) instead of openly showing dissatisfaction, opposition, or resentment to domination by the father, rather controlled the situation by a martyr-like suffering to which her offspring (particularly the daughter) pledged allegiance. This allegiance pledge, heightened by a conscious identification by the mother with her child, forced the child to twist his feelings around so that he whitened mother and blackened father. Because each step toward appreciating positives in men represented a guilt-producing stab in mother's back, all that the child could do with his resentment toward his mother was to switch it to his father. In the following chapters we shall have an opportunity to use case excerpts to illustrate this thesis.

CHAPTER XIII

HOW THE
LOYALTY
CHOICE
OPERATES

THE SCHEMATIC outlining of the workings of the loyalty bond cannot do full justice, we believe, to the intricacies of the subject. The following excerpts (many of them from non-study cases) will demonstrate, we hope, in a more vivid and concrete fashion, the kinds of open and hidden strife between the parents and how the loyalty bond helps to continue in the child the conflict existing between the parents. (See Appendix D, 7. *Case Example of Hostility Toward the Father.*)

The first example is from our study group.

Joan's mother was a pleasant, plump, co-operative woman, not too carefully groomed. Throughout the interview with the psychiatrist she was mildly tremulous until she became tearful in an emotional crisis, which will be described later. She spoke thoughtfully and positively of Joan. When Mrs. X was asked of whom Joan reminded her, she said: "At times of myself. I was fun loving, happy-go-lucky. I liked to prance around the house just like Joan does. . . . I liked to wear boy's clothes, too. Joan loves to wear her brother's shirts, but lately she is getting more feminine. I myself liked being in the Tomboy stage and for awhile we thought that Joan would never be a little girl."

Then Mrs. X revealed that although her own parents got along very well together, she had always been somewhat antagonistic toward her father. After her mother's death when Mrs. X was sixteen, her antagonistic feelings toward her father grew in intensity when he began to drink and to cavort with other women. Mrs. X thought that her mother had been wonderful, and she was trying to handle her own children as "grandmother" had, but she thought her mother had been a better mother. Although Mrs. X was rather calm throughout most of the interview, she had begun to cry when she spoke of her trouble with her husband. Before the birth of her last child she had enjoyed the sexual relationship, but after birth she was "all tired out and had a dead feeling in my sexual organs," which had persisted up until the present time. She had pleaded with her husband to permit an operation on her bladder so that this difficulty would be corrected, but he had allegedly refused. Long ago when she had first experienced this sexual deadness, her husband had told her that a person could go crazy if worked up in sexual intercourse without arriving at any climax. Mrs. X then urgently and tearfully asked, "Will you answer one question? Is this true?" She was quite relieved by the psychiatrist's reassurance that this would not drive her crazy. However, she had presented a picture of her husband's sadistically worrying her about the possibility of insanity. When Mrs. X was asked why she had chosen her husband, she replied, "Well, we both wanted a home, but I wonder if I was really in love with him." Mrs. X described him as a good person, but that he was inclined to be unreasonable and strict with the children; that as a father he somewhat enjoyed them, but not as much as some fathers. If Mrs. X and the children do something of which he disapproves, his most frequent comment to them was, "What do you want to do that for? You must be crazy."

Mr. X was also interviewed. He was a big man who appeared to be easy going, superficially good natured, not too spontaneous, and somewhat defensive in his replies. He described his daughter, Joan, as a little bull-headed but not spoiled, and that she probably got the bull-headedness from him, because her mother was "pretty understanding." In all, Mr. X did not give too much information and seemed rather critical of his daughter rather than greatly fond of her. He was defensive about his marriage, said that he and his wife had spats now and then, just like everybody else, but that he was quite happy and that his marriage was one of the best things that had ever happened to him. When Mr. X was asked about sexual relations with his wife, he said, in a non-committal way, that they got along "OK", also that sex was not important, and that a marriage should not be split up just because the sexual relationship was not good. At no time did he reveal or give any indication of the situation which his wife had described in her interview.

In the interview with the psychiatrist Joan showed much zest and spontaneity, but it was in her play behavior that certain trends were clearly shown. Joan exhibited no inhibition in using the play box, when it was offered her. Upon seeing the little doll Joan remarked that this was her baby brother. She then picked up the gun, clicked it, and compared it with the gun she had at home. Next, she picked up the clay and said it reminded her of kindergarten. With envy in her voice she told how her brother had wandered away from home and that the strangers who returned him had given him free ice-cream and candy. About her daily life, she said she liked to play with boys and with guns. When asked if she had any fun with the girls, she appeared somewhat disinterested and went on to say, "I'm going to get a bike so I can visit fires where the horse stables are." Joan told of several horse stables that had caught fire and that she wanted to see where this had happened because she was very much fascinated by the idea of horses being burned up in a fire. Finally, the dreams she described revealed a preoccupation with masculine symbols. In one of them she had dreamt that a snake was winding itself about the neck of a little boy who was playing in the yard.

The school report on Joan at the age of nine stated that she was very well adjusted, very co-operative and friendly with the teachers, and mixed well with her classmates, had a serious attitude toward school work, and worked up to mental capacity. However, the school report at thirteen showed a drop in adjustment, co-operation with the school program was only average or fair, attitude toward school work was carefree, and she was not working up to mental capacity.

The case of Joan and her mother illustrates most of the concepts outlined in the previous chapter. The reasons for Mrs. X's early dislike of her father and idealization of her mother is not clear. Rather early in life Mrs. X became competitive with men (she liked being in the Tom-boy stage), and apparently enjoyed, through her daughter, a revival of competition with men in the form of Tom-boyism. Joan herself clearly showed the competition with males and there is a decided hint that if she dropped the anti-male feelings, she would drop mother. This state of affairs probably accounted for the poor adjustment at puberty, one side of her being attracted to boys, while the other side, in a loyalty bond to her mother, tells her that she should compete with and demolish men. The mother's relation to her husband was not too clear. We would wonder how much of it was the husband's actual sadistic tendencies and how much the mother was trying to provoke this aspect of him in order to prove to herself how bad men are.

A non-study case with similar features but with enough intensification that the child was referred to the Institute for Juvenile Research, is that of Betty. Betty was referred to the clinic because of stubbornness and aggressiveness in school; she would not heed the teacher's requests, and during recess time she would aggressively hit both the girls and boys. Her mother reported that Betty had behaved at home in a similar fashion since the birth of her brother when she was three years old.

During the interview with the psychiatrist Mrs. Y was very seductive in her confidentiality. She confided a secret to the psychiatrist that she had allegedly never told anyone before. At the age of nineteen she had gone to a doctor who did a vaginal examination on her and massaged her breasts, which she thinks had been "a pass" at her. In describing her background Mrs. Y said she was the youngest of four children. When she was six, her father, an outgoing lawyer, had divorced her mother because she would not socialize with him and wanted him to stay at home. After the divorce the father would not support the family and as a result mother often sued him for non-support, at which time Mrs. Y had to appear in court to take up the gauntlet against her father. Mrs. Y was quite ambivalent toward her father. She regarded him as neglectful and cruel both toward her mother and toward herself.

In regard to her daughter, Betty, she said that the child reminds her of herself in not being afraid to express her own opinions. Mrs. Y spoke positively of her husband and said that she got along well with him. She described him as being passive and accommodating. Her first husband had been brutal to her and she divorced him after three years. Whereas she had originally experienced pain during sexual intercourse, now she was able to enjoy it somewhat with her present husband. However, she has always had pain during her menses. For ten years she had not been able to conceive and had gone to physicians who could not find any organic cause.

Betty, the daughter, was very seductive in the interview, sitting with her dress pulled up and smiling flirtatiously at the psychiatrist. When she was asked to draw, she chose to draw a boy and the first thing she drew in the picture was his penis. Throughout the whole interview there was much talk about and reference to the penis. She built up the blocks into a tall cylindrical form, she told of dreams in which she petted a snake, and she modeled a snake out of clay.

In the case of Betty, her mother, and grandmother, the attitude toward men was more violent and bitter than in the earlier described case of Joan. This case also illustrates a feature noted in many clinic cases. This feature is essentially that the mother was originally attracted to a dominant and strong figure like her own father, then would marry him only to encounter such clashes of will that the marriage breaks up and the mother marries a more passive, accommodating man. Thus, in contrast with Joan's mother, Betty's mother did not submit masochistically to provoked brutality but married a man whom she could dominate and control. The impact of masculine competitive attitudes on mother's femininity was clearly seen in her many symptoms in the sexual reproductive areas.

The following excerpt from a clinic case illustrates the presence of father-hate and competitiveness with men in a very young girl. Anita Z, a four-year-old was referred by her mother to the clinic because of "strong antipathy to her father and an abnormal attachment to her mother." She would not remain alone with her father, argued with him, and called him names. The father was quite concerned over this situation and desired his daughter's affection. This behavior had begun two years previous to referral, shortly after her brother Tom had been born. Since his birth, Anita's favorite comment had been, "I want to grow up to be a boy like Tommy, then I can cut my hair short and Daddy will be the Mommie." Anita carried out the wish to be a boy by insisting on wearing boy's clothes and by cutting her long hair on every possible occasion. She did not want to play with other children, tenaciously held on to her mother, and requested much attention.

Mrs. Z revealed that she had been somewhat Tom-boyish as a young child and that Anita reminded her of herself in that respect. She described her mother as having been dominating and her father as passive and silent. However, her strong feelings were connected with her own marriage. Sexual incompatibility developed between Mrs. Z and her husband soon after his return from military service. Accompanying this incompatibility was her husband's destructive criticism of her. "He tears me to pieces with his remarks. Nothing I do is right. I have no way of fighting back." Because her husband prefers some "unusual and perverted" foreplay preceding intercourse, Mrs. Z has refused to accommodate him. At the time of the interview theirs was a marriage in name only, sexual relations were non-existent; father and mother remained civil to each other but there was no affection.

The case of Anita illustrates the acting out of father hate by the daughter while the mother is seemingly helpless to retaliate against the really or allegedly brutal husband. Here was not the situation of mother handing over to the daughter her original hate for her own father. Instead, the small daughter seemed to be acting out mother's bitter feelings toward her husband (the girl's father).

A clinic case which involving a mother and two daughters (Mrs. W, Barbara, and Pat) may illustrate how one daughter is chosen for the loyalty bond while the other is not. Mrs. W, who was an adored sister of nine brothers, idealized her mother as a "wonderful woman," but characterized her father as "liking to be the center of attention, disliked by his children although our mother did not seem to be bothered by his personality. He did the meanest things to me such as putting a hole in my beach ball and chasing my boy friends away."

Mrs. W's own marriage had gone well except for some mother-in-law trouble until four years ago when she caught her husband cheating, and one thing led to another until finally a divorce was obtained.

Barbara, aged eleven, was referred because of bed-wetting, nervousness, and whining in a child-like way for company. Mrs. W described her in matter-of-fact, cool tones as "always picking at people to keep on playing with her, always bothering her uncle (my brother) to play with her. She is just like my husband because both expect people to do a lot for them. Sore and angry if I go out with my new boy friend, frequently asking me where she can find her father if something happens to me." In the psychiatric interview Barbara showed her liking for men and her competition with women. As for the former, she related very well to the male psychiatrist and her main theme was how to get her father back or how to get the dog back that her father had given her. As for the latter, Barbara was very fascinated with having been a pall-bearer at the funeral of a small girl cousin, and wanted to be a pall-bearer again; also when Barbara and her sister were seen together by the psychiatrist, Barbara was quite competitive, supplied answers for Pat, and at one point pulled down Pat's dress when the child's knees and thighs seemed to be too exposed.

Pat, aged seven, was referred because of "convulsions." Mrs. W described her younger daughter with much warmth as "the pride of the family," "very well liked," "very good around the house," "like myself in that we are both good natured." Pat's convulsions began at the age of six months and occurred once every year. One convulsion occurred the morning after mother's divorce had come through. Pat had been feeling ill and her mother wanted to give her an enema, which Pat had always fought off. Mother threatened to call the doctor, and Pat gave in to mother, but five minutes after the enema had been given she had a convulsion.

Mrs. W revealed that Pat had always hated doctors and men, and then she added, more parenthetically, that she herself was the same way, although recently she had somewhat gotten over her dislike for men. A year before her parents' divorce an incident occurred which heightened Pat's already existing fear of men. The incident involved a quarrel between her parents in which her father had hit her mother. Pat had heard her mother scream and after this incident Pat was afraid to go to bed at night for fear her father would hit her mother.

In the psychiatric interview Pat showed, in contrast to her sister, a marked inhibition about being on close terms with a man. She consented to go with the psychiatrist only if her sister accompanied her. She was a little apprehensive at first, but later relaxed somewhat. In the doll play she placed the father doll downstairs and arranged a footstool for him. She then put herself and a potty in another room and placed a cabinet flush against the door. (The barrier against the wished-for father was obvious.) Her mother was not included in this doll play.

Since the relationship with the psychiatrist was going well she was asked if she minded if her sister left. She began to cry and her sister had to console her and play with her. In a later conversation, Pat revealed that she had been afraid that there was to have been an operation on her that day. She was reassured that this was not to have been the case. She told of being afraid of a dirty sink and of having been dirty, because if she is dirty she gets a whipping from her mother. When Pat was asked to describe any scary dreams, she told, with much animation, of a dream of a dead man from a grave who grabbed her and took her below. She had tried to call for her mother but her voice had been very faint. Another dream of her sister, Barbara, being kidnapped by a man was described as having been less scary.

The case of Pat and Barbara illustrates how the younger daughter, Pat, having had less contact with the father and being more dependent upon the mother, had become more amenable to her mother's attitudes and thus had identified with her mother. Pat's fear of men is obvious: they are pictured in her mind as dangerous and *verboten;* they are for other women, but not for her. She is intimidated by her sister and her mother, both of whom are interested in men. Thus, beneath the loyalty identification between mother and Pat is a subtle defeminizing, crushing competitiveness on mother's part. (Mother took out her feelings about the divorce on Pat and had given her the enema which caused her convulsion.) Mother seemed to be saying, "Pat, as long as you stay out of the competition for men, as long as you share my conscious feelings that men are cruel, I will be your ally and will not punish you." Barbara, whose feelings for her father were too strong for her to give up her father, and too strong to accept mother's membership bid to the anti-male club, is much more openly competitive with mother and with Pat. Pat shows her fear of receiving affection from men by insisting that her sister accompany her to the examination with the psychiatrist, by dreaming of a scary, punishing re-union with the father (dead man in the grave). A less dreadful and more exciting dream of union with men, that is, taken by kidnappers, is apparently too disloyal for her to enact as the main character and so she allows, as in the psychiatric interview, her sister to play the main role. There are, of course, many other features which could be commented on, but they are not pertinent to the thesis of the loyalty bond.

The last two case examples illustrate the switching of resentful feelings from the mother onto the father in order to preserve the harmony of the loyalty bond to mother. The first is a single girl of thirty who sought psychoanalytic treatment because of chronic backaches and a general feeling of inadequacy. The description of her family was that her mother was a very nice person, full of fun, with whom she always had gotten along well. Her father, however, was pictured as impossible, demanding in an immature way, very curt and dictatorial. Her mother and father would often argue and she always wondered if each quarrel would be the last. For a long time in analytic treatment she continued to speak of her father as "simply impossible," and she had no affectionate feelings for him at all. That she had repressed hostility to her mother was quite apparent. In adolescence a neighbor woman whom the patient liked happened to die and for a long time the patient was worried for fear her own mother would die. The patient was also always worried that in some way she would be a disgrace to her mother and cause her to die. Her real lack of being mothered by her mother came out in a slip of the tongue. Once she was asked, when she was having some difficulty with her boy friend, why she didn't mother him a little. The patient said; "Well, I don't want to nag him." The mother idealization and father disparagment were very apparent in this case.

The following instance is an example of her switching of negatives from mother onto father. One day she reported a dream in which she had received a very nice present from her father. However, because this present had a more expensive price tag on it than the real price, she had become very angry with her father for this deception. After telling the dream, she said; "This is just like my father to play such a trick on me." When she was asked if this really ever occurred, she thought for a minute and then reluctantly admitted that she now remembered that it had been her mother who had perpetrated this deception. This girl also had considerable penis envy and had frequent fantasies of having her boy friend tied up with his penis bound with wire. The patient would then unbind the wire and help the man.

The other case was Dorothy, twenty, who had a very close attachment to her mother. Dorothy was an only child whose parents had been divorced when she was only seven, which resulted in a division of her sympathies between her mother and father. Her hostility toward men was rather well concealed, and not so marked as in the foregoing case. There had been a succession of infatuations with young men with whom she felt herself deeply in love, but when any one of them had become serious, she would begin to find fault with him. Some of her dreams and fantasies had involved eggs being squeezed. In conscious associations she had recalled that she did have a destructive thought toward her boy friend's testicles: "Would it pain him very much if his testicles were squeezed?"

The transfer of negatives from her mother onto her father was shown in the following example. At one point in the therapy she said she had a great fear of drunken people which she felt must have come from a fear of her drinking father. However, on questioning, she realized that her father had drunk only occasionally and was never abusive and had never done anything to frighten her. She then recalled that when her mother drank, it used to frighten her because her mother would then change from a sweet, kindly person to a shrewish, raucous woman. This transference of negatives was demonstrated again during one of her therapy sessions when she had come in full of resentment and distaste for her fiancé. Although initially she could not discover what he had done to incur her antagonism, questioning revealed that she had not been paid her salary by her woman employer. Since she could not be consciously resentful toward this woman because the employer was a sick woman, she transferred her resentment to her fiancé.

The loyalty bond features are not as prominent or unmistakable when we consider the mother-son relationship as when we dealt with the mother-daughter situation. In spite of the lessened prominence, in all of the examples there can be seen the repercussions on the male offspring when the mother has a bitter feeling toward her own father. In essence the repercussion is that the son, as a representative of the male sex, shall pay for the injury done mother by her own father.

The first case example from our study group is that of Robert and his mother. The case reveals the familiar features of the grandparents having been overtly compatible, but mother disliking her father, and not being able to understand how her own mother could put up with her father. Instead of mother becoming completely the defenseless, martyred sufferer in her own marriage, she chooses a weak and non-masculine man. The confusion for the son as to what is really masculine must be considerable.

Mrs. C., Robert's mother, was a short, dark-haired woman, apparently calm, who had revealed her anxiety by chain smoking throughout the interview. She looked at the male psychiatrist with a hungry, seductive expression. She began the discussion of her childhood by saying that it had been a very happy one. When she was asked if there had been any cause for unhappiness, she said; "No, my father had a good deal of money and provided well for his family. The only trouble was that he became so strict and fanatical about religion and we had to observe the orthodox customs. . . . He was very dictatorial, a little Caesar in the family. He was a strong type and very opinionated. My mother was quite submissive to my father, and his word was law. She was young in spirit and age, but my parents got along very well. My father enjoyed my mother. His favorite was whoever was youngest, and mostly favored the boys. I felt closer to my mother." When she was asked if her handling of her children was similar to that of her mother's, she replied that she would like to repeat the way her mother had done things because theirs was such a closely knit family life, but she does not want to be as opinionated and dictatorial as her father has been.

When Mrs. C. was asked to describe her marriage, she hesitated for a moment and then said that it was very much along the usual lines. Her husband was very creative, very friendly, but not at all athletic and was more feminine than most men. After awhile her control broke down and she spoke of her real discontent with him. She expressed great bitterness about the sexual maladjustment and said that he was not a real father to Robert, was only half a man. As to her own emotional instability, she had had psychotic breakdowns at the birth of each child; two of the breakdowns had required shock treatments. Regarding Robert, she said that he reminded her of herself in that they both are understanding and introspective.

Robert was an overly casual boy who munched on candy throughout the interview and was unevenly spontaneous. He seemed to be unaware of the psychiatrist and exhibited a take-it-or-leave-it manner. When the toy box was indicated he languidly fingered the crayolas, then easily and flatly said he did not want to play with them. When he was asked to describe his feelings for his father, he said; "Well, that isn't really any of my business, but as long as I am here I might as well tell it." Robert then reluctantly but definitely came out with evidence of his father's sadism. He revealed that when his father has been angry he would pull and twist his mother's arm. Sometimes his father had dragged him away from the table by the arm or while teasing him he would hit his shoulder.

Robert's concept of his father and what father figures are like may be reflected in an anxiety dream he related. In the dream he is in a deep forest "where there is a man who is a wood-chopper and his face is ugly and he goes around scaring people." How much this concept has been stimulated by his father's actual sadistic behavior and how much by his mother's hate and depreciation of men is open to question. We believe, though, from our other findings in this group, that the latter stimulus is not inconsiderable. The confusion about his father and mother, about who belongs to which sex, may be reflected in another anxiety dream in which one and one equals a thousand. He said about that dream, "I knew in the dream that it did not equal one thousand, that it was wrong; my head got mixed up and I had to wake up."

The school report on Robert had designated him as only fairly well adjusted. He was distant in his relationships to his schoolmates, only average in co-operation with the school program, not working up to mental capacity, and also showed some nervous mannerisms. The school report at twelve and thirteen revealed that although now he had succeeded in working up to mental capacity, he was still distant with his schoolmates and still exhibited nervous mannerisms.

Thus, in the case of Robert we see the repercussions on the son of a mother who hated her dominant father and envied her favored brothers. She triumphed over men by marrying a figuratively penisless man. She made her husband appear depreciated and cruel in her son's eyes, which she accomplished through her loyalty identification with her son. Robert not only cannot use his father (or other men) as a model for masculinity, but also he must be afraid of men-hating women. The only safe solution open to him is a retreat from people. The report at twelve and thirteen indicating that he was working up to mental capacity suggests that a safe retreat for him might be the intellectual area.

The next case excerpt, taken from our study group, is a good illustration of the mother who is determined that the child shall suffer for what she has suffered. Mrs. T. was plump and outwardly co-operative, but in repose her expression was depressed and she gave the impression of being a worrier. She said her son, Brian, had no faults, he was very good natured and easy to get along with, more mature and serious than the average boy and even more so than the older children in the family. "Brian is much more considerate of me than the other children are." With a laugh, she said, "He is planning to grow up and go to work so his mother doesn't have to work any more." Mrs. T. said that Brian was more like herself because he was thoughtful and worried more than the other children did. "He always looks out for me."

The description which she gave of her troubles in life was typical of those given by mothers who said that their child reminded them of themselves. During the whole pregnancy she had been sick and nauseated and had had severe backaches. She had constantly wished she had not tried to have this child; also, since she had wanted a little girl, she had been greatly disappointed at the birth of Brian. Although the labor had not been difficult, Mrs. T. said she had been badly torn. Her present health was not good; she had fibroid tumors, headaches, and backaches.

In describing her own childhood Mrs. T. said that her father had married twice and that she was the third child of the second marriage. She had wanted to go further in school but her father would not permit it. Of her father she said: "He is a bull-headed Dutchman with old-country ideas. . . . He wanted all the children to stay at home. Although he was very strict, I was not afraid of him. I would speak out anyhow."

Mrs. T. described herself as a worrier and remarked that her mother was the same way. Her mother was a very quiet, submissive person: "If she wanted something from my father he would refuse, but if my father wanted a new tractor or something, he would get it. He got what he wanted whereas my mother never got a thing." At the end of the interview when talking about the past and present she said: "I never in my life had a doll, and that was my father's fault."

The interview revealed that Brian was very ill-at-ease and shy.

He was impassive, frequently looked away from the psychiatrist, and was afraid to be at all spontaneous. If he was asked a question which he did not immediately comprehend, he asked with a snarl, "What?" In spite of some minor relaxation later he continued to be a serious, worried boy with a curious admixture of self-assurance. Frequently during the examination he seemed to be looking out at a distance as though he were reflecting on some problem that concerned him a great deal. After some encouragement he played with the toys and in his doll play he picked up a doll family and arranged them. When they accidentally fell down, he said, "Now they're all dead." Then he picked up a paint brush with which to paint their faces, but instead he knocked them all down again with a sweep of the brush. Following this, Brian tried to undress the father doll by taking off the shirt, and then he pushed the mother doll in the face with the paint brush and knocked her down. Later when he was asked what his ambition was, he said, very unusually, "I would just like to be myself." Brian's repression of his anger toward his parents, particularly his mother, was demonstrated when he said, that he never got angry with them or felt resentment toward them. He took his troubles to his mother because she was the only one at home to whom he was close.

In the case of Brian there are rather clear indications that he was being punished for what his grandfather had failed to do for his mother. Essentially, the punishment was that Brian should provide his mother with the wherewithal of life and enjoyment, he should provide her with the doll that her father never gave to her. His mother used her martyrdom and her loyalty membership to keep her son ensnared to her. While Brian verbalized no resentment toward his mother, in his play he had succeeded in hitting her in the face with a brush. Under his serious, worried surface there seemed to have been a smoldering resentment which may break out in later life.

Although many other cases could be described in detail, space does not permit more than a few brief illustrative excerpts:

Punitive mother: Mother of Allen, a study child, relatively maladjusted during latency and at puberty, said, regarding her father: "He was sadistic. My mother was domineered by my father and I think she enjoyed it." Regarding the son, "When Allen was two and was still vomiting, I became so angry that I made him eat the vomitus. I see now it was a mistake, but I did it because my father made me eat everything."

Seductive mother: Mother of Tom, a provocative, facetious study child also relatively maladjusted during latency and at puberty, said to the psychiatrist: "Talking to you makes me so nervous because your voice just goes through my whole body." About her dreams: "I have dreams of intercourse with other men and of being chased by robbers. Being chased by robbers isn't scary because if they are going to get me, I might as well relax and enjoy it." Regarding her father and her husband: "My father was stubbornly, meanly quiet which dampened my mother's love of life. My husband is the same way." Regarding her son: "Tom is a very sensitive, affectionate boy, like myself. When I am lonesome because my husband is out of town, I take Tom into bed with me."

Domineering mother: Mother of Bill, a study child, well adjusted during latency but relatively maladjusted at puberty, said regarding her way of handling the boy: "He does everything I tell him without dilly dallying. He is going to do as I want him to do." Regarding her husband: "He is home every day at four-fifteen and he better not come later than that. He doesn't tell Bill any different than I have said. They do as I say." Regarding her father: "Mean and grumpy; hit me for no reason and I just asked for more. He quarrels constantly with my mother and it isn't her fault because she is very quiet and easy going. Whenever I see him now I tell him that I have no use for him."

We have endeavored to illustrate how resentment between the parents, particularly of a hidden variety, can affect the children so that when they grow up they are ready to renew the battle of the sexes. We have seen how the mother, through suffering and a loyalty membership offer, may induce her daughter to forget what wrongs mother has done her and to band with mother against the real, exaggerated, fancied wrongs perpetrated by men. The daughter will then "hate for two." Which daughter is selected as a confederate or ally depends on many factors (as the case of Barbara and Pat illustrates). But if mother is miserable she will understandably seek company in her misery. The repercussions on the company-keeping daughter is that she is held down in her growth and in her affectionate interest in the opposite sex.

We have seen also the upsetting and confusing demasculinizing repercussions on the son when the mother has a hate for dominating men. These repercussions are intensified when the mother creates a loyalty identification bond with the son by seeing herself in him. We do not see, as we did with the daughters, a clear-cut alliance with the mother against men. Instead, we see a lessening of the son's masculinity as he, out of loyalty for the mother, cannot build up his masculinity in the usual ways, i.e., by an affectionate comradeship with his peers and older men. This way is closed to him because he would be disloyal to and out of continuity with his male-depreciating mother.

Frequently a passive attitude in adult men toward women or their wives is based on loyalty to a "suffering," "abused" mother. Because they do not want to be like their "bull-like," "abusive" fathers, they are overly careful not to cross their wives, not to suggest sexual intercourse unless the wives are willing and not to have orgastic gratification until the wives do. Thus, a loyalty bond of son to mother based in her resentment to men has severe repercussions on the boy's emotional growth.

The loyalty bond, we believe, is the factor that intensifies the continuity between generations. It, like traditionalism, and the group orientation belongs in the "permanence" category in that it tends to perpetuate sameness and to create homogeneity out of heterogeneity. In wholsome degrees it brings like-minded individuals together into fraternal organizations, individuals who recognize a part of themselves in others. It affords parents an opportunity to relive their lives, the mother in the daughter, the father in the son. In the parents' willingness to be continued, perpetuated and imitated, it provides a stepping stone in the child's learning the role of identifying with the parent of the same sex.

In an atmosphere of strife where injury and abuse have been suffered by persons impotent to defend themselves adequately, the loyalty bond takes on unwholesome aspects. The leit motif of the loyalty members is revenge as can be seen in adolescent gangs or in nations who are or who believe themselves victimized by the powers that be. The parent who has been victimized, and who has seen his own parent victimized cannot be casual about whose side the child is on. The situation is not the more wholesome one, "I am available to be emulated in part if my child so wishes" but rather, "My child has to be on my side, love my friends and hate my foes, or else!" The detrimental effects of a man-hating mother or a woman-hating father on the child's attitudes toward the sexes are obvious.

We have only touched on father's real role in these matters. To be sure, he is not blameless. He comes to his marriage from his past; he may be passive or domineering, seductive or sexually cold; he can try to win the loyalty of his children to men rather than to women. However, as we have said, we are primarily interested in how mother can affect the child's relationship to the father, all other things being equal. To take just one example: There are times when the father seems to be, or may be rejecting the daughter and injuring her femininity. The mother can make matters better by persuading the father to make up with the daughter, or by pointing out to the daughter that father didn't really mean it, that he was just in an off mood that day, that there are many other days that father has been nice to the daughter; and thus mother may be able to take the edge off daughter's wounded feelings and restore her affection to the father. However, mother in a similar incident can make matters worse by acting as an agent provocateur, by inflaming an incident that could have been resolved peacefully: "That's just like your father to do it. You still have me who thinks well of you." Mother's inflammatory intervention can, on one hand, certainly raise the daughter's mild anger to the boiling point of Hell's fury toward the father and, on the other hand, direct her sympathies toward an increased loyalty to the mother.

Opportunities for Emotional Growth

CHAPTER XIV

THE TYPES
OF ADJUSTMENT

Throughout our study, adjustment has proved to be a phenomenon important in itself and useful in enlightening us about other phenomena. Mention of some type of adjustment has been made in every one of the preceding chapters. However, because frequently some other topic was the main focus of a preceding chapter, there has not been an opportunity to view adjustment in a total fashion. In this chapter we intend to review what we have already said on the subject and to fill out the picture with some additional data.

In re-examining the phenomenon of adjustment, we can obtain a more complete picture of it only by considering the adjustment within the family as well as adjustment outside the family. The latter adjustment has been dealt with rather intensively in our consideration of the combined social adjustment score (psychiatric interview and school adjustments) and in our investigation of the one-to-one relators and the group relators (psychiatric interview adjustment much better than the school adjustment and vice versa). We had concentrated on the outside-the-family adjustment because this was deemed one of the principal tasks of this age span.

However, because the home is such a security providing area, we need to know how the child is getting along in the family while he is trying to adjust outside of it. The fact that mother's evaluation and feeling about the child's adjustment were frequently at sharp variance with the school's and the psychiatrist's, would make us wonder whether one type of adjustment was not being achieved at the expense of the other type.

In viewing this opinion difference, we should keep in mind some impressions from the preceding chapters. As we have said, problem behavior noticed by mother is a wholesome expression of growth tensions in the child—tensions reflective of a phase during which the ability to master new situations not always keeps pace with the urge to master. An unusual absence of problems from the mother's point of view may mean either that mother is especially well fitted to absorb and handle the child's growth tensions or it can mean that little growth is going on. On the other hand, the presence of many problems for mother may indicate either that the child is actively coping with his growth tensions or that he is so swamped with these signs that he cannot grow.

In order for us to answer these questions, the inside-the-family and the outside-the-family adjustments would have to be considered together. By certain procedures involving the child's combined social adjustment rating and his family adjustment rating, we were able to separate out four small groups which could illustrate the status of growth tensions. (See Appendix E, Table 36.) (A) The child was well adjusted both inside and outside the family, which possibly meant that the socialization of the child was not causing tension in the mother-child relationship. (B) The child was adjusted outside the family but not inside; the situation probably was one in which socialization was proceeding but at the cost of tension between mother and child. (C) The child was well adjusted inside, but not outside the family, probably an indication that growth and socialization have been curtailed in order that harmony be maintained between mother and child. (D) The child was not adjusted inside or outside the family; the situation seemingly was one of some interference with basic adjustability. We shall call the groups respectively: Group A— the generally adjusted; Group B—the socially adjusted; Group C— the family adjusted; and Group D—the generally maladjusted.

Before examining in some detail these four groups it might be helpful to give a birdseye view of our summary impressions. Group A (the generally adjusted) had mothers who evidenced the greatest psycho-sexual maturation. They were able to give and receive inter-personal warmth and love to their children and to their mates. The children were characterized by a vigorous, flexible, and socialized personality. Group B (the socially adjusted) had mothers who were given to over-intense feelings of love and hate and who identified with the assertive, individualistic, components in their children. The children were characterized by an overt antagonism and a lack of confidence in and closeness to their parents. Group C (the family adjusted) had mothers who avoided rivalry with their own mothers and siblings by trying to control their erotic impulse life. Fear of these turbulent feelings had made them fearful of any evidence of lively restlessness in their children who were consequently quite inhibited and deadened in their affective zest. Group D (the generally maladjusted) had mothers who were apparently unable to form stable ties with either of their own parents, and whose rivalry for dependency gratification led to defensive, hostile interpersonal relationships. The effect of this on their children seemed to have been a regressive delaying action in growing up, and an anxiety about taking the next maturational step.

We will now proceed in greater detail and take up Group A (the generally adjusted). (See Appendix E, Table 37.) We find first some familiar maternal dynamisms which were associated, as we described in early chapters, with harmonious growth. The mother, in continuity with her own past, appeared to be reliving the enjoyable aspects of her growing up, not through but with her children while she still maintained her adult responsibilities and role. The positive feelings of the mother to her own father were a characteristic of this group and helped to explain why there was a warmth and harmony with her husband. Thus, in this group there were the lowest incidence of sexual dysfunction with the husband and the lowest incidence of disagreement with him on the discipline of the child. The growth potential in the mother also was evidenced by her desire to change somewhat from the pattern of her own mother, and by her ability to effect this change. Of all the four groups, Group A was characterized by a high incidence of mothers who were both dependable and understanding of the child's individuality. In the interview with the psychiatrist and with the social worker, they were characteristically warm, spontaneous, and co-operative. Minimal in this group was the somewhat constricting binding phenomenon of mother seeing herself in the child. All in all, there emerged the picture of a reliable yet resilient family structure unified by affectionate and understanding bonds which made for both stability and self-expansion.

The vigorous, flexible, and socialized nature of these children's personality was evidenced in several ways. In general they may be characterized as showing an active, energetic protest against interruption or discontinuation of a pleasurable situation. Thus, weaning problems, open jealousy reaction at the birth of siblings, and an active rather than a passive opposition to some of their parents' commands were more often seen in this group. Their flexibility and spontaneity were evidenced by the fact that the school described them more often as leaders than followers and their moods were appropriate to the situations. The interpersonal relationships of this group were characterized by the highest degree of togetherness; all confided in one or both parents rather than (as the other three groups) confiding in a sibling or keeping their troubles to themselves. Their sad and worried feelings were most frequently related to the current social scene rather than being of an egocentric or altruistic variety.

In Group B (the socially adjusted) the major coloration of the mother's personality was a strong individualistic trend (See Appendix E, Table 38.) Although this component was somewhat self-realizing and creative, it had more the meaning of strengthening her own self in order that she not be ignored, in order that she need not kow tow to a more powerful person, in order that she make her mark in the world. The emphasis seemed to be not merely on growing, but on growing up and growing big. These mothers, as the mothers in Group A, had positive feelings toward their own fathers, but their feelings about both their mothers and their fathers were characteristically described in intense terms of black and white. Their feelings to their parents were excessively positive or negative, with much less of the reasonably positive or the ambivalent or the detached. In a way these intense feelings are characteristic of adolescence when one feels the powerless underdog and still has to make his mark in the world. A precarious self-esteem is suggested by these extremes of love and hate—overjoyed by acceptance and angered by slights. In line with this instability was the finding that Group B mothers most frequently admitted to being quite nervous and subject to moods of depression.

Characteristic of the mother's handling of the child was a marked empathy with the feelings and rights of the child as a separate individual and a de-emphasis on the warm, reliability factor. However, whereas in Group A the mothers accepted the child's individualism without seeing themselves in the child, in Group B their empathy with the child's individuality was characteristically associated with mother's seeing herself in the child. In other words, it appeared as though the child was given free rein as the vehicle or agent through which mother realized her ambitions, and thus salved her wounded precarious self-esteem.

The children were characterized by a certain touchiness about being deprived of certain rights, or attentions, and a lack of closeness to their parents. Thus, when they were asked about anger toward their parents they most frequently complained that they didn't get this or that or they didn't get to do this or that; they also least often confided in one or both of their parents. Their touchy anger, their feeling of being encroached on, their distrust of parents as confidants were quite analogous to mother's intense feelings. The result seemed to be that while the child was encouraged to make something of himself (for mother) outside the family, in the family the sparks would fly between the highly individualistic, power-needing mother and child. The child also was quite doubtful as to his ability to carry out and realize his mother's ambitions. It is similar to the situation in which the boy has been groomed by the strong, ambitious father to assert himself. Then in adolescence and young manhood when he asserts himself contrary to his father's ambition for him—friction develops.

This, then, is not the harmonious, loving family seen in Group A; instead it appears to be more of a power-seeking family with considerable drive and energy, and with the "me" components in ascendancy over the "we" components. It is reminiscent of the rivalrous and treacherous family life of the Greek gods, and we recall that the ancient Greeks were a highly individualistic and creative people, possibly in relation to their underdog relationship to the surrounding people. It is reminiscent of the jealous and omnipotent earlier Hebrew Jehovah, and we know that the Hebrews then as now are also individualistic, creative people, also possibly in reaction to their underdog position. It is reminiscent of the many other peoples, as for example the power, jealousy, and intrigue themes depicted in Shakespearian drama when individualistic and underdog Elizabethan England began to assert herself against Spain. All these have the theme, "I shall make myself more powerful than my oppressor, and more admirable than my rivals."

In Group C (the family adjusted) as in Group D (generally maladjusted), we pass from simple growing up as in Group A or growing big, as in Group B, to a block in growth. (See Appendix E, Table 39.) In Group C the children's adjustment to the mother was much better than the adjustment outside the family. It was characterized by such a preponderance of constrictive maternal influences that the end result for the children had been an almost strangulation of the impulse life. The non-growth of mother was evidenced by a lack of fondness for her own father and by a positive idealization of her own mother with a traditional imitation of her mother's motherhood pattern. There was also an over-emphasis on warm reliability, a de-emphasis on understanding the child's surgent impulses. Lastly, of a constricting nature was mother's tendency to see herself in the child.

We get the impression that these mothers were women who had avoided early rivalry with their mothers and siblings by avoiding being impulsively attracted to any pleasure situation which would cause a clash with the rival. In other words, they had to control their impulses by means of an inhibition of the zestful instinctual life. One evidence of this inhibition was that Group C mothers had the least frequency of extreme feelings about their parents. In other words, they rarely had the excessively positive or excessively negative feelings toward their parents that we noted as being so prominent in Group B.

Their fear of their own lively childhood feelings apparently made them fearful of any evidence of lively restlessness in their own children who were, in consequence, quite inhibited and deadened in affective zest. The mother's lack of empathy with the child's individualism and her tendency to see herself in the child combined to produce an obtuseness regarding the child's self-expressive needs. Since these mothers had been afraid that any lively impulse toward their own fathers might result in a hostile clash with their over-loved mothers, it was not surprising that they constantly were vigilant to nip in the bud any lively surgency which might appear in their children.

When we reviewed the reports given by Group C mothers about the development of their children, we saw evidence that these mothers were characteristically interferers with the surgent, growing, autonomous life of their children. Although they reported few difficulties in the dependent, feeding period (understandably so because the child was passive rather than independent), the toilet training disturbances reported in this group were the most frequent as compared with the other three groups. These disturbances were not in the direction of a delay in completion of habit training, but rather they took the form of a temporary breakdown of the habit once it had been established. In general it is probable that the degree of sturdiness in a final habit pattern is greater to the extent that the mother has kept the individual capacity of the child in mind when inculcating the habit. Thus, it is understandable that with the interfering characteristics of these mothers, the final toilet training habit would tend to break down somewhat. Since these mothers did not lack warmth but rather they were controlling, opportunities for overt aggressive protest by the children were minimal. The breakdown in sphincter control was perhaps a much safer protest for these children than aggressive anger or rage at the mother would have been. It should be emphasized that these were temporary breakdowns during the second to fourth year, and were not difficulties existing at the time of examination.

The lack of overt protest was seen also in relation to the siblings. These mothers reported that there was almost no jealous reaction of the children upon the birth of a sibling, and that even later, sibling rivalry very rarely existed. It is likely that these mothers, being so threatened by the appearance of angry rivalry, either suppressed it in their children or failed to perceive it. The absence of problems arising out of surgent rivalry and the absence of other problems bothering mother reminds one of the satisfied remarks mothers at times make about their children in the first year of life: "You wouldn't know that there was a baby in the house." We might paraphrase this in terms of Group C mothers: "You wouldn't know there was a growing child in the house."

The children themselves showed in the tests and interviews a variety of phenomena all pointing in one direction: a marked dampening of the lively zestful instinctual life. Thus they rarely admitted any angry feelings toward their parents; made form rather than color the determinant in the Rorschach responses; and their mood in school was fixed toward the serious side. In their dream life, Group C children were the only ones who had not spontaneously reported the anxiety dream of falling. Although this will be further elaborated in a later chapter, we might mention now that the falling dream signifies some anxiety that dangerous impulses may get out of control. We surmised that the impulse life of these children was so inhibited, that there was no occasion for a signal like the falling dream to be employed as a warning that there was impending lack of impulse control.

Finally we come to the last group, D, in which the children were comparatively not able to adjust either outside or inside the family. Here there did not appear to be any beneficial maternal influence or dynamism even of a one-sided nature. (See Appendix E, Table 40.) The mothers, in addition to lacking positive feelings toward their fathers, had similarly unaffectionate feelings to their mothers. Their basic feeling toward authority figures might be reflected in the fact that these mothers were the least comfortable and co-operative in the interview with the psychiatrist and with the social worker. In relation to their children, they were neither dependable nor understanding. Not even an egocentric linkage to the child was evidenced by the mother's seeing herself in the child was a feature of this group. Our general impression was that they were women who had apparently not formed positive stable ties with either parent. Furthermore, since they felt that they had gotten but little from their own parents, they were in the emotional position of a child still seeking childhood gratification in the form of more dependency and understanding for himself.

Because mother was still seeking for childhood gratification, she regarded other persons, such as her husband and child, as rivals. Examples of this tendency were noted frequently in this group. A few mothers had thinly disguised resentment that their husbands had gotten a raise in salary or status, putting it in such terms as: "He is getting too conceited," or "He is so busy now that he has no time for me." As for the children, one mother felt quite ignored when relatives praised her daughter for her drawings and had not paid any attention to some paintings that mother had made.

The rivalry with their husbands may be illustrated by two trends in the data. Group D mothers had the highest frequency of disagreement with their husbands about the child's discipline and the least frequency of seeing the husband in the child. This suggested to us that mother was in a rivalrous position with her husband and was trying to exclude him from possession of their child. This type of behavior was reminiscent of the insecure behavior of the small child who does not want to share his toys. He is afraid that once a toy is out of his possession or out of his control, he might lose it forever. He does not refuse to hand over his toys because he is actually using them, but is suspicious that they may be taken away permanently. This mother will fight with father over the child, not out of real interest in the child, but to hold on to what she has.

As for the children themselves, the only diagnostic phenomenon that seemed characteristic of this group (besides the difficulty in adjustment) were two trends which were possibly concerned with maturation. These children had the highest frequency of delay (not breakdown) in establishing toilet training habits, *and* the highest frequency of wishing to be younger than their present age. Our speculation about these trends is that by virtue of the highly unsatisfactory maternal atmosphere, the child is not able to grow because he is anxious about taking the next maturational step. It is not clear from our level of data whether the cause of this is that he does not have enough outer maternal interest coming in to support his growth steps, or that he finds it dangerous to grow beyond the rivalrous envious mother, or that his mother is living out her infantilism through keeping the child infantile.

Regarding toilet training habits, there certainly is a lack of inducement for the child to learn the habit. Why should he give up the pleasure of urinating and defacating as he wishes when there is little warmth and understanding offered him in return? Perhaps he senses the underlying feeling of the ungratified rivalrous mother: that he should grow up quickly and sign away his birthright to a warm, reliable and understanding relationship, so that she will not have to be bothered with his clinging and so that she can secure these gratifications herself. If he does begin to receive these gratifications elsewhere, he is made guilty by mother's plaintive wish, wail, or expression: "What about poor me—I'm not getting anything out of life." Thus we feel that these children have a need to go back to the early period; they intuitively sense their lack of inner strength confortably to take the next maturational hurdle; they possibly are fixated at the earlier level because the immature and ungratified mother alternately frustrated them out of rivalry or overgratifies them out of guilt and identification.

With the detailed examination of the four groups concluded, it will be well to review them again in a general way. Our aim was to give as unified a viewpoint as possible regarding behavioral adjustment during this age span. Accordingly, we combined the psychiatric and school evaluations to obtain an outside-the-family adjustment score and we took the mother's evaluation to represent the inside-the-family adjustment. We then isolated four smaller groups which represented different situations along the outside family and inside family gradient: Group A, who adjusted outside and inside the family; Group B, who adjusted much better outside the family; Group C, who adjusted much better inside the family; and Group D who did not adjust well inside or outside the family.

Our results can be viewed in several general ways. From the aspect of direct maternal handling we can consider that dependability and understanding of the child is high in Group A; understanding and promoting the child's individuality is high in Group B; constrictive dependability is high in Group C; and neither aspect is prominent in Group D. The repercussions on the child of these traits in the mother are understandable. Maternal dependability and understanding in Group A has produced children who adjust well in two main areas, home and society; the maternal promotion of individual rights and success in Group B has produced touchy, individualistic children who get into conflict with their touchy and individualistic mothers; the maternal atmosphere of constrictive safety and harmony in Group C has produced children whose lively and instinctual life is inhibited; the maternal atmosphere of rivalry for childhood gratifications has produced children in Group D who are fearful, or resentful about growing up.

The four groups can also be viewed from the aspect of the past-present continuity in mother. In Group A, mother relived with and through her child the enjoyable aspects of her own childhood. Since the mother had grown up sufficiently she does not have to press her child or husband to achieve what would gratify her life, she need not be fearful of impulse gratification, and she does not have to fight with her husband and children over who gets more gratification. In Group B, there was a reliving through the child of mother's own power and needs for recognition which dated from her later childhood, especially adolescence. In Group C, there was a reliving again, more through the child than with the child, of mother's fearfulness of a lively, stimulating pleasure from the instinctual life. In Group D, there was little evidence of mother's either reliving with or through her child her own childhood needs or fears. Rather, it seemed that for the mother the child was considered a rival or an obstacle to mother's own gratification.

With this re-examination, we conclude our systematic consideration of adjustment as a phenomenon pertinent to the topic of normality. We have used the child's observable features—how happy or zestful is he and how is he adapting to the environment—as our definition of adjustment and as our criterion of normality. We have seen a rather wide range in the matter of adjustments. At the top are those children whose adjustment has been so continuous or widespread that we would tend to think of them as possessing a basic adjustability which would carry over from situation to situation. These are the children who adjusted well in latency *and* in puberty—the children who adjusted well outside *and* inside the family. The growth-promoting features of their emotionally mature mothers have been pointed out.

In the large middle zone are those children whose adjustments have not been continuous nor generally wide-spread. Their adjustments have been rather specific, with no guarantee of carry-over to another type of adjustment. These are children who adjusted well in latency *or* in puberty—who got along best outside the family *or* inside the family. Their mothers have matured more in some directions than in others, thus giving more support to certain areas of the child's growth than to others.

At the bottom of the range are those children who seemingly have not adjusted, even in a specific way. They have not adjusted well in latency or in puberty—not gotten along outside the family or inside of it. This inability would tend to make us think of a lack of basic adjustability. The growth inhibiting features of their emotionally immature mothers have been indicated.

We shall be interested in the next chapter whether there are phenomena more interior than observable adjustment which might enlighten us about normality.

CHAPTER XV

❦❦❦❦❦❦❦❦❦❦❦❦❦❦❦

THE INTERIORS
OF NORMALITY

WHEN, at the end of the last chapter we used the term "basic adjustability" we were suggesting that there is something interior and intrinsic which may be associated with optimum normality. The term "adjustment" has no such connotation. It simply refers to an exterior event, to a successful mastery by the child of one specific segment of the environment. As we have described, the child may adjust to his family, but not to the social scene, or to the school but not to the psychiatric interview, or during latency but not at puberty. The majority of our study children showed this type of differential adjustment. However, a certain number, as we said, had such continual or widespread adjustment "that we would tend to think of them as possessing a basic adjustability which would carry over from situation to situation." Similarly, a certain number had such a paucity of successful adjustments that it "would tend to make us think of a lack of basic adjustability."

Thus, when we think in terms of basic adjustability we are shifting our focus toward a quality possessed by the well-functioning *interior* psychic apparatus. As to what this well-functioning apparatus is like and what makes it that way, throughout the book we have described certain pertinent concepts and impressions. We propose in this chapter to review, amplify, and consolidate what has already been set forth.

Most of the concepts described in the earlier chapters can be fitted into a schematic account of personality growth and its vicissitudes. Thus, in each growth stage, the child encounters stresses. If the stress is excessive the ego of the small child is flooded with painful feelings.

[148]

such as rage, anxiety, guilt, depression, shame, etc. One way of avoiding painful feelings is to avoid all stimuli which can cause these feelings. The child represses, makes himself unconscious of inner feelings and outer stimuli which can cause pain. For example, if he is in the growth stage of attraction to the opposite sex, and the excessive stress consists of his mother threatening him with the possibility of his "going crazy" if he plays with his penis, out of great anxiety, he will repress or forget that he had a pleasure giving penis and will block off the stimuli coming from girls.

Blocking off the inner and outer stimuli leads to two results: (1) the growth phase is blocked off, repressed into the inaccessible unconscious—the drives and energy pertinent to that growth phase becoming unavailable for further growth; (2) energy which could be used for growth is being expended in maintaining the repression, in guarding against the emergence of the repressed painful stimuli. The consequent personality has been characterized by various writers as: it is *fixated in growth*, it is *impoverished of energy*, it is *unintegrated* with one-half guarding against the emergence of the other half, it is always *fearful* that the pain producing stimuli will burst forth into consciousness, it *inflexibly constricts* itself so as not to be open to painful stimuli, it lives under the *tyranny* of the *pain producing unconscious*.

In contrast to this unfavorable chain of interior events is the chain leading to the well-functioning personality. Here the stress is wholesome, it produces a certain dosage of anxiety which, in turn, stimulates the child to find a solution to the growth problem. Because the anxiety leads to eventual mastery and adaptability rather than to pain, the constellation of stimuli does not have to be repressed into the inaccessible unconscious. On the contrary it can be present in consciousness and because of this its mastery can be improved and its integration with preceding and succeeding masteries can be more easily accomplished. Thus the resultant healthy personality has been characterized by various writers as fearless, integrated, flexible, governed by the more conscious psychic layers, and in continuity with itself.

What has our study informed us about these interiors of normality? In general, we may say that although this was not the area most conducive to investigation by our methods, we found nothing which contradicts impressions gained by more refined and appropriate methods and much to support these impressions. We will not pause to document this last statement since evidences of it are abundant in the previous chapters.

We should like, however, to dwell on how the study enlightens us about the very important phenomenon of stress—important as it is the first link in the chain of interior events. From wholesome stress issues the favorable chain leading to mastery and integration and flexibility; from unwholesome stress an unfavorable chain leading to psychic pain, repression, and inflexibility. (See Appendix D, 8. *Works by Others on Stress.*)

The undesirable effects of excessive stress, of course, are more discernible than are the desirable effects of wholesome stress. Clinicians dealing with emotionally disturbed patients are much more apt to see the consequences of excessive stress. And even we, in studying much more "normal" material, have found these consequences to be more vividly describable. Thus, for example, we noted the constrictive stress faced by the child whose mother was not only traditional but also had no understanding of the child as a separate individual; the confusing stresses faced by the child whose mother incited him to rebellion, and yet squelched the rebellion; and by the child whose mother stimulated his dependency needs and yet was not able to gratify them. These excessive stresses produced in the child inflexible and poorly adaptive personality mechanisms, such as schizoid withdrawal, passive resistance, and premature self-sufficiency. Also we described the excessive strain on the mother when she is faced with the fatiguing energy-draining situation of being unfamiliar with or conflicted about the child. And we saw the effects of such undue stress, particularly with the first-born. (See Appendix D, 9. *Inflexibility.*)

Although we have mentioned the favorable results of wholesome stress, the question may be asked: Do we have any evidence that wholesome stress is desirable? Could not an argument be made that any stress is undesirable—that the best milieu for personality growth is one which contains no stress? Although we do not have direct evidence against this line of argument, we do have some indirect evidence which suggests that *some degree of stress acts as a stimulant for adaptability and adjustment.*

Our evidence centers around a phenomenon which we have touched on from time to time in the book—namely sleep disturbances. These disturbances consist of the child waking up from an anxiety dream and calling out to the mother. Their obvious relation to stress consists, of course, in the fact that the child, to have such dreams, must be under stress during sleep.

Now, how "normal" is it to have stress during sleep, to have, that is, sleep disturbances? If the reader examines the protocols in the Appendix, he will see that almost all of the children (and mothers) report quite lurid emotion-charged anxiety dreams. This in itself would indicate that sleep-disturbing, anxiety dreams are normal, in the sense of not necessarily indicating psychopathology.

But there was another finding which indicated that such disturbances were not merely non-pathologic, but actually associated with good adjustment. This finding was, in effect, that *the best adjusted latency children were reported by their mothers as having had an occasional sleep disturbance either during latency or in the preschool period* (but *not* in both periods). Less well adjusted were (1) those children reported to have had chronic sleep disturbances (preschool and latency), (2) those children reported never to have had a sleep disturbance. (See Appendix E, Table 41.) One implication of the finding is that it is "better" during childhood to have an occasional sleep disturbing anxiety dream than to have chronically frequent anxiety dreams or no anxiety dreams at all. Translated in terms of stress, it is better that sleep be occasionally stressful than that it be frequently stressful, or not at all stressful.

At first we were surprised by the finding that an occasional sleep disturbance was associated with good adjustment. We had thought of sleep in its most usual sense—a physiological state the purpose of which was to give rest to the body. Psychoanalytic theory had propounded that the best, most normal sleep is the dreamless sleep. Shakespeare had written of sleep as "knitting up the raveled sleeve of care." Thus it seemed paradoxical that the child's good adjustment could be associated with occasional anxiety dreams which disturbed the peaceful and restful sleep.

However, the paradox can be resolved if we resort to another concept of sleep. According to this concept the person is not idle while sleeping. He is sometimes busy digesting the stimuli and problems of the day. In popular language, he sometimes "sleeps on a problem"—in psychoanalytic language, by means of dreams he is attempting to discharge and integrate excitations from his waking life. (See Appendix D, 10. *Sleep Disturbances.*)

The foregoing constitutes our evidence in support of the hypothesis that a wholesome dosage of stress is necessary for psychic growth of the child. We have dwelt on the phenomenon of stress because not only is it the first link in the chain of interior events, but also it is the only link that is under a person's conscious control. Once stress has occurred, the rest of the events proceed almost automatically. We cannot consciously decide whether we will repress or sublimate, whether we will be governed by our unconscious or by our conscious, whether we will be integrated or conflicted, whether we will be flexible or inflexible, but we do have some control about the amount of stress we allow ourselves to encounter and that which we will allow our children to encounter.

We should like, in the concluding part of this chapter to speak more generally and abstractly. Our comments will not be directly related to anything specific as adjustment, latency, child and mother, etc. Instead, they will take the form of speculations, attempting to link psychic growth with other biological phenomena. A major portion of these speculations will be concerned with concepts of permanence and change.

At the beginning of this chapter we used the term "adjustability" as a bridge between the specific exterior event, adjustment, and the interior psychic apparatus which has the potentiality for adjusting. Now we would prefer to describe this potentiality as the capacity for psychic growth. In trying to define this capacity, we find we cannot escape linking it intimately with the learning process. Thus, we might define the capacity for growth as the capacity to learn emotionally as well as intellectually. Adding the time factor, we might say that it consists of the capacity to learn age-appropriate functions and to enjoy the performance of them. Although the functions to be learned and enjoyed have considerable variety, with increasing age they have less of the individual, egocentric, self-preservative orientation and more of the super-individual, altruistic, race-preservative orientation. This change in orientation is what we usually speak of as an indication of maturation.

Growth or learning might be thought of as a sequence in the first part of which new things are taken in by one and in the second part the new things are made one's own. Put in biological terms, in the first part the organism, having a hunger or appetite, approaches the environment with an open mouth and takes part in the environment. In the second part, it digests the part taken in, distributes the breakdown elements to its own specific components, and eliminates the non-usable waste products. In the sequence what was once part of the environment is now one's own.

This sequence of events can be most generally described as internalization. (Aspects of it enter into such psychoanalytic concepts as incorporation, introjection, and identification.) The end results of the sequence can show variations in terms of how much was originally ingested and how much of what was ingested became digested. The closed mouth would ingest very little, the wide open mouth very much, the selective mouth being probably more likely to ingest only what would be most easily digested.

In our discussion of the main task of the latency period—the ability to take in and master new things from the outside—we interpreted our findings in oral terms. It will be recalled that the most feasible way of accounting for the data seemed to be in terms of the child's reaction to the first outside—the mother. An early, gratifying, predictable and non-dangerous mouth experience with her enabled the child to approach the latency period with an open mind. An early, frustrating, unpredictable and dangerous mouth experience with her prevented the child from coping adequately with the new outside during latency.

Taking in the "new" and converting it into something that resides within the person are facets of the change-permanence concepts. Unless there is a capacity for ingesting new things, there will be no opportunity for change. Unless there is a capacity for digesting the new and making it one's own, there is no opportunity for permanence. If the change capacity was heavily predominant, the person would be chameleon-like, very adaptive to the environment but with no inner permanent core or continuity. If the permanence capacity is largely predominant, then the person may be in the position of the Bourbons who learned nothing and forgot nothing.

The change and permanence concepts appeal to us as the most basic way of understanding longitudinal growth and cross-sectional adjustment. In both areas a happy blending of capacities for change and permanence is essential. In growth it is the ability to ingest the changing new and the ability to digest it so that it becomes a part of the permanent self. In adjustment it is the ability to have lively, changing, zestful impulses and the ability to contain them in a more permanent regulating framework.

Several other considerations have made change and permanence attractive as basic concepts. One is the matter of typical anxiety dreams. These are dreams which, according to Freud are dreamt so universally and so much and in the same way by people that they must have a common, constant typical meaning. Previous work by the writer (and confirmed in this "normal" study) revealed that by far the two most common typical anxiety dreams were: (1) the attacked dream—a dream in which the dreamer is in danger from some outside threat and he is relatively or absolutely immobilized;

(2) the falling dream—a dream in which the dreamer is falling from some height and is relatively unable to stop his precipitate motion. Furthermore it was found that there were individual differences concerning these two dreams: some people (adults and children) reported that they had had the attacked type of dream but never the falling type, some the falling, but never the attacked, while the majority reported the occurrence of both types of dreams but differed as to which type was the more anxiety producing.

In studying the children's behavior and the influences issuing from the mothers, we were impressed with the link between the falling dream and the phenomena of change and the link between the attacked dream and the phenomena of permanence.

Certain findings suggested to us that these typical anxiety dreams might reflect the change and permanence orientations in the mother-child continuity. (See Appendix D, 11. *Typical Anxiety Dreams.*) Ideally, the mother should be close enough to the child to provide an atmosphere of security and permanence and yet distant enough to produce an atmosphere of freedom for changing and individual expansion. Yet most mothers are not ideal in this respect. They are usually oriented more in one way than the other. They are usually a little too close and involved or a little distant and not involved. Thus, it is possible that the child's attacked dream is stimulated by a maternal atmosphere in which the mother, being close and involved, intrudes her ideas and wishes on the child, overemphasizing the permanence aspect. And it is possible that the child's falling dream is stimulated by a maternal atmosphere in which the mother is overly separate and discontinuous from the child, thus over-emphasizing the change aspect. (See Appendix D, 12. *Permanence and Change.*)

The dreams themselves seem to represent pictorially this state of affairs. In the attacked dream, first there is an encroachment, a drawing near, by the external object to the point where the dreamer's bodily integrity or individuality is endangered. This external object may be a symbol of the dependable, identified, engulfing mother. Secondly, the movement in the dream is quite inhibited, in fact, in extreme cases where the anxiety is greatest the dreamer is paralyzed and unable to escape the destructive encroachment. In a way, the dreamer is in conflict since the dependent part of him wants to please the encroaching, tying, binding mother by allowing her to engulf his individuality, while the more autonomous part of him protests and struggles against this infringement of his individuality. In another sense, since such a mother discourages (or does not take kindly to aggressive or disloyal protest on the part of the child) all he can do in his rage is to shout against heavily insulated walls and to be fearfully paralyzed by the resounding echoes of his own rage. Thus we have read into the attacked type of dream all the features of the binding, permanence dynamisms with their repercussive inhibitions.

On the other hand, the falling dream seems to represent pictorially the state of affairs when the change dynamisms are present. The situation in this dream is much different from that of the attacked dream. The external object is not encroaching, the fear in the dream is that there is nothing there and no one to cling to, to stop the fall. Instead of fear that the external object will dangerously encroach, there is the fear that the object will dangerously withdraw. Furthermore, instead of movement being inhibited or paralyzed, as in the attacked dream, here it is headlong and uncontrollable. Thus we were led to surmise that the dream may symbolize a situation where mother's acceptance, facilitation, or stimulation of individualistic impulse released by the child, brings him into the dangerous situation of having uncontrollable impulses without much of a binding tie to curb the headlong movement downward.

Another consideration regarding change and permanence is derived from our impression about interpersonal continuity and individual continuity. Interpersonal continuity provides the individual an opportunity to ingest or take in new things from the outside person, thus it belongs in the change category. Individual continuity provides the individual with a feeling of inner sameness, the result of digesting what is peculiarly pertinent to the individual, thus it belongs in the permanence category.

Freud's theory of anxiety embraces the essentials of interpersonal and individual continuities which we have assigned respectively to the change and permanence categories. He postulated that the original danger situation for the infant was that of being all alone and helpless, unable to deal with the intense feelings stimulated by hunger, pain, cold, fear, and rage. Because of this helplessness, there would be danger for the infant of being annihilated by the flooding in of extreme, intense stimulation. Thus aloneness was the first and greatest danger. Anxiety developing later acted as a warning signal that there was a possibility of the child's re-experiencing that first and greatest mortal danger and that he had better defend himself against this possibility by various means.

Freud described two main subsequent anxieties of early childhood: fear of loss of love (separation anxiety), and fear of injury to the body or genitals (castration anxiety). The separation anxiety (a fear that the mother's presence, love, or support will not be there to protect the child against the dangers of aloneness), can be considered an anxiety about the disruption of an interpersonal continuity, i.e., the mother-child continuity. Castration anxiety, however, reflects the danger of disruption of the individual or personal continuity. It denotes the anxiety over losing a part of the self.

We might say, then, that separation anxiety is a threat to one component of growth, a threat to the opportunity to change by ingesting new things from the outside. Castration anxiety, on the other hand, is a threat to the other component of growth, a threat to an inner core of permanence and continuity, onto which new things take hold. (It is of interest that the predominant psychoanalytic emphasis has been on castration anxiety. It is not improbable that this is in part the fact that Freud admittedly had no personal experience with the falling dream—a dream which we have placed in the "change" interpersonal category.)

Another consideration regarding change and permanence also derives from psychoanalytic theory. Freud conceived of the psyche as a mechanism for dealing with instinctual energy. The primitive id, a reservoir of turbulent, instinctual energy, was constantly seeking discharge, release, and gratification along the lines of the pleasure principle. Sometimes opposed to, sometimes helping the id were three regulators, the ego, the ego-ideal, and the superego, which were guided more by the reality principle than by the pleasure principle, and which aided the person in being at restful peace with the world and himself. We tend to see in the energetic pleasure-loving id, the features of "change" whereas in the rest-producing regulators the features of "permanence."

Two other applications of change and permanence to psychoanalytic theory might be contained in the following. Freud's later theorizing concerned the opposites of Eros (the life instinct with all its lively *change*) and Thanatos (the static, *permanence* producing death instinct). Kubie's theory about the creativity issuing from the preconscious layer of mentation might be considered in a similar way. There is a polarity between the rampant, pulsating unconscious which has rhyme without reason, and the highly ordered realistic conscious which knows only reason. The creative integration of the two is accomplished by the mid-system, by the preconscious which knows lively rhyme and structuring reason.

The last consideration pertaining to change and permanence derives from the universality of these concepts in non-psychoanalytic areas. The change-permanence duality has for ages been of considerable interest as a source of rich conceptualization for almost all areas of human thought and speculation. In the myths which account for the world's creation there is the making of structural order out of turbulent chaos by supernatural intervention. In mythological, religious, or historical accounts apart from creation there are such symbols of regulation as the ten commandments and monotheism. In philosophy there are similar polarities such as process and form, and thesis and antithesis leading to synthesis. There is an interesting analogy to physics where there has been a longstanding question as to the nature of matter. Is matter essentially waves of energy, or is it composed of particles? These opposites are very similar to the opposite of lively dynamic change and static structuring permanence. Some physicists, in order to make a unitary concept out of this duality, have suggested, somewhat in jest and somewhat seriously, using the term "wavicle."

Thus we believe that the evidence hints in the direction that such universal characteristics as permanence and change can be useful concepts in understanding personality. The permanence dynamism seems to have an inhibitory effect on the impulses, wholesome or unwholesome, whereas the change dynamisms seem to have an impulse-freeing effect, again wholesome or unwholesome. The wholesomeness of the inhibition resides in its stabilizing functions; the unwholesomeness in its paralyzing, constricting repercussions. The wholesomeness of impulse-freeing is obviously in its animated, zest giving functions; the unwholesomeness is obviously in its making for chaotic turbulence, for a lack of inner, continuous self-core.

The reader may wonder if, on the basis of the foregoing, we advocate any changes in theory, either psychoanalytic or non-psychoanalytic. Our belief is that there is no major change necessary. The proviso is added, however, that no change is needed so long as one aspect of theory does not dominate and encompass all other aspects of the theory, and so long as the theory remains open to change. The principal reason why one or the other theoretical aspect has become predominant is that the psyche is extremely complicated. This complexity which produces specialization in the study of the psyche also produces the specialist who naturally regards his facet of study as more significant than other facets. Thus the psychiatrist who works with psychotic patients will emphasize one aspect, those working with neurotics another aspect, and those working with delinquents still another facet.

Rather than a change in theory, it seems necessary to co-ordinate and refine the theory giving the proper weight to each of its aspects. An example of the lack of co-ordination in psychoanalytic theory was seen in our attempts to account for our findings on sleep disturbance. According to one theoretical approach, sleep disturbances should be associated with maladjustment inasmuch as the best normal sleep is the dreamless sleep. Yet according to another theoretical approach sleep disturbances could be normal because they indicate that the child is not overprotected from life's stimuli. Each theoretical insight might be valid in itself, but the correctness of its application to particular phenomena has to be decided by careful investigation and not by armchair deduction. The task of giving each separate theoretical aspect its proper weight is by no means an easy one. It compares in difficulty with properly weighting the many factors involved in predicting the weather, or in predicting economic trends.

Apart from the theory itself, do we suggest any changes in terminology? In spite of this book having been written in non-technical terms, we are not prompted to urge a new nomenclature. The technical terms in orthodox Freudian theory are quite satisfactory in dealing with the phenomena within the individual. The terms introduced by so-called neo-Freudians are equally helpful in understanding some of the phenomena occurring in interpersonal or group situations.

We do have one suggestion which refers to an increased usage of the term "continuity." There is no term in psychoanalytic terminology which has quite the connotation of connectedness as does the term continuity as used in this book. Due to the emphasis in studying and treating highly disturbed patients, the more common terms in psychoanalysis tend to denote what pulls the personality apart, while there are fewer terms having to do with what hold the personality together. There are terms denoting some amount of connectedness already in use, but all of them seem to have some limitation. Thus the term integration has more of the meaning of pattern; identity, the meaning of personal integration and cohesion rather than interpersonal connectedness; symbiosis has the idea of connectedness but in an intense degree inasmuch as it means that two objects are so mutually interdependent that the death of one will result in the death of the other.

An example of the difficulty encountered in trying to denote connectedness by using terms which imply disconnectedness is seen in the case of separation anxiety and castration anxiety. They imply the loss of something, a loss of connectedness. Separation and castration do not lend themselves to positive statements; it is awkward to say that the individual is striving for non-separateness or non-castrativeness. However, we can say in the positive that the individual is striving for continuity, and in the negative that he has an anxiety about discontinuity.

We believe, then, that the usage of the term "continuity" would be rewarding in psychoanalytic theory. It is not only useful in describing the connectedness within the person and between persons, but also in linking psychoanalytic theory with other theories pertaining to living organisms. For example, whereas the term "castration anxiety" has significance for psychoanalysts and should be retained, it would not be a part of the common language between a psychoanalyst and a geneticist. Continuity and discontinuity, however, might prove more acceptable as a common term for these two different disciplines.

This last consideration we believe important in regard to our other theoretical task of enriching psychoanalytic theory and solving some of its unsolved problems. We believe that an intercommunication with other sciences is necessary for the accomplishment of this task. In the past the direction of the flow has been from psychoanalysis outward so that, for example, anthropology and literature have been enriched or stimulated by psychoanalytic concepts and insights. We think that the flow should be in the opposite direction also; that the growth of psychoanalysis will in part result in the adoption of analogies and concepts from other biologic and human disciplines. There have been recent efforts in this direction, one example being that of psychoanalysis employing certain concepts regarding communication, concepts borrowed from the field of cybernetics.

One example of an unsolved problem is the question of what concepts to use in studying the interaction between two or more people. If the study of mother-child unit should be expanded (and this indubitably is true) to the study of the whole family, how will we conceptualize the interaction of four or five people? John Rickman recognized the paucity of psychoanalytic concepts in this regard when he said that although we do have a satisfactory one-body psychology, we also need a two-body psychology and a three-body psychology. One discipline from which concepts can be borrowed from is group psychology; another is animal ecology which treats of the interaction and mutual dependency of the organism and its environment.

Another unsolved problem is the question of why certain psychological motivations and attitudes rather than others are transmitted to a particular child. Although psychoanalysis has theorized about how the child internalizes parental attitudes (through the process of identification), it has not accounted satisfactorily for the variations in what is internalized. The transmission of psychological motivations might be investigated by using analogies from the field of genetics where the study of biological inheritance of physical characteristics is well underway.

Still another unsolved problem closely related to the preceding, pertains to the process by which the external imprinting influences interact and combine to form specific phenomena in the child. We have described the variety of nuances possible by the permutations and combinations of various maternal dynamisms. For example, a rebellious mother who is controlling with her own child, seemed to produce a different effect in the child than a rebellious mother who is understanding of the child. Thus, the resulting characteristic of passive resistance is different from the characteristic of active resistance even though these phenomena had one element in common: the rebellious mother.

The picture that emerges in regard to the imprinting repercussions is that of a particular psychic phenomenon being the result of the interaction or fusion of particular elemental factors. A slightly different combination of elemental factors may produce not merely less or more of a phenomenon, but may produce another and entirely different phenomenon. If this is true, we cannot expect to explain highly complex psychic phenomena just in terms of the separate elemental constituents. In each step or combination, a few phenomena may appear, quite different from the preceding combination, and the properties of the new phenomenon would have to be studied. The restriction to simple, elemental factors would result in an impasse similar to that faced by those who try to account for the nature of proteins solely by the concepts of inorganic chemistry. Thus, in addition to turning to genetics for an understanding of the blending of characteristics, we might have recourse to chemistry for some analogies. Just as basic elements, hydrogen and oxygen, combine in a certain proportion to make an entirely new product, water, so do the maternal imprinting dynamisms combine to form a psychological phenomenon which has properties and effects of its own.

We believe that the field of animal psychology would yield many facts and concepts which might be useful for several of the other unsolved problems. One borrowed concept which has been used in this book, for example, is that of "imprinting." The term "flexibility" is highly analogous to the animal psychologist's term "plasticity." The implications for therapy of the term, "plasticity" are seen in the remarks of David Katz who said: "Should the . . . young bird lose its own mother, the more plastic the animal is the more readily it accepts a foster mother." The mode of transmission of hate to the father figure, as described by us, seems to have an animal psychology parallel in that, "One worker had produced experimental evidence which shows that kittens start to kill mice and rats earlier if they see their mothers do so. If they never see rats and mice killed, they can be brought up along together very peacefully with rats."

Finally, clues as to how the human child grows up, individuates himself and forms a new family might be gained from the following description of how the chick family breaks up. "The actual breaking up of a family is actively initiated by the mother hen herself. The chick learns through a series of unpleasant experiences (being pecked by the mother) that the hen's attitude toward him has changed. When separated from the mother the chicks form a fraternal group and cling together. Thus the duration in the family is largely determined by the duration of the maternal instinct in the mother hen."

In general, we believe that our theoretical understanding of personality growth and functioning can be increased by a refinement and co-ordination of present theory and by borrowing concepts and analogies from other related disciplines. Also, since theory grows or is changed when it is confronted by new facts, it is necessary to continue with research activities. As Kris has suggested, the principal area for such research would seem to be that of the normal. Exploratory pilot studies, like the one we conducted, have their usefulness in setting up hypotheses which can be affirmed or disproved by later and more rigorous procedures. Of great value are long-term studies in which the child is directly observed in his development from infancy through adolescence. Studies such as these are already underway in various research centers. These studies, especially those concerning not only the child, but also the whole family, promise much for our enlightenment of normal personality functioning and growth.

CHAPTER XVI

IMPLICATIONS

OUR MOTIVE for embarking on this study, it will be recalled, was not only to gather information for the sake of information, but also to help in our actual work with children and mothers. It is our belief that some helpful guide lines did emerge from this study. We hope to demonstrate here how these guide lines bear on diagnosis and therapy at a child guidance clinic and on mental hygiene in the family and society.

The use of the words "guide lines" and "implications" is pointed and deliberate. The complexity of the individual personality and the compounding of that complexity by the variety of personalities do not allow for any sure prescriptions for mental health. Thus we conceive of this final chapter as conveying a philosophy which has to be appropriately particularized in individual cases.

DIAGNOSES AT A
CHILD GUIDANCE CLINIC

There are many types of diagnostic labels which may be applied to the child. The most known are of the specific clinical variety, e.g., conduct disorder, psychoneurosis, psychosis, etc. Their purpose is to designate what kind of psychopathology exists in the child. We will not dwell on this type of diagnosis inasmuch as it is outside the scope of a book on normality. Rather, we shall dwell on two types of diagnosis which are much more difficult to assess.

One type deals with the severity of the disturbance—whether the symptomatology is within normal limits or not. It may be called a valuative diagnosis because there is an unquestionable value in the symptoms being within normal limits rather than outside of them.

This valuative normal-abnormal diagnosis is the one which prompts the diagnostician to recommend therapy. For example, a child may be referred for rebelliousness to the school teacher. It is rather easy to make a clinical diagnosis of conduct disorder. However, to determine whether the rebelliousness is within normal limits for this particular child is not always easy, and it is on this determination that the disposition of the case rests.

We found in our study that it is risky to make a diagnosis on the child of optimum normality or decided abnormality just on the basis of adjustment in one particular area or on the basis of adjustment according to one particular evaluator. In only a small minority of cases were the school, the psychiatrist, and the mother agreed that the child was well adjusted or that the child was not adjusted. (If it were to include the psychologist's impressions from the Rorschach Test, the number of cases in which there was total agreement would be still smaller.)

This lack of unanimity led us to conclude not that each evaluator was wrong, but that each evaluator was only partially correct. The evaluator could be totally correct if he limited himself to the modest statement, "In the particular adjustment area of the child which I, with my experience, am especially equipped to observe, I consider the child to be well adjusted." The school has had more experience in seeing the child in a social group, the psychiatrist more of the child in a one-to-one relation, and the mother more of the child in the family situation.

As we have indicated previously in this book, the majority of our study children were neither optimally well adjusted (normal) or decidedly maladjusted (abnormal). Rather, they had differential adjustments, excelling sometimes in group or one-to-one, or family adaptations. They could be considered in the averagely normal range.

Similarly, it seems risky to make a definite diagnosis of optimum normality or decided abnormality just on the basis of adjustment during one age. Very few of our study children were well adjusted in the preschool period (according to mother's report) *and* in the latency period, *and* in the pubertal period (according to the follow-up school reports), and very few were emotionally maladjusted over that period of time. The majority had differential adjustments—better at some period, worse at others. Thus they could be considered as belonging to the averagely normal range.

An equally important idea of the child's normality is obtained by the diagnosis of the mother. We have stressed throughout the book how intimately the child's growth potential is linked with the mother's emotional maturity. Because the child is dependent on and close to his mother, she will influence him in two ways: (1) she will provide the stressful or non-stressful climate in which his growth will occur; (2) she will be a principal source for attitudes which the child will take over, internalize, and make his own.

The other type of diagnosis of the child deals with the kind of person the child is. It is a non-valuative diagnosis. It does not stimulate the diagnostician to change the child for the better, as he would be stimulated in the case of an abnormality diagnosis. Whereas the latter has value connotations, i.e., where should the child be placed in a certain scale, this diagnosis merely asks what the child is like. If properly carried out, it gives an idea of what the child's capacities, limitations, and directions are like.

So much of the book has been given over to a description of the many kinds of children in the normal range, that it would be highly repetitious to mention them again. However, we would like to re-emphasize how the personality diagnosis of the mother aids us in making a non-valuative personality diagnosis of the child. It is by virtue of the continuity of generations that we can understand the child through the mother. As we have said earlier in the book, the dependency of the child requires him to maintain a continuity with the earliest maturing person—the mother. The mother herself has a continuity with the child because, in varying degrees, he represents some aspect of herself and her second childhood.

The continuity principle, however, has to be used as a flexible guide rather than a rigid rule in diagnosis. When we indicated, for example, that the rebellious mother is associated with the rule-breaking child, we meant that it is more likely than not that rule-breaking in the child would issue from rebelliousness in the mother. We did not mean to convey the idea that there is a strict, compelling one-to-one relationship.

The personality differences between siblings are the most striking evidence that the continuity principle has to be used flexibly. Undoubtedly the constitutional factor plays a large part in one child being different from another. But even within the continuity principle there are factors which attenuate the strict generational correspondence. One factor consists of mother not being exactly the same person over a period of years. She may be more mature after a space of years; also she may be particularly fatigued or irritable from undue stress at one period of her life and not at another. The different siblings would be affected accordingly. Another factor consists of mother having many facets even at one period of time. For example, one of her children may represent her bad self, and is hence criticized, worried over, and rejected. Another child may represent her ideal self and is therefore overevaluated and pushed to power and achievement. Still another child might be fortunately overlooked by the pathogenic mother so that he can escape to another adult who is more benign. A third factor in attenuating the strict generational continuity is the intrusion of continuities from the other parent. The different possible blendings of the two sets of continuities may produce different end pictures in the various siblings.

From all the preceding there can be little doubt that the making of a valuative normality-abnormality diagnosis and of a non-valuative personality diagnosis is a rather complicated task. It is less simple with the more fluid, plastic, growing child than with the more consolidated adult. In fact, the more the diagnostician expects to find the child exclusively preoccupied with the growth problems of a particular age period, the more perplexing his diagnostic task will be. At any particular time, the child's past, present, and future are clearly in view. In the latency child who is coping with the current growth step of mastering the environment outside of his family, we caught glimpses of the past preschooler and the future pubertal child. Although it may be more convenient for us to think of the child as neatly disposing of one growth phase before proceeding to another, this does not seem to be the case. While the major part of a growth integration occurs at a particular age period, there is always a past integration which needs more integrating and a future integration upon which the child is beginning to work. Thus *we can view the continuity and identity of the child not only as a series of discrete integrations, but also as a continuing process of integrating.*

THE STANDARD OF NORMALITY

Because of the complexity in making a diagnosis, errors are inevitable. While some errors are insignificant and others are self-correcting, still others may have decided consequences as to the advice given parents, the recommendations of treatment, and the goal of treatment. It is particularly with the valuative diagnosis of normality and abnormality that consequential errors may appear. For this reason, we believe it is highly important to address ourselves to the question: *What standard or degree of normality should be the goal in personality growth and in therapy?*

There are of course two possible dangers attendant upon an improper standard: the danger of it being too high and the danger of it being too low. The first danger is more likely to be present in those who are enlightened, mental health conscious, and overexposed to psychopathology, while the second is more likely to be present in those who are unenlightened and unaware.

There is no doubt that if we have a better idea of the proper standard of normality, it would help us in diagnosing whether the deviation from the standard was sufficient to warrant therapeutic intervention and in deciding when to terminate therapy once therapeutic intervention had occurred. This, in part, it will be recalled, was the dilemma which prompted our study: Should we withhold therapy from a mildly disturbed child on the chance that reassurance to the mother and normal growth would heal the disturbance, or should we intervene on the chance that there would be little or no self-healing?

Although our study did not include therapy, the natural question which would have occurred to us once therapeutic intervention had occurred, would have been: When should it stop? If it should stop when the patient (adult or child) becomes "normal" and if the therapist's standard of normality is so ideal that the patient cannot achieve it, then not only might the therapy be unduly prolonged but also the patient and therapist might leave it with a mutual sense of failure. Much less likely to occur is the opposite, where the therapist's idea of normality is so over elastic that not only might the therapy be overly brief, but also the therapist and patient may leave it with a false sense of having achieved something. These same considerations apply when the parents' standards are too high or too low.

We obviously have a choice as to which danger requires more discussion. We feel it would be much more rewarding to address ourselves to the dangers attendant in the overly high standard and the reasons behind such a standard. Primarily we feel so because the "normality" pendulum has swung in such a way that the overly high standard tends to be possessed more frequently by the very people upon whose enthusiasm, sympathy, and skills the future of mental health efforts depend. We are not referring to the experienced, older diagnosticians and therapists, but rather to the beginning therapist and the newly enlightened laity.

Perhaps the main reason for the overly high standard is the failure to appreciate fully the variety of psychological types and the legitimacy of a variety of life solutions. The standard then tends to be overly high because it is narrow. There is a tendency to speak of "the normal child," "the adolescent," "the mature personality," etc., as though there was only one kind of normal child, adolescent, and mature personality. If a person does not fall into that one kind he is liable to be viewed suspiciously and efforts are made to bring him around to conformity to the one kind—efforts which may prove frustrating to both the person and the helper.

It is apparent from the preceding chapters that our position lies in the opposite direction, in the direction of the plurality of psychological types and in the direction of the life solutions being quite individual. The pluralism is of course due to the fact that each personal end picture and the life value systems are the result of particular environmental influences being worked in particular ways by individual capacities, temperaments, and traditions.

By thinking in terms of types, in effect we are taking a mid-position between the unity pole of "everybody is the same," and the variety pole, "everybody is different." Perhaps our position results from our own need to blend permanence and change factors. The unity pole position, while quite useful in teaching and communicating a soild framework, seems to us too constrictive and strangulating to be used for anything more than a working reference point. On the other hand, the variety pole position, while doing full justice to the uniqueness of each individual, tends (in us at least) to produce chaotic feeling and a great difficulty in teaching and communication. Thus, the notion of types, a notion which combines unity and variety, appeals to us as a working compromise. It is quite likely that the unity position which we are cautioning against represents the usual first stage in mastery of a subject, a stage in which one has to learn the rules before one, in the face of exceptions, learns when to break them.

Although we have throughout the book spoken of various types (traditional, rebellious, group relators, etc.), we would like to dwell briefly on two types which vie for the distinction of representing the only standard of normality. One is the somewhat conflicted, broad-vista'd type more often found among the intellectuals, intelligentsia, and artists. This person may have had a problem in integrating multiple and contradictory personality components which probably arose from having a mother who was conflicted within herself or in conflict with the father. His advantages lie in his ability to empathize with others who are in conflict, and in his ability to be more open to new answers to old questions. His creativity may be in large part due to his need to give an aesthetic shape to the still unintegrated components inside of him and the mysteries outside of him. His disadvantages may consist of a feeling of restlessness which constantly spurs him to search for the larger meaning, an impracticality about more wordly, smaller meaning matters, and an indecisiveness about people which militates against sustained, direct action.

The other is the less conflicted, narrow vista'd type, more often found in the general population. This person may have avoided conscious or unconscious conflicts by rather permanently closing himself off from certain of life's vistas. Rather than being involved like the first type in a chronic, mild conflictual uncertainty: "shall I do this or that," "is it this way or that way," this person has consciously or unconsciously decided (or it has been quite early decided for him by a single-minded mother or by unusual solidarity between the parents) that, "It is definitely this not that." His advantages consist of being able to act in a sustained, direct, productive way and to have immediate time-tested answers to the mysterious question of life. His disadvantages lie in the direction of being less able, because of the constriction of life's vistas, to empathize and identify with other people's views. Always a potential disadvantage is that although he has avoided conscious conflict by repressing a part of himself, that repressed part may be still protesting and producing unconscious conflict.

As to which of these two types should claim the laurels as the one and only true standard of normality, we can only restate our position that either standard alone would be too narrow, that each type has certain advantages and disadvantages, that each type has to work out his particular life solution satisfactorily. Persons of the first type, being leaders in intellectual matters, may raise a strong but small voice in their behalf. The less penetrating, but much larger voice is raised by people of the second type. Thus in a majority vote the second type would win. Because persons of this type are not in conflict, because they seem sure of themselves and their goals, and because they are practically useful to society, these persons are more often thought of as normal by the laity than are those persons of the first type.

Like others who have been impressed with the variety of people and types in our society, we feel that the variation is not purposeless, that it has a social value. That variety is stimulating, that cross-fertilization improves the breed is well known. But that variety is valuable in an ecological sense, in the sense of promoting the interdependence of people, in the sense of helping to conserve one's energy—this value, although recognized intellectually, is not so acceptable emotionally because of personal prejudices about one's own type being most valuable and about the value of self-sufficiency.

Besides the illustration of this point in the particular social contribution of the conflicted, broad vista'd, and the unconflicted, narrow vista'd, we can point to another example. It will be recalled that at least three well-adjusted types resulted from the interaction of mother's motherhood aspirations and the accomplishment of this aspiration: the adequate traditional, the adequate rebellious, and the adequate dependent. It is now suggested that the social contribution of the adequate traditional is to carry forward the past in a flexible way; that of the adequate rebellious is to supply aggressive energy toward combatting old evils; and that of the adequate dependent is to supply the warmth and affection necessary for enjoyable interpersonal contact and group cohesion.

If our sample of the 54 children and their mothers is at all representative of that part of the continuum extending from optimally normal to averagely normal, we get a certain broad view of the constituents of our society. There appears to be a division of social labor, both the optimally and averagely normal contributing according to their particular personality assets and motivations. Even some of the decidedly abnormal may make a contribution in an artistic or creative sense. By virtue of the generational continuity, not only is the total social climate in some way handed down to the next generation, but also handed down are the particular psychological contributions or orientations of each family. Thus, if we look at our society as it is rather than as it should be, it contains various psychological types, each possessing various degrees of adaptibility and flexibility and each potentially quite contributory to some aspects of our society.

The second reason for an overly high standard is, we believe, a cultural one and consists of the notion of limitless self-improvement. It would affect parents particularly even though therapists could not escape some of its repercussions. This notion is probably a by-product of our American social heritage which is compounded in equal parts of "expanding frontiers," "land of opportunity," "social mobility," and "there is nothing you cannot do if you really put your mind to it."

The enlightened parent whose enlightenment has been due to a capacity and desire for self-improvement would like to see his children continue in the direction of self-improvement. Frequently the implicit expectation from the child is not, "Whatever you can make of your particular self will be acceptable," but rather, the pressuring superlative, "I'd like to see you make the most of your potentialities." The resultant picture of the optimally normal child approaches that of the maximally normal—a child who is not only emotionally stable but also versatile and creative. Anything less than this might tend to create a feeling of disappointment in the parent and a feeling of failure in the child.

The limitless self-improvement notion could lead to the formation of an emotional-psychological elite, into which no one is really qualified to be admitted and yet into which everyone is trying to enter for purposes of status. A case in point is David Riesman's typology of traditional, inner-directed, outer-directed, and autonomous people. His typology is useful as a non-valuative diagnosis of the changing social scene. However there are connotations of value; the autonomous person, the superman, being representative of an emotional and psychological elite with all the consequences of people striving to enter that elite.

We believe that although this high degree of normality and versatile adaptiveness may be approached by a few individuals, it is too high to be feasible as a working standard of normality or criterion of mental health. Our reasons for believing so are twofold.

The first is based on the infrequency of optimally normal people. In our relatively healthy sample of study children, only 13 out of 54 (roughly 25 per cent) met the rough criterion of optimum normality. These 13 were well adjusted in latency as well as in puberty: they adjusted inside as well as outside the family. As for the mothers, again about 25 per cent satisfied all the rough criteria for optimum normality in being warmly dependable, understanding, improving on their mothers, if any improvement was necessary, and having an affectionate feeling for their fathers.

If only 25 per cent of the relatively healthy study sample was optimally normal, then it is likely that if the sample had been taken from the general population, only 10 to 15 per cent would have been in that category. It seems unnatural (but, of course not implausible) that mental health should be possessed by only such a small percentage of our society. We do not include in the category of physically healthy only those with a pulse rate below 80, nor do we include in the category of intelligent only those with an IQ above 130.

The second reason arises out of the question: Is there such a thing as absolute normality? Granted that there may be a phenomenon such as basic adjustability which our 25 per cent had or approached having, could anyone attain absolute flexibility and freedom from anxiety?

We would think not. We do not believe a person can attain that absolute degree of freedom. As early as latency we saw a beginning of specialization by the child in his modes of coping with the world and himself; some children showed specialization in group adjustment; others in the one-to-one adjustment; still others were best adjusted to the mother.

It appears that as soon as a certain adaptive mode gives a reward to the child in the form of external praise, or in the form of the lessening of anxious insecurity, then the child increases his personal investment in that particular mode. It becomes more difficult to change from that mode even though by throwing out the slightly dirty water one may obtain cleaner water. Furthermore, the security of using a familiar technique by which one can gauge and avoid dangerous pitfalls, is preferable, apparently, to an experimenting with a new technique which, although having the potentiality for greater rewards, has also the potentiality for failure.

The internal structure, then, of the person dictates that when in doubt one should do what one is familiar with, or has been successful with, or both. The more a person has experienced doubt and insecurity (particularly great anxiety when under undue stress in his development) the more tenaciously will he hang onto a familiar, perhaps even totally anachronistic or quite unrealistic mode of adaptation. Apart from this extreme situation, it is true that everyone has experienced some degree of uncertainty. Thus there is with all of us an innate tendency to cling to the familiar. This clinging to the familiar will tend to limit the amount of free flexibility and adaptability available for coping with new situations.

Besides this innate tendency we have social pressures which delimit the degree of expansion of the personality. In our present competitive society there is a constant pressure upon the child to become recognizable to the nurturing and authority figures as someone who is beginning to develop a practical know-how to cope with this acquisitive, competitive society. In the school the getting of good grades, or being chosen for a fraternity, or being elected class president, or being good in sports hold out promise to the parents and to the child that pursuing the successful course will result in some later tangible reward. Thus one picks his early specialization, sometimes at the proper time, but often prematurely in order to guarantee for one's self a secure place in society.

Our society does not place a high premium on the total or whole man. Whenever a person departs from the straight line taken by his peers or colleagues—the businessman who takes off a year to go to school, the educator who takes a year off to go into business is regarded by his associates either as foolish or a traitor, or both. As a result, one who contemplates such a step would tend to think of what he might be losing in regard to his peer group rather than of what he would be gaining in his personal development.

Thus, for at least two reasons it is not possible for a person to achieve that absolute degree of flexibility which would enable him to cope with any new or adverse situation. One reason is internal: the innate tendency to cling to the familiar, a tendency which increases with advancing age as the lively impulses decrease in strength. The other reason is external: the tendency for our society to give rewards to the expert, specialized person who can do one thing very well rather than several things rather well. In view of this, absolute flexibility or normality would seem to be a utopian concept like perpetual motion or the machine which operates with 100 per cent efficiency.

The final reason for an overly high standard is, we believe, a more technical one and arises out of therapy methods and goals. It consists of a preference for the more complete cure goal achieved by deep insight therapy rather than for the more symptomatic relief achieved by supportive therapy.

As useful as support is—either as the main facet of therapy or as an adjunct to other kinds of therapy—therapists tend to be discontent with any procedure which treats the symptoms more than the cause. Even though during supportive therapy it is likely that some emotional learning or re-learning does take place, therapists are dissatisfied with the lack of guarantee of this occurring and also with the amount and rate of learning. Rightly or wrongly, we as therapists are ambitious enough to wish to cure a patient rather than just to participate in the management of the patient. As our surgical colleagues find satisfaction in the complete extirpation of a malignant tumor, as our medical colleagues are gratified by discovering substances which rather permanently immunize the patient against certain infections, so are we most interested in a therapeutic procedure which builds up *within* the patient considerable protection against future debilitating stresses. This kind of procedure which leaves the patient with built-in strength is, of course, called deep insight therapy, the most systematic of which and the most striving for radical cure being psychoanalysis.

Thus an overly high standard of mental health may result from the high scientific value attached to a complete, radical cure of emotional disturbance which would ideally protect the patient from all future undue stresses. This tendency is most often temporarily possessed, as we have said, by inexperienced therapists to whom anything resembling psychopathology is a spur to further deep therapy. It is rarely possessed by experienced therapists who have come to appreciate that a thorough cure is somewhat more difficult than is complete removal of a tumor, that many patients can be helped considerably without a radical excision of all potential psychopathology, and that some patients whose life situation is chronically difficult do have to be managed for a considerable time in a supportive way.

Does this stopping short of a radical cure represent merely fatigue and disillusionment on the part of the older, experienced therapist, or may it have a therapeutic rationale? We believe a valid argument could be made for the latter. Part of the argument has already been given: there is a limit to the amount of self-improvement and real change possible. If there is such a limit, then deep insight therapy (psychoanalysis) would have to be magical to transcend the limits of what is possible. It remains a rational, scientific procedure when it keeps within its limits.

The other part of the argument revolves around the notion of what is normal and abnormal. We have already indicated our position that there is no sharp dividing line creating a dichotomy between normal and abnormal, and that rather, there is a continuum extending from the optimally normal to the decidedly abnormal. On this continuum each person may be placed according to his potential (to borrow Kubie's term) for normality, flexibility, ego strength, maturity, or growth, and his potential for abnormality, inflexibility, ego weakness, immaturity, or fixation. Of these somewhat interchangeable terms we have been using normality and abnormality because they are in common usage and are not likely to disappear soon from our ordinary language.

The pertinence of the foregoing to mental health is that it is not the inevitable presence of abnormal potential in a person that matters so much as it is the interrelationship between the abnormal and normal potential. The emotional well-being depends on the way in which the abnormal potential is circumscribed, guarded over, safely gratified, and utilized by the normal potential. In psychoanalytic theory this is the kind of optimum interrelationship described as existing between the strong forces in the turbulent id and the regulators (ego, ego-ideal, and superego). Unharnessed and ungratified, the id can be a foe of the regulators, causing an energy-draining disintegrative split; harnessed and gratified, it can be an ally of the regulators, allowing all psychic energy to be focused on adaptive action.

Thus the goal of deep insight therapy is not the impossible and magical one of eradicating all abnormal potential, but rather the rational one of helping the person to handle his abnormal potential more wisely and effectively.

As the term implies, deep insight leads to increased self-knowledge. This is another way of stating Freud's thesis that the aim in therapy is to make the unconscious conscious. Self-knowledge consists of knowing what the self is like, what it feels, what it thinks, and what it does.

Self-knowledge also aids in better knowing what the environment is like. There are no longer any rigid projections so that unwarrantedly the environment appears uniformly evil and the self uniformly benign, nor any rigid introjections so that unwarrantedly the environment is uniformly benign and the self uniformly evil.

We have devoted some space to examining and discussing the third reason for an overly high standard of normality. We believe that the overly ambitious goal (in inexperienced therapists) of eradicating all seeming psychopathology or all abnormal potential is not feasible nor scientifically rational. The feasible and rational goal is self-knowledge, with all its implications for a happier treatment of one's self and a better awareness of the environment. Comfortable self-knowledge, arrived at spontaneously, through growth or through therapy, represents a working integration between the normal and the abnormal potentials.

Our entire discussion of the three reasons for an overly high standard of normality has gradually led us to the point of offering an affirmative thesis regarding the proper diagnostic standard. The thesis, stated in qualitative rather than quantitative terms is: The characteristics of a proper standard are (1) that it is always in terms of the particular person or type of person, i.e. it is not too narrow; (2) that though it recognizes that there is strong potential for growth, it takes into account that there is a limit to self-improvement, i.e., it is not too high; (3) that it views a person as one who through self-knowledge can more wisely, benignly, and effectively handle his inevitable abnormal potential, rather than viewing the person as one who is free of this potential or who has to eradicate or deny this side of himself, i.e., it is not too rigid.

The therapeutic implications of this standard have already been mentioned. It would help in knowing whether it is necessary to intervene therapeutically, whether there is in the child such a degree of the inevitable abnormal potential that the latter cannot be handled by the normal potential in the child and in his immediate family and in his less immediate environment. Similarly, it would aid in determining, once therapeutic intervention has occurred, whether the ascendency of the normal potential had increased sufficiently that therapy might be terminated.

GENERAL REMARKS

In closing, we would like to make a few general observations about how the mother (and father) play a role in the mental health work with the child and about the resources that persons have for self-healing.

Whatever can be done to increase mother's dependability and her understanding would preventatively decrease the amount of potential maladjustment for the child. We had noted that these capacities of mother are not constant but rather fluctuate due to stress, unfamiliarity, and conflict. An important factor which helps relieve undue stress in the mother is the co-operative understanding contributed by the father. His support as a stable person, as the economic provider, and as a companion does much to help mother over the rough periods.

Relief from stress is also accomplished by reducing the anxiety. The inexperienced parents, especially those who so far have only one child, are particularly susceptible to being at sea and not knowing what to make of their child. They are also particularly susceptible to the bogeyman introduced by the current emphasis on mental health and the possibility of psychopathological developments. As a result these parents tend to be overanxious and tense in their handling of the child—dependability and understanding suffer. (The same applies to the handling of the children by the inexperienced teacher who has not seen different kinds of children grow up, and the inexperienced clinician who reads ominous psychopathology into "normal" growth problems.)

If, for some reason, the family strengths have not been able to cope with the family problem or the child's problem, the mother may seek help from a child guidance clinic. The word "may" is used advisedly inasmuch as one of the principal obstacles to helping the most disturbed children is the reluctance of parents to seek help diagnostically and to continue in a therapy program. The reluctance is based partly on feelings of shame and inadequacy and partly on inflexibility. Our experience at the Institute for Juvenile Research is that the co-operation of the parents is in inverse proportion to the degree of the child's disturbance. In other words, the least disturbed children have the most co-operative parents. This trend is not surprising inasmuch as the most severe disturbance of the child usually springs from the inflexibility of the parents.

When mothers do seek help from the clinic, we see considerable variation in how much help they require. Some mothers are sufficiently emancipated and individuated from a tenacious, faulty past that in two or three interviews they may perceive and utilize a better way of solving their problems. Others are so inflexibly caught up in their past that it takes months or years for them to become adapted to the current situation.

Some mothers require help because they are needlessly overanxious about their normally growing child. They do not realize, as do more experienced and stable parents, that there is a comfortable margin for error. In this regard it will be recalled that in our study children definite signs of maladjustment appeared mainly when both dependability and understanding were missing from the maternal atmosphere. The mild impairment of one or the other capacity in mother did not seem crucially to affect the child's adjustment. It would help these anxious mothers to realize that *all children normally exhibit growth problems, and that if the parents are reasonably mature, there is little likelihood that these problems will become permanent or disabling.*

The phenomenon of parental anxiety requires more discussion. We have already mentioned as one of its sources the bogeyman introduced by the current emphasis on mental health. As a result, the child is viewed by the parent as a potential emotional invalid rather than as a potential normal person. The situation, however, was not always this way. Formerly parents were comparatively oblivious to the possibility of the child being emotionally traumatized in his growing up. The family in those days could be described as parent-centered. However, with the growth of the notion of democracy, equalitarianism, and the "rights of men," the pendulum swung sharply in the other direction. The family has become increasingly child-centered; it has, to the neglect of other important considerations, poured energy and anxiety into an impossible goal, that of guarding the child against any possible emotional trauma. The modern conscientious mother seems to be taking the child's emotional temperature whenever the least symptom appears. The child, sensing the mother's concern, develops exaggerated ideas of his own importance in the scheme of things.

If there is an answer to these sharp pendulum swings, it would seem to be in the direction of a *family-centered* family. With such a family, the unduly egocentric attitudes promoted by a parent-centered family or by a child-centered family would assume wholesome proportions. The energies and interests of the separate family members would be comparatively subordinated to some higher goal—the family organization. As a previous chapter has shown, this organization can avoid the pitfalls of wild anarchy and of rigid suppression. *And in any well-functioning, high-morale organization the leadership has to be assumed by the more experienced and mature members, namely, the parents.*

As for the actual treatment of the mother, a treatment which may stop or go beyond the therapeutically oriented diagnostic interview, a few implications arise from our study. When the impairment of maternal dependability and understanding exceed the margin for error, a building up of them is a complicated affair. Obviously it is more than a matter of telling mother that she is undependable or non-understanding. And it is more than informing her that she is wrong about a certain child-rearing practice.

The latter course, we believe, is risky in view of the variety of family customs. Specific prescriptions that fail to consider the particular generational continuities would not only miss the mark but would be confusing. The mother (or father) would unnecessarily be put on the defensive and made uncertain about a particular way of child-rearing which is not crucial to the child's adjustment. We found, for example, no difference in adjustment between children toilet trained at 14 months and children trained at 22 months. Thus one family may have a certain custom in toilet training or in feeding or in display of aggression which, in itself, is not abnormal or pathogenic. It is the feelings, the pressures, and the conflicts behind the customs which we believe are more important than the customs themselves.

A matter closely related to the continuity of generations is the inevitability of the parent imprinting the child to some degree. Some mothers (or fathers) are anxious not to become a formative, imprinting influence on their children. They apparently feel that making their position or stand definitely known to the child will so indelibly imprint the child that he will never be able to form his own opinions. A common example among the intelligentsia is not forcing the child to go to Sunday School and preferring the child to make up his own mind when older if he wants a religious affiliation.

This over-abdication of parental tendencies to direct and mold is based, we believe, on the unnecessary fear that the children will not change their minds as they grow up. Our findings indicated that children did improve on their own parents, that change was not only possible but frequent. Certainly a definite position taken by the parent when coupled with a capacity for accepting the child's separate individuality would offer the child a temporary scaffolding from which he could build his individual attitudes. A certain degree of imprinting is thus not only inevitable but also, in our opinion, necessary. As Santayana has said: "Specific character is a necessary point of origin for universal relations—a specific inheritance strengthens the soul. . . . otherwise he wanders from place to place . . . a voluntary exile always uneasy."

As for the self-healing aspects, we were quite impressed by the fact that among our 54 children and mothers a sizeable number had what appeared to be resilient personalities. The stresses they had gone through had matured and strengthened them. A defeat or frustration was something to learn from, rather than to be crushed by. Accustomed as we were in a child guidance clinic mainly to see psychopathology, familiar as we were with the cliche, "everybody is neurotic," we were both surprised and pleased to find many evidences of mental health and potentialities for it in our group. As others have said, the psychological apparatus does have the same type of self-healing resources as has the physiological apparatus. Just as the physiological system combats an infection by mobilizing the white cells, by blocking off the infected area, by putting the body to rest, so does the psychological apparatus combat stress or frustration by developing aggression, by warding off painful feelings through the mechanism of repression or denial, and gives the psyche an opportunity to rest by the use of regression.

While the foregoing pertains to the self-healing resources in the individual person, there are spontaneous curative facilities in the relationship between two or more people. Man's biological propensity to be a social animal enables him to benefit psychologically from the resources of other humans. One example of this is the lessening of anxiety accomplished through the supportive presence of another person. Another related example is the supplementing or complementing of one's self by a friendship or a marriage. We mentioned earlier the psychological division of labor in society which would allow each person to contribute what is natural for him and depend on others for what is natural for them. Thus, rather than the traditional person feeling that it is encumbent upon him to take the lead in changing the past, he could rest comfortably in his own mission of carrying on the past, knowing that the rebellious person will inevitably take up the cudgels for change. When psychological division of labor is not utilized, there are such repercussions of uncertainty and tension as is seen sometimes in the overburdened executive who is unable to delegate authority to others.

In our study we saw evidence of the self-healing qualities contained in the mother-child relationship and the older-newer generation relationship. It will be recalled that we noted many mothers were free enough of the past that they could at least partially undo and correct their past when the present reality necessitated that they do so. Although at times in the correcting of the past, the pendulum may have occasionally swung too far, at least the pendulum was dynamically swinging instead of being set at dead center.

This correction of the past brings to mind Franz Alexander's concept of psychotherapy, which is, in essence, that the patient undergoes a corrective emotional experience. This experience becomes corrective if and when the therapist deliberately selects from the many possible attitudes he could have toward the patient that particular attitude which is the opposite of the pathogenic attitude of the parent of the patient. In other words, if the patient's mother or father were unduly controlling, the therapist's attitude toward him would be toward empathy with the individual needs of the patient. If the patient's mother or father were unduly permissive, the therapist's attitude would be in the direction of setting firm limits.

In a way, the mental health of the mother and child appears to depend on a similar corrective emotional experience. The mother, if she had been dissatisfied in her own childhood with too little warmth or too much control, resolves to herself that with her own children she will be warmer and less controlling. Because of her partial identification with the child, in a sense, she is going through her own second childhood, but in a new, revised, and corrected edition. In other words, she is administering a corrective emotional experience to herself. The child, at times, benefits from the better corrected handling and at other times suffers somewhat from the over-swing of the pendulum. These same considerations also apply to the cycles through which society passes; the wave of permissive pleasure seeking which follows a long period of puritanical reform.

We also saw the child beginning to formulate his future attitude as a parent. Secure enough to verbalize his dissatisfactions with some of his parents' dealings with him, he seems to be resolving that when he is a parent he will be more dependable or less controlling. As we described with the mother, he is beginning to administer a corrective emotional experience to himself. In this way, each generation corrects the over-emphasis of the preceding generation.

We end these explorations, then, on a sanguine note. We believe that there is a resilient nucleus to the personality which would seem to promise much for the survival of the human race. It resembles the type of nuclear core that Thornton Wilder so imaginatively described in *The Skin of Our Teeth*. There is margin for error; there is capacity for change; and what one generation cannot achieve in its lifetime, the next generation tries to cope with. The continuity of the advance is not always in a straight line forward; successive generations, like a sailboat heading into the wind, must tack this way and that in order to utilize the energy of the prevailing historical forces.

An opposite, pessimistic note has been prevalent in recent literature, psychiatric and otherwise. Several things have combined to produce this pessimistic orientation. One of these is the emphasis up until lately on the disruptive psychopathological factors in individual and group functioning. Pathologic labels have been placed on behavioral phenomena. Thus, ours has been called the "age of anxiety"; or, a nation which has two contradictory viewpoints is described as suffering from "national schizophrenia." Another and probably greater contribution to pessimism has been the actual historical events. The world, exhausted and disillusioned by two major wars, and living in dread of annihilation by a third, cannot help but be skeptical about the progress of mankind.

Notwithstanding the current historical realities, we believe it would be a mistake to allow pessimism or anxiety to be the major orientation to the human personality. The human psyche is not like a house of cards, susceptible to being blown over by any strong wind. It has been on the scene for thousands of years, and has had its good times and its bad. It does not normally occur to us to question why the heart is still beating (unless we have a cardiac neurosis). We appear to have placed the human race into a different, more fragile category, failing to realize fully that it has the same sturdy resiliency belonging to the other biologic phenomena. Its resiliency resides not only within the individual, but also in the mutually strengthening effects of different kinds of people working and living together.

Appendixes*

A NORMAL BOY
AND HIS
MOTHER

Mrs. L. was a sweet looking, nicely dressed, dark-haired young woman. Her skin was somewhat red, as if mottled from tension, and although there was some tension in her general manner, she was otherwise at ease. She related well to the social worker, who thought that Mrs. L. might have some tendency to cover up or deny any of her feelings that might be considered socially unacceptable or threatening to her. She gave the impression of having a desire to conform and do well, without showing, along with this attitude, much evidence of being pushing or dominating. The social worker felt that she is probably more rigid than openly harsh and punitive. The worker got the feeling of warmth and kindness in Mrs. L., but did not feel that there was a real closeness between mother and son, Tom.

Mother agreed with the school's opinion about Tom, saying that they, too, thought he was well adjusted, and that she considered him "average in his emotions."

The parents had been married a year and three months when Tom, a planned baby, was born. They had wanted two children but

---

*In Appendixes A and B is presented the case material pertaining to one boy and one girl (and their mothers). The boy and girl are taken from that small group (25 per cent of the total group) that showed consistent adjustment. In other words, they scored high during latency in adjustment inside and outside the family, and their puberty school report also showed good adjustment. The material will illustrate not only some of the points we have made throughout the book, but also the method of examination. The material will be presented without comment or interpretation.

not as close together as they had them. They have wanted more children, but everything seems too expensive. Mother said she would like a large family if they could afford it. Although she thought Tom and John were too close together, she felt that it has probably been easier in the long run to have them this way. She could not go anywhere, anyway, when Tom was small, and it is always a lot of work the first few years with any baby.

During her pregnancy with Tom, mother felt well physically and had very little nausea. There had been more nausea during the pregnancy with John. She was a little depressed at times, but not often. When carrying Tom she had been a little anxious because she did not know what it was all about. With John she was fearful that something would happen to her and thus leave Tom without a mother. She also dreaded the delivery with John because she knew what it was like from her previous experience. Mother could remember no frightening dreams, but said she dreamed about a home of her own and play space for the children. She thinks these two things are the biggest in her life and that she would like her children to be able to do the things she was not able to do as a child. Mother's doctor was a friend of theirs and she had a great deal of confidence in him. Both parents wanted a boy when they were expecting Tom. When she was pregnant with John, she had wanted a girl and had been very disappointed the first few days after he was born, but said she has not taken out any of her resentment on him because of it.

Mrs. L. was in labor with Tom for nine hours and did not think the delivery too hard. Anesthesia was used only at the end. Mrs. L. commented that she had been determined not to be like the other women who cried. However, she asked for anesthesia in the delivery of John and said she was not convinced of the methods of natural childbirth. Instruments were used in the delivery of John but John was not injured and she had only a few stitches. When she first saw John she was very pleased because Tom had been such a pretty little baby. She was very proud of him. The hospital had a nursery plan.

During his first few weeks Tom was a very active baby, and he has continued to be an active child. Mother commented that he was very active even during her pregnancy.

During his first year Tom was a good baby who slept well. She followed a schedule, but not rigidly. He did not cry very much, and when he did she always tried to see if something was wrong, but "tried not to spoil him." She held him and played with him when he was good, which meant when he was not crying. He never seemed to want to be bothered with cuddling and would push away and squirm when it was offered. If strangers looked at him, he cried but mother thought this was because he had had to be inside the home most of the time during his first winter. He was all right with strangers after he was fifteen or sixteen months old.

Mother nursed Tom entirely until he was four months old and then gave him a special bottle until he was eight or nine months old. He continued with the bottle until he was a year and a half, because he did not like the cup and mother felt it was more important for him to get his milk. Tom then weaned himself without difficulty. Mother had enjoyed nursing him, considering this part of her "maternal workings." John had been a bottle baby because mother had no milk. Tom was never a big eater, and she had worried about this at first, trying for about a year to get him to eat more. Finally, she realized he would not do so unless he wanted to.

Training for bowel control started when Tom was around six months and was established soon after. She did as the book said, putting him on the pot every twenty minutes at first and then every half hour, until "things took care of themselves." She did not start to train him for wetting until he was a year and a half and felt she had not been too successful until he was two, although he had readily stopped wetting the bed. At first mother had taught Tom to sit down to urinate and found it hard later to teach him to stand up. All of her friends had at that time daughters who were completely trained at a year and a half. Occasionally now Tom may wet his pants or wet the bed if he is sick. This rarely happens oftener than twice a year.

Tom walked at one year. He sat up at five months and was crawling around his play-pen at six and seven months. Mother said he had known at nine months whether a book was upside down or not. At present Tom and John have separate beds in a room that they share together. Tom shared his parents' bedroom until he was three years old. Tom does not seem to require much sleep and has not had many bad dreams. He used to lie awake for hours before he fell asleep but does not do so often any more.

At three, Tom had an upset stomach, following which he was dehydrated and had to be hospitalized for three days. At five, he developed various allergies, and he started having asthmatic attacks when he was six. Medication had seemed to control the asthma. He had a T. and A. when he was four years old, and last year he had an ear infection for which he had to be hospitalized for ten days. He had measles and chicken pox after he started school, but was not very sick with these diseases. Mother has noted that Tom seems to resent being sick so much when other children are not.

Tom has asked where babies come from, but mother thinks this matter has not "preyed too much on his mind." He thought at first that people got a baby when they were first married, but he knows now about the period of pregnancy. He has never asked about the father's part in conception, but knows there has to be both a man and woman. His parents have tried to answer his questions as he has asked them. Mother said she has tried to be natural in answering his questions because she does not think they should be suppressed. Since Tom does not have a sister she has not allowed him to see her undressed or to use the bathroom at the same time. He has asked about her breasts and knows about the difference in using the toilet. Mother has noticed no masturbation since he was three, at which time he used to "grab himself." At that time the doctor told her he was still discovering himself, but if he did this now she would consider it a problem which she would have to do something about.

In talking about which parent the children prefer, mother said that father had been the sort of person the boys had always looked up to. She used to think that they thought more of their father than they did of her because they never showed a lot of positive feeling toward her unless she was sick. In discussing her feelings about preferences, mother said she does not feel left out and that she is happy and thankful the boys have that kind of father. She does not feel that he is taking the boys away from her but rather that it is nicer that there are two instead of one to share the children. Tom has had no particular fears or worries about his parents.

When Tom was small, Mrs. L. used to spank him because she thought he was too little to understand words. Now that he is older they discipline him by making him sit on a chair or by depriving him of the bedtime story his father tells him, and this is the worst punishment because Tom enjoys the story so much. He has to be disciplined mostly for disobedience because he likes to do what he wants to do and is quite determined about it. Both parents discipline the children, except that mother is with them more than father. They agree on discipline. Mother said she had formerly thought that the children should always mind her, but that now she has a new outlook about this matter since the little girl of one of her friends died about six months ago. This event made her stop and think about what was really important in her relationship with the children. She never enjoys punishing them because it makes her feel bad and she does not like to see Tom cry. Although punishing them is no pleasure for her, she feels that the children do have to know the difference between right and wrong. If the other children in the neighborhood are punished less for the same things Tom does, she sometimes wonders if she has been unjust to him, but she really thinks the other mothers have not been severe enough with their children. She feels that the discipline she and her husband use works very well. Tom and John may sometimes think their parents are too severe with them, but they are not punished unduly, and there are many nice things for the children to offset punishments.

Mother thought that Tom did not know what it was like to be without John since he was so small when John was born. She remembered that the older boy had resented the first time that John had his bath in Tom's bathinette; Tom cried and motioned to mother that he wanted a bath himself. He was so small when John was born that he got almost the same attention. He had been told while mother was in the hospital that she would be coming home with a baby. Tom stayed with the paternal grandmother while mother was in the hospital, and father spent a lot of extra time with him.

In looking back, mother thought that perhaps she had expected perfection of the boys and had picked at them too much. Since her friend's little girl died, she has tried to relax, and she finds that her own nerves are better. She thought it was at about six that Tom became much more determined. He had been a sweet, mild boy until he was three; then he began to be more determined when he started playing with other children in the neighborhood. She thought, too, that about the age of six his size, as compared with other children, became more noticeable because he had started school, and also because John began to grow and became bigger than his brother. Mrs. L. commented that Tom is built like her brother who became very tall when he was grown, and she fully expects Tom to grow later, too. Mother thought he and John were like most brothers in the way they get along. They fuss, but they also play together. They have gone through different stages in their relationship. Last year John was egging other boys against Tom.

During the first three years of Tom's life, the family lived with the paternal grandmother. Following their move from that home, they lived in two different places, and for the last three years have rented five rooms. Worker did not note whether the family lived in an apartment or a house now.

In comparing the children, Mrs. L. said Tom is very studious and serious, while John's very good grades seem to come easily and naturally. John is happy-go-lucky and nothing ever seems to bother him. He is big for his age and plays a lot with Tom's friends. Tom objected to this only once, and he had also said he didn't want John to join his Cub Scout group. John does not say much of anything. Both boys seem to enjoy the same things and have many interests in common. Tom seems to be more stable now, while John is more contrary.

Mother described Tom as a very alert child, a more or less high-strung youngster with whom she has to deal carefully. He is tense and may cry and get upset if he feels he has been mistreated outside the home. He will tell mother about it and does not fight back very much with the other children. Mother thinks that Tom has a mature mind. She mentioned in her description of him that he is very happy in his relationship with his father. He is not an introvert but he is more on the shy side. Mother feels that his allergies (hay-fever and a number of foods) have made him high-strung, but there seems to have been a change in him in the last six months, during which time he has become much more even in nature. His allergies, too, have been better the last six months. He has been treated with hay-fever shots and drugs. Formerly he would get very high-strung and determined at times, but always got over these depressions quickly. He has lots of friends and plays for the most part with boys his own age. He feels his small size indirectly, but never talks about it directly. John is half a head taller than Tom. The parents handle this handicap by trying to emphasize Tom's other qualities and abilities, such as his reading. Mrs. L. thought Tom could be characterized as self-sufficient; he does not want any help from them. She observed that both she and her husband are somewhat determined themselves, but not nearly so much as Tom.

When Tom is angry he may slam things down and let off steam in fights with other children, but he does not get into many fights. His size is a disadvantage in fighting with other children and he frequently resorts to kicking. When he loses his temper at home, he talks in a complaining manner to his parents, who try to calm him down and explain things to him. Mother thinks that children are like adults: that they have to talk back; and she would rather have him talk back to his parents so he can get it out of his system, after which they can explain to him that this is not nice.

Mr. L. spends a great deal of time with the children, and mother thinks this is most unusual. He plays with them in the evening and spends Saturdays with them. The other kids in the neighborhood think father is a magician and look upon him as an ideal. He really enjoys it and does not do these things with the children out of a sense of duty. Mother feels that this is the whole secret of her sons being happy, i.e., having a father who does things with them.

Mother and Tom get along pretty well. She does some things with them but not so much as father. However, the children always feel free to bring their friends to their home to play and to see and meet mother. Tom confides more in his father, as if the matter were man-to-man. Although he was not cuddled much as a baby, in the last six months he has been much more spontaneously affectionate toward mother. He had always been more affectionate with father, but mother said that this had not bothered her, because she had considered Tom just not spontaneously affectionate.

Psychiatric interview with mother: Mrs. L. was an attractive and well-groomed woman with a pleasant smile. She talked rather easily in response to questions, giving thoughtful answers, but did not rattle on. There was some suggestion of firmness and control and undoubtedly she does control her own feelings. She sacrificed zest to accuracy. However, she laughed appropriately and easily and not from anxiety. She said she wouldn't say she was shocked that Tom was referred as well adjusted—maybe a little astonished but not too surprised—because she thinks Tom has been a nice, normal, little boy this year. Last year he was going through a phase of being quite determined, but he has gotten pretty well over that now and is getting to be more like the future adult he will become. Now mother can reason with him and explain things. The psychiatrist asked what kind of boy mother saw in him, and she said he is quite high-strung and emotional. He gets along with other children, though, and feels secure in his home. He is inclined to be reserved—not an extrovert. He is a serious minded child. The psychiatrist asked Mrs. L. if there were any faults she could think of, and she laughed and said that at school he never seems to finish his work and at home he gripes about things, "but I guess he is like most other children that way." The psychiatrist asked mother what she thought his best personality trait was. She thought for a bit and then said that he has friends and is friendly and is considerate of other boys' feelings; he has a pleasing personality and doesn't push his ideas on anyone. When asked of whom Tom reminded her, she said, "Well, he is like his daddy in being somewhat reserved." When asked about conflicts within herself in raising him, she said: "Up to a year ago perhaps I set too high standards for him. I picked on imperfections, but since a friend of mine lost her three-

year-old daughter I have given up on nagging and want to see that
he is happy." This death of her friend's daughter certainly changed
mother's viewpoint. Asked about conflict with her husband about
raising Tom, she said: "No, although he is more calm and easygoing
than I. He doesn't agrue with me over the nagging that I did with
Tom."

When asked about her childhood, Mrs. L. said: "I think I had a
very happy childhood. Of course my mother died when I was twelve.
I won't say that I was unhappy after my mother died, but the family
sort of drifted apart. We got a lot of attention from my mother. We
never knew what a baby-sitter was; mother never went off and left
us." When asked to describe her mother further, she said that she
was very quiet and reserved, never took part in any activities, just
stayed at home. It was a rare event for her mother to go four blocks
from home. She was quite busy with her domestic activities. "Mother
died of a cerebral hemorrhage rather suddenly. Father, on the other
hand, was more with mother and her siblings. He would tell them
stories in the evening, sing and play games. He has always been a
very happy person. He has always liked children and would play with
them. He plays with his grandchildren and likes younger people."
Her father was a coal miner for a number of years and then worked
for the school as an engineer. He was always a good provider and a
steady worker. The psychiatrist asked mother if she thought her
father had any faults and she said, "Possibly he was a bit strict when
I was in high school, but maybe he thought it best." Mrs. L. was the
youngest of five siblings; having two brothers and two sisters. Mrs. L.
is five years younger than her next older sister. One of the sisters died
of measles when mother was three years old. Mother said she got
along OK with her siblings. They have drifted apart in recent years
but are not estranged. Mother thinks that being the baby made her
the favorite. The psychiatrist asked her to compare her handling of
the children with her mother's and she said, "I'm more energetic in
getting the boys into activities and out of the house, and I do use a
baby-sitter sometimes when I go out of the house." Mother received
a B.S. degree in education and taught school for years. She always
wanted to be a teacher when she was a child, and she used to play
at it. She did enjoy teaching to some extent, but she said this with
some hesitation. Mother doesn't think she would like to return to
that kind of work because it definitely requires a lot of patience.

The psychiatrist asked her about her present health and she said:
"I can't say I've been in the best of health, but I'm not sickly either;

sometimes I don't feel good. I had an anemic condition and I get tired easily. Occasionally I feel that way two or three days in a row. In the spring and fall I feel wonderful, but in the winter I have these ups and downs. I feel closed in." When the psychiatrist asked her about nervousness, she said: "I guess I am on the nervous side, especially when I don't feel good. Little things upset me and at those times I get impatient and irritable." Asked about nervous fears she said: "Only some worry about my own health. Once I was worried that I had a goiter. My imagination went wild a bit." Psychiatrist asked mother about angry feelings and she said she gets angry now and then when she is tired or upset. Mrs. L. was asked about how she handles her anger. She said: "I hold it in for a while and then I have to let off steam. My first impulse is to overlook the incident and I make a determined effort to control the anger, but when I do blow off I feel much better." With her children she first tries to hold in the anger and then blows off but with her husband she tries even more not to get angry, and she has never had a really big fuss with him because there has never been any occasion for it. He is quiet, nice, and good natured. With her friends she acts about the same as with the kids. Mother doesn't think she is too much on the compulsive, orderly side. She does like a clean house, but a little dust doesn't upset her. Regarding worrying, she said, "Yes I am a worrier about the kids' health, their school marks, and when we get a big doctor bill."

Regarding sleep, mother said she sleeps fairly well but she does wake up early in the morning. If she doesn't go out in the evening she tries to get to bed by 9:30. Mother said she doesn't dream often and can't think of any recent dreams. When asked if the dreams were pleasant or unpleasant, she said, "Well, the only dream I can recall, and it has repeated itself since childhood, is that I am going to school and am embarrassed because I have no shoes or stockings on." Asked about dreams of herself in danger, she said no, but that she occasionally has dreamt of a death or a birth. Then she said, "Now I remember the last dream I had. It seems that my husband was talking to another girl in the office and I snatched at her hair in an angry way." Asked definitely about the attacked dream, she said she did have a dream of a big moving ball that tried to engulf her. The unpleasant part was being swallowed up by this ball. She could not remember any dreams of falling. She did recall a dream of people dying, and once dreamt of her father dying. Mother said that this didn't bother her much. The scariest of all dreams was the one in which she was at the point of being swallowed up by the ball.

When asked about her moods, she said: "I wouldn't say I was grumpy all the time; I guess I'm in a fairly good mood." Mrs. L. doesn't get much recreation. She plays golf and ball with the boys in the spring and does a good bit of hiking. She does not like to be shut in or closed up. She enjoys being with other people, playing cards. She plays golf with her husband. When asked if she had dislikes, she said, "Yes. I don't like extraverts or those who try to dominate. I don't like forceful people."

"Asked to describe her husband, she said he is very calm, and rather easygoing. He does not complain much, is a creative person, not especially an outdoor athletic type, but more on the sensitive, artistic type. She said that he devotes much time to the children and to her and is quite considerate. She thinks their marriage has gone very well and that they are compatible. Mr. L. is a copywriter for an advertising agency and has always worked steadily. He spends more time with her and the children than the average father does. He is not interested in "going out with the boys." Mother thinks that she enjoys people more than he does.

Mother did some dating before marriage and had some high-school crushes. Sex information came through the grapevine after her mother died. She states that she achieves a climax when she is in the mood. Frequency of intercourse, at the present, is two or three times a week and a week may go by in which they have none.

At the end of the interview, the psychiatrist asked mother if she had any questions with which he could help her, and she asked the psychiatrist what he thought of Tom. The psychiatrist spoke reassuringly of Tom's present condition, and mother seemed relieved.

Psychiatric interview with the child: Tom was an alert, friendly, small, eight-year-old who rose to greet the psychiatrist in the waiting room. He was full of zest, yet respectful, and talkative when given the green light. He was moderately restless, however, both at the beginning and at the end of the interview. At times his attention would wander and he had less affect and attention than one would expect. There was also some nail-biting during the hour. In spite of his restlessness he was not too curious about the clinic and there also seemed to be a mild amount of defensiveness.

When the psychiatrist asked him about fun, he said he had a game called Gold Finch, which is about birds, and which he played about 60 times last week. When asked with whom, he said with his brother and sometimes with his father. He likes to play baseball, too, as well as football. He would rather play outside than be on the inside. He said, "My mother wouldn't let me stay inside on a good day." Asked if there was anything he could do just by himself, he said, "Well, solitaire, I guess." He disclosed that he had more fun with other kids than just by himself. He listens to the radio every night and he likes things like *Broken Arrow, Tom Mix, The Cisco Kid,* and *The RB Ranch.* In the movies he likes Tom Mix and also *The Lone Ranger.* Asked about reading, he said, "We get our reading from doing our stamp collecting and playing Gold Finch," but he doesn't do much reading of books otherwise. Asked specifically about murder mysteries he said he likes some of them in which there are hold-ups, but that he doesn't like those in which there are murders. The psychiatrist asked him if such shows made him dream, and he said, sometimes. He likes to memorize parts of movies and make a dream out of them. He adds a few things of his own to the dream.

At this point the psychiatrist indicated the toy-box. The boy was quite interested but held back a little through politeness. He needed some permission to fish around in the box and then he did so with interest. He told the psychiatrist that he likes to mold clay; then he played with the gun, fingered it for a moment, and seemed undecided what to do next. Asked what he would like to do, he said he would like to draw. The psychiatrist told him that they would do that a little later. While talking to the examiner he was cutting up the wax paper with the scissors. He finally picked up the dolls, but was interested chiefly in their mechanics and moved their arms and legs about. (At this point he was somewhat restless, distractible, and clumsy in his play. There seemed to be no organized activity.) He then told the psychiatrist that his brother liked darts. (Tom did not take anything out of the box, but pushed the toys around within the box to see if there was anything he would be interested in.)

The psychiatrist then turned to the fantasy questions and asked about the three wishes. There was a slight anticipatory smile as he told the examiner that his first wish was that he would like to be captain of a baseball team, and then he stopped. Reminded that he had two more wishes, he said, "Well, to be a train engineer, and third, I would like to own a ranch." With a thousand dollars, he said, "Oh, I'd buy a car, buy a home, and train accessories for my electric train." His ambition is to be a train engineer. He would like to be sixteen rather than his present age. When asked why, he said so he could skip a lot of school that way, and then he grinned. Asked if he didn't like school, he said that there were other things he liked better—the game of Gold Finch for example.

When the psychiatrist asked Tom about his emotional feelings he admitted that he gets angry when bigger kids won't let him join in their baseball games. The psychiatrist said at this point, "When you are bigger you'll play, too." He said, "Baseball will be my hobby." Asked with whom else he got angry he said, "With my brother when he doesn't hold the cards correctly in Gold Finch." Asked about anger toward his mother, he was somewhat abashed, and said, "Well, sometimes when she does such things as put my bike away and says I can't play with it." Occasionally he gets angry at his father, as when his father comes home late and won't let Tom go down and see him. Asked if he likes his father, he said, "Yes, and you ought to see my brother. He walks behind father and takes steps just like him." Asked about sad feelings he said, "Yes, like when I can't play baseball with the boys and sometimes when I lose at games." He admits worrying, for example, when his mother sends him to the store to buy things and he doesn't have enough money. Asked what he did then, he said, "Well, I just buy the more important things." All the while Tom was fingering the toys and then with a mischievous smile he clicked the gun. The psychiatrist asked him at whom he was shooting and he said, nobody. Then he quickly closed the box and the psychiatrist, feeling that the boy had reacted to his question, said that he didn't have to close the box just because the psychiatrist said he might shoot somebody.

Tom sleeps in a bunkbed and occupies the upper berth. He has no preference for top or bottom. He said he and his brother change off. He said he dreams occasionally, and when asked what kind of dreams he has, he said, "Oh, about circus, cowboys and Indians, and also about movies." Asked if they were good or bad dreams, he said they were half and half. Questioned about his good dreams, he said, "Well, I dreamt once about a circus. Some child was giving water to an elephant. The elephant started talking and said, 'Don't give me water, I have enough.' Then the elephant squirted the water through his trunk into the boy's face. It was almost like it was a fireman's hose." The psychiatrist said, "It's a good thing you weren't the boy," and he said, "I'd like it if I were the boy." Asked about scarey dreams, he became mildly defensive and exhibited some blocking. He said he doesn't have very many. Asked what the scariest was, he said: "Well, Tarzan swimming in the ocean and he comes to a dark cave and an octopus ensnares him. Tarzan takes out his knife and begins cutting at the tentacles. Then Tarzan comes up against a shark and the shark gets the best of him and Tarzan gets all scratched up." The examiner asked Tom if he had ever had a dream in which he was in danger—not Tarzan, but he himself. He said, no, that he almost never dreams about himself. When asked about dreams of falling, he said, "Oh, yes. I had a dream in which a drawbridge went up and I fell off. It was lucky I landed in a boat." Asked if he ever dreamed of his family in danger, he said, no. At this point the psychiatrist asked him which was the scariest dream of all he had related, and he said, "I guess the falling dream." Asked if that was more scary than the one about Tarzan, he said, yes.

Regarding his family, he was rather more direct than the average child. He doesn't know if there is a real boss; he said it is half and half. He thinks that his father is a little more strict than his mother. He says there are no favorites in the family, but he admits being closer to father. However, he does take his troubles to his mother.

He needed no prompting at the end to go ahead with the drawing, and he drew without paying too much attention to the psychiatrist. In response to the psychiatrist's question about the picture Tom was drawing, the boy talked about it, saying complimentary things about it. Then he added, "They don't allow cameras in submarines or else a spy could take pictures."

ᕮᕮᕮᕮᕮᕮᕮᕮᕮᕮᕮᕮᕮᕮᕮᕮᕮᕮᕮᕮᕮ

A NORMAL GIRL
AND HER
MOTHER

MRS. J. was tall, thin, and dark-haired with large features and heavy make-up. During the interview with the social worker she related well and seemed at ease, except for some initial nervousness. She was spontaneous, eager to present information, and gave the impression of wanting to do the right thing and to do it well. She placed emphasis on self-control, obedience, and consideration of others in her expectations of her children. She did not show much sensitivity to or understanding of feelings, and although she appeared a rather narcissistic and controlled person, she impressed the worker as being fairly warm.

The parents agreed with the school's opinion of Caroline. She has been a pleasure to her parents.

Mr. and Mrs. J. were married while he was still in school, but Carolyn was a planned child. She had wanted a baby before she got any older but she thought he had agreed to it simply because he was expected to. She has always loved children but she remembered having asked her mother why everyone always got so excited about a baby being born. However, while she was pregnant she found that it was exciting. At one point she remarked that she has a sister who had tried for ten years to have a child.

Throughout the nine months of pregnancy Mrs. J. had been miserable, she had constant nausea. The same had become true with Robert, but with him it had not been quite so bad. Although her condition was good for the most part, she had a feeling of weakness and was not strong. Dysentery the last few weeks caused her to lose almost all the weight she had previously gained. She also had very bad headaches, and the thought of going back to the hospital (she had been ill much as a child) was very distasteful to her. The doctor who took care of her had been too busy to give her the attention she would have liked, but he had taken an interest in her because of her earlier illnesses. She has always been a worrier, particularly about money.

Both parents had wanted a little girl, and Mr. J. recently told Caroline that she has been everything mother wanted when they were expecting her. Mother had danced for years herself and wanted a little girl who would be both a dancer and a "personality" girl.

The hospital had a nursery plan. Delivery had been very difficult and the doctor thought later that a caesarian section would have been advantageous. Mother was given some gas at the last and she was not sure whether instruments were used. She had an episiotomy with thirty-six stitches. Later she developed a vaginal infection and was really not able to walk comfortably for four or five months following Caroline's birth.

Caroline was born with her face down. During delivery her jaw had been pushed to one side and the father has always thought this accounted for her occlusion. It took months for the jaw to adjust itself. When mother first saw Caroline she looked just like a little boy because she had no hair. In fact, she remained bald until she was three years old, but after the doctor prescribed thyroid her hair started to grow.

Caroline was a very active baby during the first few weeks and has continued so. During her first year she seemed to be a happy child. She rarely cried, but when she cried after eating Mrs. J. let her cry it out until she fell asleep. As an infant, Caroline's fingers seemed always to be moving. Mother had a certain time for holding the baby, but she did not pick her up much because she was so very tiny. Caroline went to everyone and cried only occasionally.

Caroline was nursed for four months. She never ate well from either breast or bottle and never finished an entire bottle. At eighteen months she was weaned and appeared to accept it. She learned how to drink from a cup readily, but she never finished this either. Mother worried a great deal about her not eating because she did not see how the child could live on such a small amount of food. Mr. J. had to help his wife to overcome this fear. She had to learn that there was no use fussing and fighting with Caroline, because it did no good. Mother had to learn to give the child smaller portions, and Caroline had to learn that she had to eat these smaller amounts. Father has

really worked at the eating difficulties, although Caroline still dawdles
and dreams over her meals and this infuriates her mother.

Toilet training started when Caroline was eight or nine months
old and completed at two years. Mrs. J. said she followed the Children's Bureau's book on *Child Care from One to Six* meticulously
and kept it on the night stand by her bed. She worked right along
with the schedule suggested by the book and found it easy. She said
Caroline was forced in all these things because they were in the Army
then. Caroline has to urinate frequently at school and occasionally
wets her bed. This has happened for three or four months in the past
year.

Caroline had measles and chicken pox during her preschool years,
and mumps after she started to school. She was very sick with the
measles because they did not break out and the doctor did not know
that she had them. She has had hay-fever since she was about three
and has been treated for it with drugs. She is allergic to weather
changes. A tonsillectomy was performed when she was two and a
half because of her bad sore throats. Due to weakness following the
operation, she had something like convulsions when she came home
from the hospital. For that reason Mrs. J. catered to her unwilling-
ness to eat, but her father insisted on her eating and, at the time,
Mrs. J. thought her husband was mean.

Caroline walked at one year. Mother could not remember when
she had started to talk, but thought it was about the usual time. She
said she should have brought Caroline's baby book with her.

Since Robert was born, Caroline has had her own room. During
her early years Caroline slept in the room either with her mother or
with both parents. There were a lot of changes because they moved
so often when father was in the service. A few years ago, for about a
year, Caroline was occasionally hysterical in her sleep. She would
kick and scream, and although her eyes were open she was asleep
and hard to waken. Now she has only an occasional bad dream.

Caroline has not asked many questions about sex, but she knows
about a seed and how the baby grows inside the mother. She and
Robert used to bathe together, but recently she decided she did not
want to do so any longer. She once said it was funny that she and
Robert were so different. She decided it was just like being born
colored or white, that she was a girl and Robert was a boy, and that
she was lucky and happy to be a girl. Mrs. J. thought this illustrated
very well how Caroline seems to decide things for herself. Mother is
ready to tell Caroline about menstruation, but is waiting "until she is

ready and can accept it." Because she dances with older girls, Mrs. J. is sure Caroline knows something about physical development in adolescence. At home Caroline pretends that she has some breast development, and tells mother that she thinks she will look better when she does develop because then she will be fatter. Mrs. J. has not wanted to tell her very much until she is ready because she sits and thinks about these things and gets very concerned. Two or three years ago mother found Caroline and her cousin masturbating in bed with the sheets. The cousin had told Caroline to do this, explaining that it would feel good. Mother was very upset and worried about it and finally asked the cousin's mother not to let her little girl play with Caroline any more. This went on for a long time, but gradually stopped. Mother was afraid to put much stress on the matter for fear she would arouse Caroline's curiosity further. Mother has told her to keep herself clean, and not to handle herself—that it is not lady-like and not right unless she is washing herself.

Mother thinks Caroline is closer to her although she respects and admires her father. She thinks Caroline has a terrific crush on her father, as she calls him handsome and cute, and remarks on how well he and mother dance together. Caroline says father does not really mean it when he says things that irritate mother, and she tries to find excuses for him. If mother or father is sick she becomes very concerned and feels very badly if mother is at all unhappy. It is she who tells Robert that he should be considerate of mother when she does not feel well.

Discipline for Caroline and Robert differs. If Caroline talks back to the girl who lives with them she is deprived of some pleasure. Mother does not have to hit her, and she does not want to do so anyway, because Caroline is so tiny and frail. When disciplined Caroline is very disappointed, but she has to accept it. Mother loves it that she can sit back and talk with Caroline and the child knows that what mother says has to be carried through. Father is more stern and strict and has never had to sacrifice what he wants to do as mother has, because the children always do what father wants them to do. Father does more of the disciplining than mother, and although they agree, father usually carries through what he says more consistently than mother, who sometimes weakens. They never argue about discipline because Mrs. J. feels her husband knows more about it than she does. When she has to discipline the children, she is sorry but she feels sure of herself and comfortable about it, because she knows there was a reason for their needing whatever discipline they get.

Prior to Robert's birth father was in the Service and the family lived in a number of different places. Since Robert was born the family has lived in a six-room apartment, which they rent.

Caroline knew just before mother went to the hospital that they were going to have another baby. She seemed very happy about Robert and was "just darling to him." Their life was very confused at that point, because father was in the service and mother had been terrified when she discovered that she was pregnant again. She resented it very much and said that Caroline was still preferred. "Caroline was a darling, sweet child throughout." Robert was not treated at all as Carolyn had been as a baby. As a child, Mrs. J. had been sick with a rare blood disease and her ability to have Caroline was surprising and therefore the little girl's coming was a wonderful event to them. Their feeling about Robert and the fact that Caroline was still preferred, meant that Caroline did not see Robert get a lot of extra attention.

Caroline and Robert are friendly one minute and fighting the next. Robert teases Caroline a lot about her eating and calls her "skinny." At this Caroline becomes angry and upset, and although she tries to ignore him, she really cannot. Robert's kind of teasing is most annoying and has taken place only in the last year. Caroline always thought Robert was so "cute and adorable." When he teases her friends, however, they fight back. Mother thought this was because her friends are stronger than Caroline, who is not a fighter. Also, mother did not think that the teasing would stop if Caroline fought back at Robert, because he would just enjoy the fighting.

Mrs. J. said Caroline had been no problem except with regard to eating. Mother belongs to the Association for Family Living and has attended their lectures and read many of the books which they suggested, particularly those designed to help parents with their children's questions about sex. Also, the parents were a part of a marriage group and follow-up study given by Professor Ernest W. Burgess at the University of Chicago. It was Mrs. J.'s feeling that Caroline had been easy to train—"a real pleasure." Mother suggested that the girl might be too independent and that perhaps she herself had been too wrapped up in the child's positives. She said she knew she should not compare Robert unfavorably with Caroline, but that he is so different and so much harder to handle.

In comparing the children, mother said that Robert is more highstrung, rough and tough, while Caroline is dainty. The boy is a much better eater. Caroline is less concerned about her appearance, although she always wants to look "nice." Robert is a comedian who will do "sneaky things," which Caroline will not do; but if on occasion she does them, she will tell mother immediately what she has done. Mother has always impressed upon the children that they should never lie.

In describing Caroline, mother said that she bubbles over with personality. She is warm and extremely sensitive. To illustrate the sensitiveness mother gave several examples. The paternal grandfather had lived with them until his death three years ago. Caroline still mentions him about once a week. She would never hurt another child, and even if children teased her about her teeth, she would try to find some way to get around it so she could still be nice to them. When a friend moved away and did not write to Caroline, she was very upset. She is a dreamer and has no conception of time at all. Frequently she does not hear when she is spoken to. She is very advanced in her dancing and also very critical of it, never satisfied with herself. She loves to be around people, is very vain, and would love to be beautiful. She plays with both boys and girls (two of her best friends were also in our study). She is very complimentary and is always flattering people. At present she is having some orthodontic work done and has had to wear a head-gear at night for the past few months. Although she thinks it is awful, she wears it willingly. She feels that things might have been worse—she might have been born with only one eye or only one leg.

Caroline gets excited and emotional when she is angry and shows temper, but she gets over it quickly. She gets angry chiefly at her brother and shows her feeling by upbraiding him, saying that she hates him and thinks he is horrible. She rarely talks back to her parents, and her eating is about the only thing they fight about. Mother dislikes and disapproves of the child's talking back to them. Actually she talks back to mother and not to father. She talks to mother in a very "old-ladyish manner"; she may try to calm her mother and will tell her that father has had a hard day, etc.

Caroline gets along better with her father. Robert gives mother "love like no one ever heard of," but he respects father. He is sweet and thoughtful of mother, but he makes mother angry by not doing what she asks him to do. He also told mother he is scared of father. Caroline and her mother get along just fine together. The girl confides in both parents and is extremely affectionate. Mother said she is not so surprised at her being so sensitive because both she and the maternal grandmother were like that, and Caroline has probably inherited it from them.

Psychiatric Interview with Mother: Mrs. J. seemed to have a good relationship. There was an appropriate mixture of spontaneity and receptivity. She was quite co-operative, spoke frankly, and seemed to show a basic warmth. During the interview she was rather free and easy in manner, but appropriately so.

Mrs. J. said she was not astonished at the referral, but flattered. She thinks the girl is adjusted. When asked what kind of girl Caroline is, mother said, "Just a pleasure—she has wonderful personality and charm." Asked if she had faults, mother said, "Yes, definitely—dreaminess and no conception of time, but her disposition is ideal." Asked about other faults, she said, "No, just dreaming and not eating." When asked whom she reminded her of, she said: "Well, not a pattern, a little bit of each. She is alert and quick and has a sense of humor from her father." The psychiatrist asked what the child got from her mother, and she said: "Well, sensitivity and trying to please. My disposition is also to think of other people. That's my way of meeting people." Asked about the dreaminess, mother said: "I was that way, too. I was worse when I was younger." She admitted that her dreaming bothered her own mother. For example, mother would go into a reverie after she had had a date when she was an adolescent. Mother said there is some conflict between the parents as to raising Caroline, and that father thinks she wraps her life around the children too much. He wants more attention and he is still a baby. Mother smiled at this point. Mr. J. thinks that he is getting enough attention from his wife, but doesn't want any interference. Mother doesn't think there is much doubt within herself about how to raise Caroline. She revealed that Caroline didn't cry much as a baby, and not often now. Mother said you can hurt the child deeply, but she controls it—she doesn't weep.

In speaking about her childhood, mother opened with the statement: "Well, I had a sister. We were very different. I had an extreme inferiority complex and we didn't get along. As I got older, I developed a rare blood sickness and was very ill. When I was fifteen I was the center of attention. My parents were so happy when I got well that I received a lot of confidence from them. Before that I felt very inferior. My sister seemed so beautiful, smart, and independent, and she would fight restrictions, whereas I would always mind. I thought my father preferred her because they were so much alike. I had a wonderful home and was very happy. My father often played with us and he was a great pal. My mother also was very understanding. It was such a wonderful home that we couldn't understand why anyone would rush to get married. Up to the time I was fourteen my sister made me believe that I was much beneath her. I think my dad admired her spunk. My mother didn't like my sister too much. She liked me better because I was understanding and behaved better."

When asked further about her father, she said: "He gave us a wonderful feeling of a father's relationship to children. I was so naive that I thought all fathers were that way—so devoted. When I got married I was simply amazed that my husband would object to doing anything for the kids. He was a hard worker and provided well. My blood sickness took all the money my father made and then the business went into bankruptcy. Our income was cut down very much. My mother went to work as a checker and cashier." Mrs. J. revealed that her father had a temper and occasional moods, but mostly a wonderful disposition. When his temper came out, you would be amazed. "He'd be like a baby for three days." He was very intelligent. On the other hand, Mrs. J. felt that her mother was very emotional, high-strung and super-sensitive, very intelligent and a good thinker. She had been a school teacher. She was a great worrier and manufactured things to worry about. She spent time with her own children. "One thing my mother hadn't done which I do, is that she never built us up. With my mother the teacher was always right and the neighbor kids were always right. Mother never bragged about her own children. She never built us up." The psychiatrist asked if there were any other differences in her own handling of the children, and she said, "No, just that I build my children up, whereas my mother did not." Regarding the relationship between her parents, she said, "My mother was super-sensitive and my daddy was a great tease. He wouldn't tell her things for fear of worrying her. Then, when it did come out it was a great shock. When my mother was teased, she would flare up. My dad would giggle and my mother would get more mad." When asked what she would be teased about, she said, "Dad would tease her about her closeness with money. My father was very extravagant. He tipped lavishly and that would annoy mother. Sometimes he would do it purposely in order to see her get excited." Mother was the second of three children. She had a sister two and one-half years older and a brother eight years younger. She thinks her father preferred the brother and guessed her mother did too. Mother felt much closer to her mother, whereas her sister was much closer to the father. She still clashes with her sister, but she and her brother get along fine. Mother revealed that she, herself, was a shy, obedient, understanding child. Mrs. J.'s education was interrupted in her fourth year of high school due to sickness. Then she took a few courses and at seventeen began modeling and selling clothes. She worked up through marriage and until the time she was five months pregnant. Now occasionally she does free-lance modeling and she has enjoyed it.

Regarding her present state, Mrs. J. said her health is fine. Of her nervousness she said, "I think so, although less nervous than I used to be. I have learned to accept things." Asked about her worrisome nature mother said: "If I am away from home I worry about the kids' welfare. My husband has worried me more than the kids. He is not easily satisfied, not a happy person. He likes frequent changes, so since marriage, I've never had a secure feeling. This bothers me much more than things getting on my nerves, because I'm rather easily satisfied." Regarding angry feelings mother said, "I get them occasionally." The psychiatrist asked her for what reason and she said: "Well, if I am late in meeting my husband and have a justifiable reason, I get angry at him because he won't give me a chance to explain. Also, I can get very angry at his sisters. I like being with them because they are fun, but they are very self-centered. Still I don't let my husband know about this." She admitted that she does get angry with the children if they don't mind or if they disobey. Mother said she used to have a violent temper, but now she waits until she calms down, then she tells the kids how angry she had been. With her husband she used to hold back her anger, but not so much any more. It is better for her, she said, when she can release her anger, but her husband doesn't understand this and says that mother is not as sweet as she used to be. The psychiatrist asked mother what changed her so that now she talked up to her husband more, and she said: "I guess I got more sure of myself. I felt from life experience that I had common sense, so then I felt I had something to say about things too." She used to feel happier when she restrained her anger but now when she lets it out she feels better and more relaxed in inside. Now she feels smarter and wiser. Before, she apparently felt happier because she felt life was just a bowl of cherries. As she went from restraining her anger to releasing it, she felt more confident, and because she felt confident she was able to talk up. Mother doesn't think she is especially fussy in a compulsive way but does like things systematic and orderly. Mother said she does worry because of the hot water that her husband has her in constantly. She said she sleeps fairly well. She needs a lot of sleep and rest. She dreams a good deal, but the dreams are mostly neutral. She used to have screamy nightmares, especially after she was sick and in her first years of marriage.

Now when she is upset she takes triple bromides which relax her. When the kids are sick, mother is OK, but one week later when they are well again she gets terrific migraine headaches. She could not remember any recent dreams. The psychiatrist asked her the worst dream she ever had and she said it was about the death of someone. "Someone was lying in his casket and it horrified me." Asked what was the worst dream she ever had in which she was in danger, she said, "Well, I remember a dream of falling, like down a deep hole." She was then asked directly about attack dreams, and she recalled one of burglars coming in to steal things and commanding her not to move or call out. She has not dreamt of others in the family in danger. When asked, at the end of all these dreams which was the most scarey, she put them in this order: Most scarey was the attack dream; second was the casket dream; and third was the falling dream.

Mrs. J. said she is usually in a good, cheerful mood, and at this point said, "I might tell you that I have many fears, like fear of dogs." She was asked about blues and she said, "Not often except when I start to feel sorry for others or myself." The longest she had ever felt blue was for two or three days, but this rarely happens. Asked about being enthusiastic or elated, she said: "Oh, yes, very much. I get very enthusiastic over something good that happens to my husband or the kids." She revealed that her husband is extremely enthusiastic about his own interests. She does not get as enthusiastic about something happening to her as happening to others. When asked about recreation, she said she wished she could travel as much as she once did. Now-a-days she goes to the theater just as she did as a kid. She has fun with people, she likes to be with them very much, and she has many friends. She does have dislikes, and she likes natural people. She dislikes people who are trying to impress or people whose main interest is making money. She said: "I like girls who are out doing things or working. I have no interest in women who play cards or lead humdrum lives."

Asked about her husband she said: "He likes attention and frequent change. I'm the only one he hasn't changed. He changes work, and the furniture in the apartment. He can change the furniture in the apartment once a week if I let him. He can't accept things that are displeasing without making an issue of it, even such things as the weather or minor inconveniences." She then asked, somewhat plaintively: "Do people outgrow that? I've waited for him to settle down, but he has wonderful ideals that can't be broken down. I think he has a softer disposition now. He doesn't want to be that way, but he is. He is quite opinionated. He has great likes and dislikes. I might feel that way, but I try to see the other side of things. He is quite wrapped up in his own problems and is quite self-centered."

When Mrs. J. was asked about their marriage and she summarized it by saying: "It isn't dull. Marriage is quite difficult. I must have craved some type of excitement to stick it out, because it has been very exciting. We have had some very happy and some unhappy times." When asked about the happy ones, she said, "When my husband is contented, I feel so much better, and I am happy to see him happy." Mother said she dated somewhat before marriage, but her husband seems always to have been around. Her mother prepared her for the menses and sex and the things were discussed openly. Asked about sexual adjustment she said, "Well, that came perfectly normal and natural." About satisfaction in sex, she said: "Well, I do everything to please my husband. If I were unhappy with him, I wouldn't have sex with him, but if I am just tired, I put myself in the mood. I always get an orgasm if I am happy with him. I wouldn't have relations otherwise." The frequency is once every one or two weeks. "My husband is wrapped up in his own thoughts so much that he doesn't give too much thought to sex." At the end of the interview the psychiatrist asked mother about any problems she might have. She said, "That dreaminess of Caroline's. I don't like that and I wonder what's going to happen." Mother still takes Caroline downtown for fear she will lose her way if she gets excited.

Psychiatric Interview with Child: Caroline was a pleasant, obliging, rather homely little girl who was soft but still had zest. She seemed to make a point of getting along with people. There was an anticipatory smile or grin playing around her mouth all the time. However, when talking seriously, as about some abuse, her smile came off. She spoke directly and spontaneously but did not go to extremes. She had a comfortable, trusting relationship to the psychiatrist, and was not defensive. She was animated enough so that when she got involved in telling a dream she acted it out somewhat.

Regarding fun, she said she liked to dance, does toe dancing, and said that she was going to dancing school that day. She likes to play and do arithmetic in school. Upon questioning she said that she preferred arithmetic to playing. When asked about playing she said, "Yes, I like to jump rope, play ball, and play with dolls." Sometimes she plays baseball with her father. Asked if she had any fun with her mother she said, "Oh, yes, we go shopping together and she takes me every place, practically." She said she has more fun playing outside with others. By herself, she can look at television or play with dolls.

On television she likes *Howdy-Doody* but doesn't like wrestling. She has to get to bed by eight o'clock. She likes *The Lone Ranger* and *Hop-a-long Cassidy* on the radio. She doesn't see movies very often. She has seen only *Red Shoes* and *Cinderella*. She likes to read—especially fairy tales. She reads *Snow White* all the time. When asked if she likes murder mysteries she said, with a shudder, no, but that her brother likes them.

At this point the psychiatrist indicated the toy-box. She fished around in it, peering in and then picked up the crayolas. The psychiatrist said that they would draw later and then she picked up the dolls and said, "No, that's baby stuff." Asked if she minded playing with baby stuff, she said with a grin, no, but that she'd rather be grown up. She said she likes to play with clay and then she began to fashion some. Asked if she played with dolls at home she said, "Yes, but the ones here are small and for babies." When questioned about what she did with dolls at home, she said, "Well, I have a doll bed and my doll has measles and I take care of her." She continued to work with the clay. At this point the psychiatrist went on to her fantasy life and asked her for the three wishes. She gave a reflective smile and said first she would like to have a lot of fun. Then she said, regarding what she was fashioning with the clay, that the tail would be too long for a dog. Asked if she liked dogs, she said, yes, but that she didn't have one because her mother doesn't like them. When asked about a thousand dollars, she laughed and said, "I'd give it to my mother, or my father, or both of them, or put it in the bank." The psychiatrist asked her if she would spend any of it and she said, "No, it was too much money." She would rather be younger than she is. She would rather be as she was at six. When the psychiatrist asked why, she said, "Well, I would get to do different things. As a grown-up I have to give up those cute dresses and pinafores." At that point she said she had finished the clay doll, and when the psychiatrist exclaimed over it she was quite pleased. She said her ambition was to be a dancer.

Asked about her emotional feelings she said, yes, she gets angry once in a while. Sometimes she doesn't realize that she is doing something wrong like taking candy before dinner. Then her mother gets mad and Caroline gets mad at her mother and cries. She added, "But I didn't realize I was doing anything wrong." The psychiatrist asked her who else makes her angry and she said, "Well, my brother. He hits me." Asked if she hit him back, she said, "Yes—but not hard, because he threw a ball at me once." She did get angry at one girl who didn't play ball fairly. She doesn't get angry at school teachers because she likes them. She is afraid to get angry with her father.

She feels angry but she is afraid to let him know. When asked what made her angry with him, she said, "He won't let me turn on the television set." Asked what would happen if she showed anger toward him she said, "He'd feel bad or get angry and spank me more." She admitted that she gets sad feelings at times. When her girl friend Susan went away to California, she missed her. Now she is angry because Susan doesn't write her. Another time she felt sad when her aunt disappointed her by not taking her to see *Red Shoes* the second time. She doesn't think she worries too much.

Caroline sleeps in a bedroom of her own. She does dream once in a while, short dreams, and mostly nice dreams. Asked about her nice dreams, she said she remembers part of one and then proceeded to tell about a bad dream which she said was a good one. In the dream the teacher was taking her to the principal, and she fell in the quicksand and was sinking. Below the quicksand was a machine, and a lot of bad men were there who wanted to steal children. These men were sort of interested in children and were not too bad, still Caroline tried to get away. The real bad man had a mustache. The scariest part was that something was pulling her down and the sand started covering her face like powder. "The worst part was that they said they would drop me in the river when they got me." When the psychiatrist asked her about falling dreams, she said, "Oh, yes," and illustrated by gestures a dream of falling a thousand feet from a tower. Asked about the attacked dream she said: "Oh, yes, a drunken man was after me and I couldn't run. It was midnight. He caught me and buried me in the ground. I finally got out. Susan was in the dream but she stayed behind. I warned her to stay away. This drunk was strangling people in a lane." She had not had dreams of others in danger except for Susan in this dream. When asked to compare the attacked and falling dreams, she said, "They were both pretty scarey," but she thought the attacked dream was somewhat more scarey than the falling dream.

Concerning the family, she said both parents are strict, but father more so, because he is boss. She said there is no special favorite; that she feels closest to all. She takes her troubles to her mother, or sometimes to her daddy, too, because her mother always asks daddy the answer to the problems. While drawing Caroline asked many questions about another patient, a girl classmate of hers. Was she nice, and did the psychiatrist talk to her dad and mother, and so on. She looked at the psychiatrist frequently during the examination.

VARIETIES OF
NORMALITY
(54 PROFILES)

INTRODUCTION

IN THE following pages, 54 short protocols will be presented. Each protocol represents one child and his, or her, mother. They are arranged by sex of the child and by the combined social adjustment rating. For the child we have limited the protocol to: (a) school report, (b) relationship to psychiatrist, (c) play activity, and (d) dreams. The numeral in parenthesis after the anxiety dreams represents the child's rating of how comparatively important the dream was, (1), e.g., indicating the most unpleasant.

For the mother we have limited the protocal to: (a) her idea of the child's problem, (b) the degree of impairment of her mothering qualities (only the kind of impairment of dependability is specified), (c) her ability to relate to the interviewer, (d) her dreamlife (manner of elicitation is the same as for the children).

GIRLS

Combined Social Adjustment—Very well adjusted

CASE 1.

I. SCHOOL

Latency: Very well adjusted.
Puberty: Very well adjusted.

II. PSYCHIATRIC

Relationship: Rapport quick and complete; affect adequate; verbally communicative.

Play: Fashions clay into figure of boy.

Dreams: Occasional—mostly good dreams.
1. Pleasant dreams: "I'm getting a new home."
2. Spontaneous anxiety dreams: "Burglar coming into house" (1).
3. Elicited anxiety dreams: "Falling from wagon" (2).

III. MOTHER

Child's problem: Previous: None. Present: Doesn't confide in mother.

Mother's personality: Related very well.

Mother as mother: Dependability impaired (fluctuates with father and economic circumstances); understanding unimpaired.

Mother's dreams: Rare; mostly pleasant. "Of dead relatives who were fond of me."
1. Spontaneous anxiety dreams: "Burglar breaking into house and upsetting things."
2. Elicited anxiety dreams: None.

CASE 2.

I. SCHOOL

Latency: Very well adjusted.
Puberty: Very well adjusted.

II. PSYCHIATRIC

Relationship: Rapport quick and complete; affect adequate; communicative.

Play: Rejects dolls as "baby stuff"; fashions clay into a dog.

Dreams: Occasional—mostly nice.
1. Pleasant dreams: "I fell into quicksand and then into a machine and a man interested in children tried to seize me."
2. Spontaneous anxiety dreams: "A drunken man—a strangler—caught me and buried me in the ground" (1).
3. Elicited anxiety dreams: "Falling a thousand feet from a tower" (2). "My girl friend and others getting murdered" (3).

III. MOTHER

Child's problem: Previous: Finicky eater. Present: None.

Mother's personality: Relates averagely well.

Mother as mother: Dependability unimpaired; understanding impaired.

Mother's dreams: Frequent; neutral dreams.
1. Spontaneous anxiety dreams: "Someone died and is lying in his casket and I'm horrified" (2). "Falling down a deep well" (3).
2. Elicited anxiety dream: "Burglar comes in to steal things" (1).

CASE 3.

I. SCHOOL

Latency: Very well adjusted.
Puberty: Fairly well adjusted.

II. PSYCHIATRIC

Relationship: Rapport quick and complete; affect adequate; communicative.

Play: Unimaginative; stands dolls on their feet.

Dreams: Occasional—mostly nice dreams.
  1. Pleasant dreams: "In mountains in which there are candy trees and houses."
  2. Spontaneous anxiety dreams: "Robbed, choked, and stabbed to death by a burglar" (1).
  3. Elicited anxiety dreams: "Falling when I jumped off a mountain to escape a man" (3). "My brother killed" (2).

III. MOTHER

Child's problem: Previous: None. Present: Talks too much to strangers.

Mother's personality: Mother relates averagely well.

Mother as mother: Dependability unimpaired; understanding unimpaired.

Mother's dreams: Frequent; pleasant and unpleasant.
  1. Pleasant dreams: "I'm in a show seeing people nicely dressed."
  2. Spontaneous anxiety dreams: "I knife a man who's trying to knife my husband" (2). "Chased by a ghost" (1). "Falling off a mountain" (3).

CASE 4.

I. SCHOOL

Latency: Very well adjusted.
Puberty: No report.

II. PSYCHIATRIC

Relationship: Rapport immediate and complete; affect adequate; very communicative.

Play: Unimaginative; makes the dolls stand.

Dreams: Occasional—"used to be scarey."
  1. Pleasant dreams: "Can't recall." "Can't remember."
  2. Spontaneous anxiety dreams:

"Snake crawled around me but a man shot it" (1).
  3. Elicited anxiety dreams: "Falling off a roof" (2).

III. MOTHER

Child's problem: Previous: None. Present: None.

Mother's personality: Relates very well.

Mother as mother: Dependability impaired (anxious about dependency); understanding impaired.

Mother's dreams: Occasional—neutral.
  1. Spontaneous anxiety dreams: None.
  2. Elicited anxiety dreams: "Falling off a ladder" (2). "Married couple I know are in an accident" (1).

CASE 5.

I. SCHOOL

Latency: Very well adjusted.
Puberty: Very well adjusted.

II. PSYCHIATRIC

Relationship: Rapport quick and complete; affect bubbling; communicative except in the area of the feelings of anger.

Play: Examines dolls; fashions hat out of clay; puts hat on doll.

Dreams: Frequent—"some funny, some nice, and some nightmares."
  1. Funny dreams: "Stranger takes place of bridegroom; bride angry, throws rolling-pin at him."
  2. Pleasant dreams (funny dreams): "I'm a fairy."
  3. Spontaneous anxiety dreams: "Kidnapped by bad men" (1). "In boat with father—we both drown" (2).
  4. Elicited anxiety dreams: None.

III. MOTHER

Child's problem: Previous: None. Present: None.

Mother's personality: Relates only fairly well.

Mother as mother: Dependability impaired (not dependable or warm); understanding impaired.

Mother's dreams: Seldom—neutral.
1. Spontaneous anxiety dreams: "Disappointed that my mother didn't give me enough money for a good dress. I ripped apart the sweater she gave me" (2). "Large and small people of odd shapes" (2).
2. Elicited anxiety: "Falling off a roof" (3). "My two daughters hit by a car" (1).

CASE 6.

I. SCHOOL

Latency: Very well adjusted.
Puberty: Very well adjusted.

II. PSYCHIATRIC

Relationship: Rapport immediate and complete; affect bubbling; Communicative.

Play: Imaginative doll play with family dialogue; fashions clay snake.

Dreams: Occasional—some good; mostly bad.
1. Pleasant dreams: "Dentist pulls wrong tooth, comforts me by saying I will be a good dancer." "Boy keeps me out too late dancing."
2. Spontaneous anxiety dreams: "Man chases girl friend and me trying to hang us—we shoot him" (1).
3. Elicited anxiety dream: "Boy tried to push me into a hole with broken glass in it—girl friend rescues me." "Boy plucks out my eye" (1).

III. MOTHER

Child's problem: Previous: None. Present: Undesirable friends.

Mother's personality: Relates very well.

Mother as mother: Dependability unimpaired; understanding unimpaired.

Mother's dreams: Seldom.
1. Spontaneous anxiety dreams: None.
2. Elicited anxiety dreams: "Man after me" (2). "Falling off steps" (3). "My mother dying" (1). "My brother dying" (2).

CASE 7.

I. SCHOOL

Latency: Very well adjusted.
Puberty: Very well adjusted.

II. PSYCHIATRIC

Relationship: Rapport quick and complete; affect bubbling; communicative.

Play: Investigative; examines doll family in play.

Dreams: Frequent—mostly scary.
1. Pleasant dreams: "Girl I liked lived right next door."
2. Spontaneous anxiety dreams: "Man knocking on door and saying, 'Oh, let me come in there'" (2). "Woman in black is a burglar—I hide under the bed" (1).
3. Elicited anxiety dreams: "Man in a car chasing me and my brother" (3).

III. MOTHER

Child's problem: Previous: "Didn't want to go to school alone." Present: None.

Mother's personality: Relates well.

Mother as mother: Dependability impaired (anxious about dependability); understanding impaired.

Mother's dreams: Occasional—neutral dreams.
1. Spontaneous anxiety dreams: Frustrated effort. "Couldn't find my clothes in order to dress quickly" (2).
2. Elicited anxiety dreams: "Vaguely recall someone after me" (4).

"Frequently dream of falling from a high building" (3). "My children are hurt" (1).

CASE 8.

I. SCHOOL

Latency: Very well adjusted.

Puberty: Well adjusted (work not up to mental capacity).

II. PSYCHIATRIC

Relationship: Rapport quick and complete; affect bubbling; communicative.

Play: Arranges doll family by size; clicks the gun; fashions clay into figure of little girl.

Dreams: Occasional—pleasant and unpleasant.
1. Pleasant: "I'm getting married." "My sister is getting married."
2. Spontaneous anxiety dreams: "Boys strangled by snakes; their mothers blame me" (1). "While swimming I'm caught in a whirlpool" (2).
3. Elicited anxiety dreams: "Man kidnaps me" (3). "Falling from the Empire State Building" (2).

III. MOTHER

Child's problem: Previous: Cries, screams, and has temper tantrums if left alone. Present: Tries to get out of going to school.

Mother's personality: Relates very well.

Mother as mother: Dependability unimpaired; understanding unimpaired.

Dreams: Seldom—neutral.
1. Pleasant: "Living where I did as a child, waiting for my mother to come home."
2. Spontaneous anxiety dreams: "The world coming to an end; everybody confused" (3).
3. Elicited anxiety dreams: "Frankenstein after me" (1). "Jumping off a second-story building" (2).

CASE 9.

I. SCHOOL

Latency: Very well adjusted.

Puberty: No report.

II. PSYCHIATRIC

Relationship: Rapport quick and complete; affect bubbling; some difficulty in verbalizing fantasies and feelings.

Play: Imaginative doll play; baby hurt —daughter helps sick mother— father hit by a truck—daughter cares for him.

Dreams: Occasional—mostly nice.
1. Pleasant: "I get a new doll." "My sister gets a new doll."
2. Spontaneous anxiety dreams: "Bad people or lions or tigers coming out of closet toward me" (1).
3. Elicited anxiety dreams: "My girl friend is in some trouble" (2).

III. MOTHER

Child's problem: Previous: Initial poor adjustment in each new grade. Present: Not forward enough.

Mother's personality: Relates only fairly well.

Mother as mother: Dependability impaired (anxious and resentful about dependency); understanding impaired.

Mother's dreams: Very rarely—unpleasant.
1. Spontaneous anxiety dreams: "My daughter was hurt" (1). "My husband was killed" (1). "Falling from a building" (3). "Walking down stairs which had no sides to them" (3). "Tall man standing over my bed" (2).

CASE 10.

I. SCHOOL

Latency: Very well adjusted.

Puberty: No report.

II. PSYCHIATRIC

Relationship: Rapport quick and complete; affect adequate; some difficulty in communicating dreams.

Play: Merely handled doll family, moving arms and legs.

Dreams: Hardly ever. Can't remember. "Crazy ones."
1. Pleasant dreams: "Can't remember."
2. Spontaneous anxiety dreams: "A tiger is loose. Everyone and I am running" (1). "Falling off a street-car" (2).
3. Elicited anxiety dreams: None.

III. MOTHER

Child's problem: Previous: None. Present: Resents sibling.

Mother's personality: Relates very well.

Mother as mother: Dependability unimpaired; understanding unimpaired.

Mother's dreams: Very seldom—no particular type.
1. Spontaneous anxiety dreams: "Something terrible happened to my husband" (1).
2. Elicited anxiety dreams: None.

CASE 11.

I. SCHOOL

Latency: Well adjusted (distant with teacher; solitary with classmates; not working up to capacity.

Puberty: Very well adjusted.

II. PSYCHIATRIC

Relationship: Rapport quick and complete; affect adequate; communicative.

Play: Fashions snails out of clay; fingers the dolls.

Dreams: Occasional—mostly scary.
1. Pleasant: "Being on the farm with grandma."
2. Spontaneous anxiety dreams: "Frankenstein coming down the street; a gorilla coming up the street; and I am in the middle. They jump at me and are going to eat me up" (1).
3. Elicited anxiety dreams: "Frankenstein pushes my bed into the wall and I am falling" (2).

III. MOTHER

Child's problem: Previous: Afraid of father when he came home from the Army. Present: None.

Mother's personality: Relates very well.

Mother as mother: Dependability unimpaired; understanding unimpaired.

Mother's dreams: Occasional—unpleasant.
1. Spontaneous anxiety dreams: "My dead father is still alive and is still finding fault with me" (2). "I am being stabbed and shot by someone" (1). "As a child dreamt of drowning" (2). "My dead grandfather standing over my bed" (1).
2. Elicited anxiety dreams: "Falling from mountain" (3). "Saving my brother from drowning" (2).

CASE 12.

I. SCHOOL

Latency: Very well adjusted.
Puberty: No report.

II. PSYCHIATRIC

Relationship: Rapport quick and complete; affect dampened; communicative.

Play: Not interested in the dolls or toys.

Dreams: Occasionally—mostly unpleasant.
1. Pleasant dreams: "Can't remember."
2. Spontaneous anxiety dreams: "Four big, fat gorillas after me."
3. Elicited anxiety dreams: None.

III. MOTHER

Child's problem: Previous: None. Present: "Ignores mother's requests."

Mother's personality: Relates only fairly well.

Mother as mother: Dependability impaired (resents dependency); understanding impaired.

Dreams: Frequent—mostly unpleasant.
1. Spontaneous anxiety dreams: "Going again to my father's funeral" (3). "Going to my own funeral, and seeing myself in a casket" (1). "Swimming out too far" (2).
2. Elicited anxiety dreams: "Falling from a window" (2). "About father dying before he actually did die" (3).

CASE 13.

I. SCHOOL

Latency: Well adjusted (not working up to capacity).

Puberty: Fairly well adjusted (solitary with classmates; not working up to mental capacity).

II. PSYCHIATRIC

Relationship: Rapport quick and complete; affect adequate; communicative.

Play: Handled doll; preferred to use crayons. "Clay gets my hands too dirty."

Dreams: Frequent—mostly nice.
1. Pleasant dreams: "I'm an angel." "I'm in a castle."
2. Spontaneous anxiety dreams: "Our baby-sitter drank soap suds. Her hair turned gray and her teeth rotted. She chased me" (1). "Falling from a building" (2).
3. Elicited anxiety dreams: None.

III. MOTHER

Child's problem: Previous: Separating from mother on beginning school. Present: Separating from mother.

Mother's personality: Relates very well.

Mother as mother: Dependability impaired (anxious about dependency); understanding unimpaired.

Mother's dreams: Seldom.
1. Spontaneous anxiety dreams: (As child) "Fellow in black cape chasing me" (1). "Going to hell and on the edge of the fire" (1).
2. Elicited anxiety dreams: "Falling" (2).

Combined Social Adjustment—Well adjusted

CASE 14.

I. SCHOOL

Latency: Fairly well adjusted (nervous habits).

Puberty: No report.

II. PSYCHIATRIC

Relationship: Rapport quick and complete; affect bubbling; communicative except about dreams.

Play: Shoots gun; imaginative doll play in which father is protecting family against rustlers.

Dreams: (She cannot distinguish well between day dreams and night dreams.)
1. Pleasant dreams: "Being with Roy Rogers."
2. Spontaneous anxiety dreams: "A slave girl who is thrown into the fire."
3. Elicited anxiety dreams: None.

III. MOTHER

Child's problem: Previous: Difficult to toilet train. Present: Disobedient, slow in doing things.

Mother's personality: Relates averagely well.

Mother as mother: Dependability impaired (fluctuates with economic security); understanding impaired.

Mother's dreams: Rare.
1. Spontaneous anxiety dreams: "At school without shoes, and am embarrassed" (1) "Lost my purse" (2).
2. Elicited anxiety dreams: "Falling off a roof" (2).

CASE 15.

I. SCHOOL

Latency: Very well adjusted.
Puberty: Well adjusted (distant with classmates).

II. PSYCHIATRIC

Relationship: Rapport quick and complete; affect dampened; blocked in verbalizing feelings and dreams.

Play: Gives father, mother, and baby dolls a ride on the top of a truck; then has just father and baby ride.

Dreams: Denies dreams of any type.

III. MOTHER

Child's problem: Previous: crying too much. Present: Determined to have own way.

Mother's personality: Relates very well.

Mother as mother: Dependency impaired (anxious about dependency); understanding unimpaired.

Mother's dreams: Occasional; rarely unpleasant.
1. Spontaneous anxiety dreams: "Hanging from a bridge and the bridge wouldn't go down—afraid of the water I'm going to drop into" (1).
2. Elicited anxiety dreams: "Vaguely recall being chased by a man" (2).

CASE 16.

I. SCHOOL

Latency: Fairly well adjusted (not working up to mental capacity).

Puberty: Very well adjusted.

II. PSYCHIATRIC

Relationship: Rapport quick and complete; affect dampened; communicative.

Play: Picks up clay, then the dolls; no play or investigation.

Dreams: Frequent—"Bad ones and nice ones."
1. Pleasant dreams: "Have everything I want." "I'm a princess."
2. Spontaneous anxiety dreams: "Bad men coming after me" (2).
3. Elicited anxiety dreams: "Falling off a mountain" (1). "My brother, father, and mother falling off a mountain" (3).

III. MOTHER

Child's problem: Previous: Poor marks in school. Present: Poor manners.

Mother's personality: Relates only fairly well.

Mother as mother: Dependability impaired (fluctuates with father's condition); understanding impaired.

Dreams: Occasional—weird dreams.
1. Spontaneous anxiety dreams: "People have small heads and big heads" (1). "Sister-in-law lying dead in her coffin and she winked at me" (3).
2. Elicited anxiety dreams: "Vaguely recall someone after me" (3). "Falling through space" (2).

CASE 17.

I. SCHOOL

Latency: Very well adjusted.
Puberty: No report.

II. PSYCHIATRIC

Relationship: Rapport slow and incomplete; affect dampened; communicative.

Play: Fashions clay bowl; examines dolls.

Dreams: Occasional—"Bad dreams".
1. Pleasant dreams: "That I got a little puppy."
2. Spontaneous anxiety dreams: "Walking with parents and sister; suddenly they are gone and I am lost. It is dark" (2). "My sister dying" (1).
3. Elicited anxiety dreams: "I am accused then chased by someone" (3).

III. MOTHER

Child's problem: Previous: Rough, playing with boys. Present: Cries easily.

Mother's personality: Relates averagely well.

Mother as mother: Dependability impaired (anxious about dependency); understanding unimpaired.

Dreams: Very seldom.
1. Spontaneous anxiety dreams: "Being bombed" (2). "Man in white robes saying, 'I'll get you eventually' " (1). "Snakes after me" (2). "Falling through space" (3).
2. Elicited anxiety dreams: None.

CASE 18.

I. SCHOOL

Latency: Very well adjusted.
Puberty: Very well adjusted.

II. PSYCHIATRIC

Relationship: Rapport slow and incomplete; affect dampened; communicative.

Play: Unimaginative doll play; stands dolls up in order to have a family picture taken.

Dreams: Occasional—"Mostly dreams I like."
1. Pleasant dreams: "My mother takes teacher's place in school."
2. Spontaneous anxiety dreams: "Mother placed my brother and me on a plank adrift in the ocean. We had nothing to eat for a long time."
3. Elicited anxiety dreams: None.

III. MOTHER

Child's problem: Previous: None. Present: None.

Mother's personality: Relates averagely well.

Mother as mother: Dependability unimpaired; understanding impaired.

Dreams: Occasional—mostly pleasant.
1. Pleasant dreams: "Dancing with other men."
2. Spontaneous anxiety dreams: "Burglar trying to break into house" (2). "Seeing my real mother alive" (1).
3. Elicited anxiety dreams: "Chased by someone; I couldn't scream" (2). "Sensations of falling" (4). "My father and sister in an auto accident" (3).

Combined Social Adjustment—Fairly well adjusted

CASE 19.

I. SCHOOL

Latency: Well adjusted (not working to capacity).
Puberty: Well adjusted (not working to capacity; distant with teacher).

II. PSYCHIATRIC

Relationship: Rapport slow and incomplete; affect uneven; general difficulty in verbal communication.

Play: Fashions bed and pillow out of clay; presses doll's face harshly into clay; plays with truck and guns.

Dreams: "I can't remember—I just can't remember."
1. Pleasant dreams: None.

2. Anxiety dreams: None.
3. Elicited anxiety dreams: "Falling."

III. MOTHER

Child's problem: Past: None. Present: Shyness.

Mother's personality: Relates averagely well.

Mother as mother: Dependability impaired (fluctuates with economic security; understanding impaired.

Dreams: Rare.
  1. Spontaneous anxiety dreams: "A disjointed hand wrapping itself around my leg" (1).
  2. Elicited anxiety dreams: None.

CASE 20.
I. SCHOOL
Latency: Fairly well adjusted (worries some).

Puberty: Well adjusted (distant with teacher; not working up to capacity).

II. PSYCHIATRIC

Relationship: Rapport gradual and complete; affect adequate; communicative except in area of feelings.

Play: Placed all the dolls on mother's shoulder, then all the dolls on father's shoulder; has baby doll crushed by the other dolls; clicks the gun.

Dreams: Occasional—mostly bad.
  1. Pleasant dreams: "My parents died and some nice people adopted me."
  2. Spontaneous anxiety dreams: "Kidnapped by men but I escaped" (2). "Bogey man or witches put me in an oven and eat me up" (2).
  3. Elicited anxiety dreams: "Falling from the Empire State Building" (3). "Kidnapped and shot by brother and sister" (1).

III. MOTHER

Child's problem: Previous: None. Present: Not feminine enough; argues with mother.

Mother's personality: Relates only fairly well.

Mother as mother: Dependability impaired (resents dependency); understanding impaired.

Dreams: Rare.
  1. Spontaneous anxiety dreams: "Riding on an elevated train which did a loop-the-loop" (1). "Tigers after me" (2).
  2. Elicited anxiety dreams: None.

CASE 21.
I. SCHOOL
Latency: Fairly well adjusted (easily worried).

Puberty: Very well adjusted.

II. PSYCHIATRIC

Relationship: Rapport gradual and incomplete; affect dampened; general difficulty in verbalizing.

Play: Unimaginative; doll family scene of mother cooking and father reading the paper and children playing.

Dreams: Occasional—"Nice dreams."
  1. Pleasant dreams: "I'm playing with my doll."
  2. Spontaneous dreams: None.
  3. Elicited anxiety dreams: None.

III. MOTHER

Child's problem: Previous: Asthma, enuresis, and tantrums. Present: None.

Mother's personality: Relates very well.

Mother as mother: Dependability impaired (anxious about dependency); Understanding unimpaired.

Dreams: Occasional—unpleasant.
  1. Spontaneous anxiety dreams: "Falling off a cliff" (4). "One of

my children run over by a car"
(2). "My mother dying" (1).
2. Elicited anxiety dreams: "Wild
animals after me and I can't
move" (3).

CASE 22.

I. SCHOOL

Latency: Fairly well adjusted (stubborn; attention seeking with teacher; has nervous habits).

Puberty: Fairly well adjusted (seeks attention from teacher; interferes with classmates; nervous habits; not working up to capacity).

II. PSYCHIATRIC

Relationship: Rapport gradual and incomplete; affect deadened; communicative.

Play: Looks at toys but doesn't touch them.

Dreams: Frequent—"Mostly nice."
1. Pleasant dreams: "That I had a party."
2. Spontaneous anxiety dreams: "Someone breaking into the house; I pushed him out and he fell on broken glass" (1). "A wild animal after me" (1).
3. Elicited anxiety dreams: None.

III. MOTHER

Child's problem: Previous: Resistive to piano lessons in summer. Present: None.

Mother's personality: Relates very well.

Mother as mother: Dependability unimpaired; understanding impaired.

Dreams: Never "or rarely."
1. Pleasant dreams: "My mother being alive again."
2. Spontaneous anxiety dreams: (As child) "Neighbors' barn on fire. I call my parents."
3. Elicited anxiety dreams: None.

CASE 23.

I. SCHOOL

Latency: Well adjusted (not working up to capacity).

Puberty: Fairly well adjusted (distant with teacher; solitary with classmates).

II. PSYCHIATRIC

Relationship: Rapport gradual and incomplete; affect uneven; communicative.

Play: Mother doll slaps father doll and children dolls, knocking them down. Mother and father embrace. Mother lies on father. Mother spanks little girl. Later child fashions a shark out of clay.

Dreams: Frequent—mostly scary.
1. Pleasant dreams: "about Santa Claus."
2. Spontaneous anxiety dreams: "Taking care of my little sister, and I lost her" (1). "Skeletons and ghosts about to attack me" (3). "I am real little. Two giant ants are going to eat me" (3).
3. Elicited anxiety dreams: "Mother, me, and my three sisters on a mountain. One by one we fall off—I the last" (2).

III. MOTHER

Child's problem: Previous: to go to the dentist. Present: Daydreaming; constantly needs correction.

Mother's personality: Relates averagely well.

Mother as mother: Dependability impaired (fluctuates with economic security and with father; understanding unimpaired.

Dreams: Occasionally—usually pleasant.
1. Pleasant dreams: "I am in my teens having a good time with the crowd."
2. Spontaneous anxiety dreams: "My father dying" (2). "My brother dying" (2). "That my

mother was dead" (1). "Rats after me" (3).

3. Elicited anxiety dreams: "My daughter is drowning and I can't reach her" (2).

CASE 24.

I. SCHOOL

Latency: Well adjusted (distant with teacher; solitary with classmates).

Puberty: Very well adjusted.

II. PSYCHIATRIC

Relationship: Rapport gradual and incomplete; affect dampened; communicative.

Play: Fashions duck, snake, and flower out of clay; lines dolls up giving baby doll to sister rather than to mother.

Dreams: Occasional—"some nice, some scary."

1. Pleasant dreams: "Can't remember any."
2. Spontaneous anxiety dreams: "My dog jumped into a tree with a porcupine, and got stuck. I pulled porcupine's tail by mistake and got scared" (2).
3. Elicited anxiety dreams: "A giant caught me and ate me" (2). "Falling off a fire escape" (3). "Mother and father in the hands of kidnappers who are blackmailers. Police rescue them" (1).

III. MOTHER

Child's problem: Previous: Keeping things to herself. Present: Thumbsucking and worrying.

Mother's personality: Relates only fairly well.

Mother as mother: Dependability unimpaired; understanding unimpaired.

Dreams: Rare.

1. Spontaneous anxiety dreams: "Falling through space."
2. Elicited anxiety dreams: None.

CASE 25.

I. SCHOOL

Latency: Well adjusted (some nervous habits; not working up to capacity).

Puberty: No report.

II. PSYCHIATRIC

Relationship: Rapport slow and incomplete; affect dampened; general difficulty in communicating.

Play: Fashions animal out of clay; fingers dolls.

Dreams: Occasional—"silly ones."

1. Pleasant dreams: "Looked in a mirror and saw I had on winter clothes." "Animals and lions fighting with each other. It's not scary."
2. Spontaneous anxiety dreams: None.
3. Elicited anxiety dreams: None.

III. MOTHER

Child's problem: Previous: None. Present: None.

Mother's personality: Relates averagely well.

Mother as mother: Dependability impaired (fluctuates with father's state); understanding impaired.

Dreams: Frequency—seizures of nightmares four times a year.

1. Spontaneous anxiety dreams: "Men approach me" (1). "Drowning" (2). "Going under anasthetic" (2).
2. Elicited anxiety dreams: "My father stretched out dead" (3). "My husband in an accident" (3).

CASE 26.

I. SCHOOL

Latency: Well adjusted (not working up to capacity).

Puberty: Very well adjusted.

II. PSYCHIATRIC

Relationship: Rapport gradual and incomplete; affect uneven; communicative.

Play: Fashions cup and saucer out of clay; has brother and sister dolls shake hands; the same with the mother and father dolls; has doll family listen to radio; brother doll spanked by mother and father, but sister is never punished.

Dreams: Occasional—"mostly nice," "some scary."

1. Pleasant dreams: "Going to night clubs." "Getting married."
2. Spontaneous anxiety dreams: "I hide in the closet when skeletons or ghosts come into the house" (1).
3. Elicited anxiety dreams: "My sister hurt her knee and bled" (2). "A little boy cut his arm" (2).

III. MOTHER

Child's problem: Previous: None. Present: None.

Mother's personality: Relates averagely well.

Mother as mother: Dependability unimpaired; understanding unimpaired.

Dreams: Frequent.

1. Spontaneous anxiety dreams: "Packing for trips and always forgetting something" (3). "Gorillas chasing me over roof tops" (1). "Falling from high cliffs" (2).

BOYS

Combined Social Adjustment—Very well adjusted

CASE 1.

I. SCHOOL

Latency: Very well adjusted.
Puberty: Very well adjusted.

II. PSYCHIATRIC

Relationship: Rapport quick and complete; affect bubbling; communicative.

Play: Examines toys; clicks guns; cuts waxed paper with scissors; no organized play activity.

Dreams: Occasional—"half good; half bad."

1. Pleasant dreams: "At circus. An elephant squirts water through his trunk into a little boy's face."
2. Spontaneous anxiety dreams: "Tarzan beats off an octopus, but loses to a shark" (2).
3. Elicited anxiety dreams: "A draw-bridge went up and I fell off" (1).

III. MOTHER

Child's problem: Previous: None. present: High-strung; self sufficient.

Mother's personality: Related very well.

Mother as mother: Dependability unimpaired; understanding unimpaired.

Dreams: Not too often.

1. Spontaneous anxiety dreams: (This is repetitive.) "I am embarrassed going to school without shoes or stockings" (3). "Husband talking to another girl. I angrily pull her hair" (4).
2. Elicited anxiety dreams: "Big, moving ball about to engulf me" (1). "Father dying" (2).

CASE 2.

I. SCHOOL

Latency: Very well adjusted.
Puberty: Very well adjusted.

II. PSYCHIATRIC

Relationship: Rapport gradual and incomplete; affect adequate; communicative.

Play: Rejects. "No fun playing with these toys."

Dreams: Occasional—"mostly good."
1. Pleasant dreams: "On a pony." "Having a pony." "Having a million dollars."
2. Spontaneous anxiety dreams: "Falling down a man-hole" (2). "In jungle, a snake bit me. I fell dead" (1).
3. Elicited anxiety dreams: None.

III. MOTHER

Child's problem: Previous: Bit people. Didn't want to go to school. Present: Faints or gets sick. Obstinate with parents.

Mother's personality: Relates very well.

Mother as mother: Dependability unimpaired; understanding unimpaired.

Dreams: Infrequent—mostly unpleasant.
1. Spontaneous anxiety dreams: "Dogs or hyenas after me" (2). "My husband dead" (1). "I am to be electrocuted for having killed somebody" (2). "Falling from a mountain" (3).
2. Elicited anxiety dreams: None.

CASE 3.

I. SCHOOL

Latency: Very well adjusted.
Puberty: Very well adjusted.

II. PSYCHIATRIC

Relationship: Rapport quick and complete; affect adequate; communicative.

Play: Clicks gun eagerly; rest of toys rejected as "kids' stuff."

Dreams: Frequently—"mostly good."
1. Pleasant dreams: "Can't remember any."
2. Spontaneous anxiety dreams: "I am with good guys losing a shooting war to the bad guys." "When I fired the machine-gun I fell on my hind end."

3. Elicited anxiety dreams: "Lions and tigers are closing in on me. I jump up, knock their heads together and escape" (1). "Fall 50 feet into water. Crocodiles try to bite my rear end" (1). "Rescuing my boy friend" (2).

III. MOTHER

Child's problem: Previous: Cried when away from mother. Present: Fights with cousin.

Mother's personality: Relates very well.

Mother as mother: Dependability unimpaired; understanding unimpaired.

Dreams: Seldom.
1. Spontaneous anxiety dreams: "My husband dead" (1). "Someone chopping off my head" (2).
2. Elicited anxiety dreams: "Sensation of falling" (3).

CASE 4.

I. SCHOOL

Latency: Very well adjusted.
Puberty: No report.

II. PSYCHIATRIC

Relationship: Rapport quick and complete; affect adequate; communicative.

Play: Rejects toy box; says nothing of interest there.

Dreams: Not too often—"half nice, half scary."
1. Pleasant dreams: "Going to the world's fair."
2. Spontaneous anxiety dreams: "My little sister fell off an elevator" (2). "I fell off an elevator" (1). "Green face coming toward me" (3).
3. Elicited anxiety dreams: None.

III. MOTHER

Child's problem: Previous: Nervous; blinked eyes when with a teacher he disliked. Present: None.

Mother's personality: Relates very well.

Mother as mother: Dependability impaired.
(somewhat resentful of dependency); understanding unimpaired.

Dreams: "In spells—sometimes frequently."
1. Pleasant dreams: "Having a wonderful time with the kids in a car we ordered." "My father coming back to life."
2. Spontaneous anxiety dreams: "My son drowning" (1). "My daughter fell out of a window" (1)."I am running on a railroad track away from something" (3).
3. Elicited anxiety dreams: "Falling through space" (2).

CASE 5.
I. SCHOOL
Latency: Very well adjusted.
Puberty: Very well adjusted.
II. PSYCHIATRIC
Relationship: Rapport quick and complete; affect dampened; some difficulty in communication of fantasies and feelings.

Play: Doll play: patrol boy stops car so girl can cross street; fashions man's face out of clay, which turns out to be an Indian with a very long nose.

Dreams: Frequently—mostly scary.
1. Pleasant dreams: "Have a thousand dollars in pocket, but it keeps dropping out through a hole."
2. Spontaneous anxiety dreams: "Snakes after me—they bite me". "Can't shoot them with my gun" (1).
3. Elicited anxiety dreams: "Mother broke her arm in an auto crash" (2).
III. MOTHER
Child's problem: Previous: One time

stealing and firesetting. Present: Temper.

Mother's personality: Relates averagely well.

Mother as mother: Dependability impaired (fluctuates with socio-economic factors); understanding impaired.

Dreams: Occasional—some nightmares.
1. Spontaneous anxiety dreams: "At Riverview on the rollercoaster I just scream" (2). "In hell—the devil is going to stick me with pitchforks" (1). "Falling from railroad tracks or mountains" (2).
2. Elicited anxiety dreams: "My mother dead" (3).

CASE 6.
I. SCHOOL
Latency: Very well adjusted.

Puberty: Fairly well adjusted (seeks attention of teacher; is not working up to capacity).

II. PSYCHIATRIC

Relationship: Rapport quick and complete; affect bubbling! communicative.

Play: Has mother and father dolls shake hands; then sister and brother do the same; clicks gun; fashions car out of clay.

Dreams: Occasional—mostly scary.
1. Pleasant: "We have a nice new car. I grab for its handle, but can't find it."
2. Spontaneous anxiety dreams: "I got a snake in a sandwich and called my father for help" (2). "With father on bridge. I urinate, and the bridge goes up and down" (2). "Tiger and leopard after me; I can't move" (1).
3. Elicited anxiety dreams: "Burglar is after my father" (3).

III. MOTHER

Child's problem: Previous: None. Present: None.

Mother's personality: Mother relates averagely well.

Mother as mother: Dependability unimpaired; understanding impaired.

Dreams: Very seldom.
1. Spontaneous anxiety dreams: "I got my two fingers caught in the fence and they had to be cut off" (1). (When a small child.) "I was chased, cut up, put in a boiler and cooked" (1).
2. Elicited anxiety dreams: None

CASE 7.

I. SCHOOL

Latency: Very well adjusted.

Puberty: Fairly well adjusted (pronounced shyness with teachers and peers).

II. PSYCHIATRIC

Relationship: Rapport: gradual and complete; affect adequate; communicative.

Play: Picks up gun, puts it down quickly: two trucks approach each other but traffic lights prevent collision; later trucks collide; police: chase a reckless driver; married couple in car almost go off cliff; shoots gun.

Dreams: Day dreams and night dreams. "Nice and scary."
1. Pleasant dreams: "Can't remember."
2. Spontaneous anxiety dreams: "Frankenstein after me" (2). "Going to die" (1). "The house is on fire; it is coming closer" (2).
3. Elicited anxiety dreams: "Rescued mother and sister from a collapsing viaduct" (3).

III. MOTHER

Child's Problem: Previous: Feeding problem; nervous; car sick. Present: Nervous.

Mother's personality: Relates only fairly well.

Mother as mother: Dependability impaired (anxious about dependency); understanding impaired.

Dreams: Seldom.
1. Spontaneous anxiety dreams: "Bowling for first time and others picking out my faults."
2. Elicited anxiety dreams: None.

CASE 8.

I. SCHOOL

Latency: Well adjusted (interferes with peers).

Puberty: Very well adjusted.

II. PSYCHIATRIC

Relationship: Rapport quick and complete; affect adequate; communicative.

Play: Examines dolls; sets them on edge of table; shoots gun; fashions clay into a figure.

Dreams: Frequent—mostly scary.
1. Pleasant dreams: "Fun at a picnic, but a big rabbit comes out of the bushes and chases me."
2. Spontaneous anxiety dreams: "Dragon swallowed me, but he coughed me up and I knifed him in the heart" (1). "Gorilla after me. I threw poisoned fruit in his mouth and he dropped dead" (1).
3. Elicited anxiety dreams: "Falling from airplane" (2). "Mother drowning. I rescue her" (3).

III. MOTHER

Child's problem: Previous: None. Present: Tattles; feels gypped.

Mother's personality: Relates averagely well.

Mother as mother: Dependability impaired (fluctuates with father and socio-economic factors); understanding unimpaired.

Dreams: Rare.
1. Spontaneous anxiety dream: (Repetitive) "Burglar climbs in the bedroom and cuts my sister to pieces and throws the pieces under the bed" (1). "Traveling on a train in the mountains and the train approaches a broken bridge" (2).
2. Elicited anxiety dreams: "Embarrassed because I am outside and unclothed" (3).

CASE 9.

I. SCHOOL

Latency: Well adjusted (not working up to capacity.)
Puberty: Fairly well adjusted (distant with teacher and interferes with peers; Nervous habits; Tardiness; Not working up to mental capacity).

II. PSYCHIATRIC

Relationship: Rapport quick and complete; affect adequate; communicative.
Play: Shoots gun at aerial across the street; plays with trucks and cars in a safe, orderly way.
Dreams: Occasional—"mystery ones" "funny ones."
1. Pleasant or "funny" dreams: "Boy pushes me in a well and he comes down and rescues me. I go up in a basket and leave him there." "Getting a new bike."
2. Spontaneous anxiety dreams: "Gangster in a mask is going to chop my head off" (1). "My sister's head chopped off" (2). "Rescuing boy cousin from gangsters" (3).
3. Elicited anxiety dreams: None.

III. MOTHER

Child's problem: Previous: Lying once. Present: None.

Mother's personality: Relates only averagely well.
Mother as mother: Dependability unimpaired; understanding unimpaired.
Dreams: Frequent—pleasant and unpleasant.
1. Pleasant dreams: "I'm back in school." "I'm a waitress again." "My sister-in-law whom I liked very much is living again."
2. Spontaneous anxiety dreams: "Chinaman chasing me with a knife because I've murdered someone" (2). "Falling through space" (2).
3. Elicited anxiety dreams: "My father had died" (1).

CASE 10.

I. SCHOOL

Latency: Well adjusted (stubborn with teacher).
Puberty: Fairly well adjusted (stubborn with teacher; solitary with peers).

II. PSYCHIATRIC

Relationship: Rapport immediate and complete; affect bubbling, communicative.
Play: Disdains toys. "I have better at home."
Dreams: Occasional—mostly scary.
1. Pleasant dreams: "My team won at baseball."
2. Spontaneous anxiety dreams: "Five lions gang up on me. I shoot them. I kill the pursuing grandpa ape. I and the natives roast and eat a lion" (1). "Falling down into a canyon—a sharp rock goes through my stomach" (2).
3. Elicited anxiety dreams: None.

III. MOTHER

Child's problem: Previous: Afraid of being different from other boys.

Present: Fearful of being separated from mother.

Mother's personality: Relates very well.

Mother as mother: Dependability unimpaired; understanding unimpaired.

Dreams: Seldom now.
1. Spontaneous anxiety dreams: "Snakes after me" (1). "Clouds swirling around me and covering me up" (2).
2. Elicited anxiety dreams: None.

CASE 11.

I. SCHOOL

Latency: Well adjusted (not working up to capacity).

Puberty: Very well adjusted.

II. PSYCHIATRIC

Relationship: Rapport quick and complete; affect adequate; communicative.

Play: Imaginative doll play: Mother's feelings hurt by father. She leaves for a week. Son stays with father. Later father gets a job. Mother says, "Good for you!"

Dreams: "Mostly scary ones."
1. Pleasant dreams: "Never have them."
2. Spontaneous anxiety dreams: "Cobras and rattle snakes after me" (1). "I and a man stabbing each other. His knife goes deeper than mine. I die. Two weeks later he dies" (1).
3. Elicited anxiety dreams: None.

III. MOTHER

Child's problem: Previous: None. Present: Afraid of father; doesn't want to go to bed; not a big eater.

Mother's personality: Relates very well.

Mother as mother: Dependability unimpaired; understanding impaired.

Dreams: Occasional—pleasant, or neutral.

1. Spontaneous anxiety dreams: "Train going by my house and gets connected with the death of my sister when I was five" (1).
2. Elicited anxiety dreams: Chased by someone" (2). "Falling through space" (3). "My daughter falling in a well" (1).

CASE 12.

I. SCHOOL

Latency: Well adjusted (not working up to capacity).

Puberty: Fairly well adjusted (not working up to capacity; defiant to teacher).

II. PSYCHIATRIC

Relationship: Rapport quick and complete; affect adequate; communicative.

Play: Clicks gun; fingers trucks; telling what he would do with them at home.

Dreams: Occasional—"Scary."
1. Pleasant dreams: "I forget them."
2. Spontaneous anxiety dreams: "Guy with a knife trying to kill me. Couldn't defend myself" (1).
3. Elicited anxiety dreams: "Falling off the biggest mountain in the world" (2).

III. MOTHER

Child's problem: Previous: None. Present: None.

Mother's personality: Relates well.

Mother as mother: Dependability unimpaired; understanding impaired.

Dreams: Occasional.
1. Spontaneous anxiety dreams: "Nightmares as a kid. Can't recall details" (1). "Falling through space" (2).
2. Elicited anxiety dreams: "In a boat with my two kids—boat capsizes. I have to decide which kid to save" (2).

Combined Social Adjustment—Well adjusted

CASE 13.

I. SCHOOL

Latency: Very well adjusted.

Puberty: Fair (stubborn toward authority; not working up to capacity).

II. PSYCHIATRIC

Relationship: Rapport gradual and complete; affect dampened; general difficulty in communication.

Play: Clicks gun; works legs of dolls; mother doll shakes hands with son; truck pushes sister down off edge of desk.

Dreams: Not often—mostly pleasant.
1. Pleasant dreams: "I am getting a cocker spaniel."
2. Spontaneous anxiety dreams: None.
3. Elicited anxiety dreams: "Bear or tiger after me" (2). "Falling from a real high mountain" (1).

III. MOTHER

Child's problem: Previous: None. Present: Sex play with neighbor boy.

Mother's personality: Relates only fairly well.

Mother as mother: Dependability unimpaired; understanding unimpaired.

Dreams: Rare.
1. Spontaneous anxiety dreams: "My uncle had put my father on a slab which was moving closer to a buzz saw" (1). "My sister run down by a train" (2).
2. Elicited anxiety dreams: "Falling from a building" (3).

CASE 14.

I. SCHOOL

Latency: Very well adjusted.

Puberty: Very well adjusted.

II. PSYCHIATRIC

Relationship: Rapport gradual and in-complete; affect uneven; general difficulty in communicating.

Play: Clicks gun, shoots it; merely fingers the doll.

Dreams: Occasional—"Can't remember them" (then) "mostly nice."
1. Pleasant dreams: "Can't remember any."
2. Spontaneous anxiety dreams: None.
3. Elicited anxiety dreams: "Attacked by a rattle snake and a tiger at the same time" (1). "Falling off a cliff" (2). "My brother and sister in some danger" (3).

III. MOTHER

Child's problem: Previous: Fear of going to sleep or to the bathroom alone at night. Present: None.

Mother's personality: Relates only fairly well.

Mother as mother: Dependability impaired (fluctuates with father's state); understanding unimpaired.

Dreams: Frequent—mostly unpleasant.
1. Spontaneous anxiety dreams: "Enemy planes bombing our neighborhood. I am figuring how to cross elevator tracks to see what is left of my husband" (1).
2. Elicited anxiety dreams: "A murderer came through my window" (2). "Sensation of falling as I drop off to sleep" (3).

CASE 15.

I. SCHOOL

Latency: Very well adjusted.

Puberty: Fairly well adjusted (stubborn and distant with teacher; interfering with peers; not working up to capacity).

II. PSYCHIATRIC

Relationship: Rapport quick and complete; affect uneven; difficulty in communicating feelings and dreams.

Play: Rejects toys. "Not interested in these toys."

Dreams: "Many—"sometimes funny—sometimes scary and unpleasant."
1. Pleasant dreams: "Had a horse and got so mixed up so I used a wallet for a saddle, and found myself riding a bike."
2. Spontaneous anxiety dreams: "Can't remember. Hardly ever have them."
3. Elicited anxiety dreams: "An animal caught me and killed me" (3).

III. MOTHER

Child problem: Previous: Head banging and biting. Present: Stubborn and nagging.

Mother's personality: Relates averagely well.

Mother as mother: Dependability impaired (not warm); understanding impaired.

Dreams: Occasionally—mostly neutral.
1. Spontaneous anxiety dreams: (repetitive) "Walking down the street with breast exposed—embarrassed when I meet people" (3). "That my baby or my son is sick" (1). "Falling from a mountain" (3).
2. Elicited anxiety dreams: "Man after me. I couldn't run" (2).

CASE 16.

I. SCHOOL

Latency: Fair (not working up to capacity).

Puberty: Fair (seeks attention from teacher; interferes with peers; some nervous mannerisms; not working up to capacity).

II. PSYCHIATRIC

Relationship: Rapport quick and complete; affect adequate; communicative.

Play: Touches clay; takes up gun and boy doll puts them down; fashions clay into a human figure.

Dreams: Frequent—"*Re* being good the next day."
1. Pleasant dreams: "That I would never lie nor play with matches."
2. Spontaneous anxiety dreams: "I am a burglar breaking into a house" (1). "Bear after me. I kill him with a knife" (1). "A burglar jumps on me."
3. Elicited anxiety dreams: "Falling off garage" (2).

III. MOTHER

Child's problem: Previous: None. Present: Moodiness.

Mother's personality: Relates averagely well.

Mother as mother: Dependability impaired (not warm); understanding impaired.

Dreams: Not often.
1. Spontaneous anxiety dreams: "My mother or father dying. I wake up crying."
2. Elicited anxiety dreams: None.

CASE 17.

I. SCHOOL

Latency: Fair adjustment (seeks attention from teacher; not working up to capacity).

Puberty: Well adjusted (not working up to capacity).

II. PSYCHIATRIC

Relationship: Rapport immediate and complete; affect bubbling; communicative.

Play: Stands up mother and father dolls, but rejects baby doll; shoots gun; rolls truck so it crashes and catches fire.

Dreams: Not often—pleasant.
1. Pleasant dreams: "I have a lot of horses." "Me and my boy friend in a boat with a lot of girls."

2. Spontaneous anxiety dreams: "Poison snake after me" (1).
3. Elicited anxiety dreams: "I fell off a mountain and broke my arm" (2).

III. MOTHER

Child's problem: Previous: Resented brother; biting; mean. Present: Resentment of brother.

Mother's personality: Relates only fairly well.

Mother as mother: Dependability impaired (not very warm); understanding impaired.

Dreams: Frequent—Pleasant, neutral, and some unpleasant.
1. Spontaneous anxiety dreams: "Doctor found spots on my sister's lungs" (2). "My father dying" (1). "Someone trying to chase me" (2). "Falling through space" (3).

CASE 18.

I. SCHOOL

Latency: Well adjusted (interferes with classmates).

Puberty: Very well adjusted.

II. PSYCHIATRIC

Relationship: Rapport slow and complete; affect adequate; communicative.

Play: Clicks gun experimentally; puts baby doll in mother's arms; father does back bends; girl doll on his

stomach; further experimentation with dolls.

Dreams: Frequent—mostly good but some are bad.
1. Pleasant dreams: "Looking through telescope at Mars and saw a man with a round head."
2. Spontaneous anxiety dreams: "Police caught me for asking a man too many questions" (1).
3. Elicited anxiety dreams: "My brother almost got hit by a car out of control" (2).

III. MOTHER

Child's problem: Previous: None. Present: Untidy in school; pushes kids and makes them laugh.

Mother's personality: Relates very well.

Mother as mother: Dependability unimpaired; understanding unimpaired.

Dreams: Not often now—were mostly unpleasant.
1. Spontaneous anxiety dreams: (Repetitive) "I'm not married and I feel alone and as if I should be engaged or married" (1). "I and other people walking around and suddenly I realize that I and the others are all dead" (1).
2. Elicited anxiety dreams: "Someone is after me" (2). "My mother dead" (3). "Something bad happened to my children" (3).

Combined Social Adjustment—Fairly well adjusted

CASE 19.

I. SCHOOL

Latency: Fairly well adjusted (seeks attention; nervous habits; not working up to capacity).

Puberty: Fair (stubborn with teacher; seeks attention; nervous habits; not working up to capacity).

II. PSYCHIATRIC

Relationship: Rapport gradual and in-

complete; affect uneven; generalized difficulty in communicating.

Play: Rejects; too uneasy.

Dreams: Occasional—"only funny ones."
1. Funny dreams: "Giant steps on Petty the pup goes through the air; giant chases pup into a puddle and pup tries to swim (I wake up swimming)."

2. Spontaneous anxiety dreams: None.
3. Elicited anxiety dreams: None.

III. MOTHER

Child's problem: Previous: Pushing other children and crying about being hurt. Present: Wants more freedom.

Mother's personality: Relates averagely well.

Mother as mother: Dependability unimpaired; understanding impaired.

Dreams: Frequent during a nervous breakdown.
1. Spontaneous anxiety dreams: "Robbers coming into the house" (2). "My husband out with other women" (2). "I am having intercourse with some other man" (2). "Walking around in a scary house—I trip on the stairs and fall headlong" (1).

CASE 20.

I. SCHOOL

Latency: Well adjusted (some nervous habits; not working up to capacity).

Puberty: Well adjusted (stubborn with kids; not working up to capacity).

II. PSYCHIATRIC

Relationship: Rapport gradual and incomplete; affect uneven; general difficulty in communicating.

Play: Rejects; "Like my own toys better."

Dreams: Frequent—"mostly scary."
1. Spontaneous anxiety dreams: "I don't know. I forget."
2. Elicited anxiety dreams: "Something after me."

III. MOTHER

Child's problem: Previous: None. Present: "Sometimes I consider him abnormal."

Mother's personality: Mother relates only fairly well.

Mother as mother: Dependability impaired (anxious about dependency); understanding impaired.

Mother's dreams: "No time to dream any more."
1. Spontaneous anxiety dreams: (Repetitive) "Going down a flight of stairs but the ceiling, floor, and steps meet at one point and I can't see how I can get to the bottom of the steps."
2. Elicited anxiety dreams: None.

CASE 21.

I. SCHOOL

Latency: Fairly well adjusted (distant with teacher; some nervous habits; not working up to capacity).

Puberty: No report.

II. PSYCHIATRIC

Relationship: Rapport quick and complete; affect deadened; some difficulty in communicating fantasies.

Play: Only fingers gun; fashions a bird out of clay.

Dreams: Occasionally—"nice" and "scary."
1. Pleasant dreams: "Rolled up a magic carpet and flew to fairy land." "Going on a camping trip."
2. Spontaneous anxiety dreams: "I am a lion tamer in a circus, but one of the lions sprang on me" (1). "Falling off the Empire State Building" (2). "I broke a water pipe in a house under construction and the watchman chased me" (1).
3. Elicited anxiety dreams: "Boy friend fell off a ledge and I helped him back with a rope" (3).

III. MOTHER

Child's problem: Previous.: He worried too much; insomnia; upset if taken unaware. Present: Asthma.

Mother's personality: Relates averagely well.

Mother as mother: Dependability impaired (anxious about dependency); understanding unimpaired.

Dreams: Very seldom—neutral dreams.

1. Spontaneous anxiety dreams: "Lost in mid air—suspended—a terrible feeling of not knowing where you are and of falling" (1).
2. Elicited anxiety dreams: None.

CASE 22.

I. SCHOOL

Latency: Fairly well adjusted (uncooperative with teacher; not working up to capacity).

Puberty: No report.

II. PSYCHIATRIC

Relationship: Rapport slow and incomplete; affect uneven; communicative except for dreams.

Play: Shoots gun—aims it at psychiatrist; not interested in any other toys.

Dreams: Seldom—"not since the age of two." "Well, at least not since 6 or 7." "Mostly spooky."

1. Pleasant dreams: "Can't remember any."
2. Spontaneous anxiety dreams: "Frankenstein after me" (1).
3. Elicited anxiety dreams: "Falling through space" (2). "Something bad happening to my brother" (3).

III. MOTHER

Child's problem: Previous: None. Present: None.

Mother's personality: Relates only fairly well.

Mother as mother: Dependability impaired (not warm); understanding impaired.

Dreams: "Not for a long time."

1. Spontaneous anxiety dreams: "Falling off of something" (1).
2. Elicited anxiety dreams: "My oldest son—not this child—in some trouble" (2).

CASE 23.

I. SCHOOL

Latency: Fairly well adjusted (distant with teacher; some nervous habits; not working up to capacity).

Puberty: Very well adjusted.

II. PSYCHIATRIC

Relationship: Rapport gradual and complete; affect uneven; verbally communicative.

Play: Languidly fingers crayolas, paste, and gun, but declines to play with them.

Dreams: Often—"nice dreams and nightmares."

1. Pleasant dreams: "Can't remember any."
2. Spontaneous anxiety dreams: "Vacation over and I have to go back to school" (4). "Ugly wood-chopper went around scaring people" (3). "One and one equals 1,000" (1). "My room and furniture quite changed" (2).
3. Elicited anxiety dreams: "Falling off a cliff" (4).

III. MOTHER

Child's problem: Previous: Didn't want to play with other boys. Present: Doesn't want to play with other boys.

Mother's personality: Relates only fairly well.

Mother as mother: Dependability impaired (anxious about dependability); understanding impaired.

Dreams: "I wish you would not ask me about them."

1. Spontaneous anxiety dreams: None.
2. Elicited anxiety dreams: "My children are in danger" (1). "Some men after me" (2). "Falling through space" (3).

CASE 24.

I. SCHOOL

Latency: Fairly well adjusted (interferes with children; some nervous habits).

Puberty: Fairly well adjusted (some nervous habits; not working up to capacity).

II. PSYCHIATRIC

Relationship: Rapport quick and incomplete; affect uneven; difficulty in communicating fantasies and feelings.

Play: Clicks gun, points it at own head; imaginative doll play using clay also; family scene: mother and father are arguing.

Dreams: Often—pleasant and unpleasant.
  1. Pleasant dreams: "I have lots of money."
  2. Spontaneous anxiety dreams: "The whole family is caught in a flood" (1).
  3. Elicited anxiety dreams: "Wild animals after me" (2). "Falling of a mountain" (2).

III. MOTHER

Child's problem: Previous: Stealing. Present: Reluctant to go to school; feels gypped.

Mother's personality: Relates averagely well.

Mother as mother: Dependability impaired (fluctuates with father's state and socio-economic situation); understanding unimpaired.

Dreams: Seldom.
  1. Spontaneous anxiety dreams: "Sister being killed" (1). "Falling off a bridge" (2).
  2. Elicited anxiety dreams: "Not enough clothing on" (3).

CASE 25.

I. SCHOOL

Latency: Fairly well adjusted (stubborn and distant with teachers; solitary with peers; not working up to capacity).

Puberty: Well adjusted (distant with teacher; solitary with peers).

II. PSYCHIATRIC

Relationship: Rapport slow and incomplete; affect uneven; general difficulty in communicating.

Play: Fashions gargoyle face out of clay, first tearing head off the clay figure made by another child; makes father doll fall on back when coming home from work; father doll knocks other dolls over.

Dreams: Never.
  1. Pleasant dreams: Never.
  2. Spontaneous anxiety dreams: "None."
  3. Elicited anxiety dreams: "Monster going to eat me up."

III. MOTHER

Child's problem: Previous: None. Present: Doesn't confide about his troubles with other boys.

Mother's personality: Relates only fairly well.

Mother as mother: Dependability impaired (not warm); understanding impaired.

Dreams: Often—pleasant and unpleasant.
  1. Pleasant: "Of my grandmother who has been dead for years."
  2. Spontaneous anxiety dreams: "Something bad is going to happen to my father" (3). "That I am either dying or dead" (2). "My son is on fire and I can't help him" (1).
  3. Elicited anxiety dreams: "Burglar in the house" (2). "Falling through space" (3).

CASE 26.

I. SCHOOL

Latency: Fairly well adjusted (not working up to capacity).

Puberty: No report.

II. PSYCHIATRIC

Relationship: Rapport slow and incomplete; affect uneven; blocking and difficulty in communicating his feelings.

Play: With encouragement shoots gun; has cars collide; police catching robber car; doll family falls down; "Now they're all dead"; Knocks down mother doll and another doll with paint brush.

Dreams: Frequent—"happy kind."
1. Pleasant dreams: "I have a million dollars."
2. Spontaneous anxiety dreams: "Spooks after me."
3. Elicited anxiety dreams: None.

III. MOTHER

Child's problem: Previous: "School said he was spoiled." Present: None.

Mother's personality: Relates very well.

Mother as mother: Dependability unimpaired; understanding impaired.

Dreams: Occasional.
1. Pleasant dreams: "We have lots of money."
2. Spontaneous anxiety dreams: "Going to a nice place—can't locate my dress, shoes, or stockings" (3). "Falling into a pit" (2). "I was married, but there was another man—someone trying to shoot me" (1).
3. Elicited anxiety dreams: "Someone dying" (4).

CASE 27.

I. SCHOOL

Latency: Well adjusted (not working up to capacity).

Puberty: Fairly well adjusted (stubborn with teacher and interferes with peers; some nervous habits; not working up to capacity).

II. PSYCHIATRIC

Relationship: Rapport quick and complete; affect adequate; difficulty in communicating feelings and dreams.

Play: Fashions boat out of clay; sets doll family on edge of table; "They're going over the edge of the cliff"; swats sister doll on rear for not being upright; hits her with rubber bands; shoots father doll; then boy doll falls over cliff.

Dreams:
1. Pleasant dreams: "What the world will be like afterwards—after I die they'd have television on watches. I wish I could live forever."
2. Spontaneous anxiety dreams: "I was in a snake pit—almost bitten by their poisonous fangs" (1).
3. Elicited anxiety dreams: "Falling off a cliff" (2).

III. MOTHER

Child's problem: Previous: Lying. Present: Too active; a show-off.

Mother's personality: Relates averagely well.

Mother as mother: Dependability not impaired; understanding impaired.

Dreams: Occasional.
1. Spontaneous anxiety dreams: "Burglar coming to rob me of my bracelet given to me by my husband. I throw bracelet into piano" (1).
2. Elicited anxiety dreams: "Falling through air" (2). "My husband and brother-in-law drowning on a sinking raft" (1).

CASE 28.

I. SCHOOL

Latency: Well adjusted (stubborn and distant with teacher).

Puberty: Very well adjusted.

II. PSYCHIATRIC

Relationship: Rapport slow and complete; affect dampened; uncommunicative about dreams.

Play: Bashful—doesn't use play material.

Dreams: Occasional—"But I forget them." "Usually good."

1. Pleasant dreams: "I can't remember them."
2. Spontaneous anxiety dreams: "Something coming after me."
3. Elicited anxiety dreams: None.

III. MOTHER

Child's problem: Previous: Sibling rivalry. Present: None.

Mother's personality: Relates averagely well.

Mother as mother: Dependability unimpaired; understanding unimpaired.

Dreams: "I dream in spells."

1. Spontaneous anxiety dreams: "A little girl got lost in the mountains" (1).
2. Elicited anxiety dreams: "Falling" (2). "Members of my family in danger" (1).

AMPLIFICATIONS

1. *METHODS OF STUDY*

A questionnaire was provided the school personnel to help them in selecting the children. First they were asked to designate the children as being either well adjusted or fairly well adjusted. Then they were asked to give information about ten items pertaining to the child's adjustment at school. These items included the child's relationship with the teacher, the school disciplinary system, and with his peers; also his usual mood, symptoms of nervousness, parents' complaints about the child, and whether his school work indicated that he was working up to his mental capacity. We added the proviso that we wanted children who represented all-round adjustment, and that the school personnel should not select only those children who were most conforming or most apt in their school work.

To obtain a range of socio-economic influences, we asked four different schools to co-operate with us in the study. One school drew its pupils from a lower-middle-class, small-home area just on the fringe of an area of high delinquency; another from a middle-class, small-home area; a third from an upper-middle-class apartment home area; and still another from an upper-middle-class, large-house, suburban-like area on the outskirts of the city.

After we had decided upon the source of our subjects, our next problem was to narrow the selection of the children in order to provide as few variables as possible. The age span to be studied had been dictated by the reasons given previously: lack of knowledge about the latency period, and the bulk of our referrals were in this age span. However, we chose to further limit the age span to eight and nine. This was done not only to reduce the variables but more particularly because it would provide us with the best opportunity to examine the latency period since the children would be just past the age in which they had become accustomed to their initiation into school life and they had not yet reached the emotional upheaval connected with pre-puberty and puberty.

White children were selected to avoid any sociological complications. In order to avoid the complications seen in broken homes, we also asked that the children selected come from homes in which both the natural father and mother were living together. Our selection was limited further to those children who had at least one other sibling. This provision was made in order to view the usual effects on the child of the presence of younger or older siblings.

Before we actually saw our first child, we discovered that there was a further selectivity operative in our choice of children. We found that of the parents contacted, only two-thirds were actually willing to co-operate with the study. Therefore, to whatever bias might have been introduced by the schools' personnel's selection of the child we now had an additional bias of obtaining only children whose parents were co-operative with the idea of the study. As the school reports were returned we were encouraged by the differences in the reports that indicated we were getting the slightly maladjusted as well as the adjusted. Finally, because only one-half of the fathers volunteered to cooperate with the study, while all the mothers volunteered, we decided to make this essentially a study of mothers and children. (See Appendix E, Table 1, *Identifying Data.*)

The research team consisted of the three usual members of the clinic diagnostic team: psychiatrist, social worker, and psychologist. The diagnostic techniques used in the research study were predominantly those used commonly at a child guidance clinic in the examination of disturbed children and their mothers. The similarities and differences between clinic and study methods will *be apparent from the following description.*

The Psychiatric Interview. The psychiatric interview with the child followed roughly along the lines of any interview with a child referred to the clinic for emotional disturbance. In such an interview, the psychiatrist meets the child in the waiting room, and usually the mother helps in the introduction. As the child and the psychiatrist walk to the interview room there is an opportunity for the examiner to put the child at his ease by some friendly remark, which may or may not bring on a friendly, spontaneous response from the child. Once in the room, the interview proper may take several forms, depending on the child and also on the temperament and philosophy of the psychiatrist. Usually play equipment is in sight and the child is invited to play with the toys if he wishes. The play equipment frequently includes dolls, doll house, guns, trucks, modeling clay, crayons, paper, etc. The child may play with the toys in a highly organized and creative way, e.g., portraying with the guns a dramatic story of a struggle between cowboys and Indians, with the dolls a domestic story of interaction between imaginary parents and imaginary children, or fashioning a dog with clay. The child may examine each of several toys in a desultory or detached manner, or curiously, to see how it works and then pass on to the next toy. Finally, the child may decline the invitation to play with such remarks as, "That's for babies. I'm a big boy." Or, "I've got that stuff at home."

While the play is going on, the psychiatrist usually watches to see what will come next, gives help when asked for by the child, and after awhile may make a comment on some aspect of the play in order to draw the child out to some verbalization. If the child does not play, the occasion for verbal interchange arises much sooner. In the verbal part of the interview, the examiner may use any spontaneous feeling response by the child as an entry into the child's hidden feelings and conflicts. Besides waiting for the child to provide an entre, either through his play or speech, the psychiatrist has at his disposal several stock questions, which have variable success in drawing the child out. Examples of such questions are: "What do you like to watch on television?" "If you were given a thousand dollars what would you do with it?" "What do you feel sad about?" "Whom do you tell your troubles to?" "What do you dream about?"

The psychiatric interview used in this exploratory study was similar to the type of interview just described. The principal difference was that a more or less uniform method was used with all the children. This uniformity was deemed desirable for the reason that it provided a constant, a uniform backdrop against which the variations of the child's behavior could be revealed more strikingly. The interview in detail started with the friendly welcome in the interview room; once inside the room the psychiatrist explained that we were interested in learning about boys and girls who were doing well in school and that the psychiatrist would like to know him a little better. Then the child was asked about his interests, hobbies, enthusiasms—in other words, asked about non-threatening areas in order to increase the rapport and trust. At this point the child was invited to play with the articles in the toy box. This toy box was standardized so that all the 54 children would be exposed to the same toy box and the same toys. This box contained dolls, trucks, guns, clay, clothes, scissors, paper, etc. After sufficient time was given the child to play (sufficient, that is, for the psychiatrist to learn how the child was going to use the toys, creatively, detachedly, or rejecting of them), he was invited into a verbal interchange in which certain areas were systematically explored. These areas were his fantasy life, his emotional feelings, his dream life, and his family life.

Psychological Test Information. Of all the tests administered by the psychologist (Stanford-Binet, Rorschach, Sentence Completion, Despert Fables, and Draw-a-Person) only two will be referred to in this report—referred to in the sense of supplementary evidence rather than primary evidence for certain hypotheses. The two tests are the Rorschach and the Despert Fables. The Rorschach ink-blot test is familiar enough not to need any description. (Both the Rorschach and Despert Fables Tests were administered in the standard fashion.) Besides the usual summary of the Rorschach scoring, the psychologist had a rating scale based on the Rorschach data for various personality functions. These functions were (a) intellectual, (b) emotional, (c) reality testing, (d) socialization, and (e) anxiety controls.

The Despert Fables Test is not as well known as the Rorschach. It consists of 20 fables told to the child, and his responses and reactions are then noted and analyzed. Five of these fables and the responses to them seem to be of value and significance in understanding the complete clinical data. An illustrative fable is: A daddy bird and a mamma bird and their little birdie in the nest on the branch of a tree. All of a sudden a big wind blows; it shakes the tree and the nest falls to the ground. The three birds awaken all of a sudden. The daddy flies quickly to one part of the tree, the mamma to another pine tree; the little bird knows how to fly. What is the little bird going to do?

The other Despert Fables useful to us were: *Fable No. 3*: In a field there is a mamma sheep and a little lamb. The little lamb bounces around all day near his mamma. Every night his mamma gives him some good, warm milk, which he likes very much. But he can already eat grass. One day his mamma says to him, "You don't need milk any more. You go and eat some nice, fresh grass." What do you think the little lamb is going to do? *Fable No. 5*: A dog goes crazy and bites his daddy and his mommy and all of his brothers and sisters. Who gets hurt most? *Fable No. 6*: On a farm there is a little baby calf and his mommy cow. The calf plays all day long with his mommy. Whenever he asks for it, his mommy gives him some warm milk, but he is old enough to eat grass. One day the farmer brings the mommy a tiny weeny little calf which is very hungry, but the mommy does not have enough milk for two so she says to the bigger calf: "I haven't enough milk for two. You are bigger. You go and eat some nice, fresh grass." What do you think the little calf is going to do? *Fable No. 12*: A family of deer is running in the woods. Suddenly a hunter comes along and shoots and kills one of them, but the others don't get hurt. Whom do you suppose he killed? *Fable 16*: The teacher calls a boy to the front of the room one day. She tells him that he must go home right away because something terrible has happened. What do you suppose has happened?

School Report. The questionnaire to the school personnel (from teacher, adjustment teacher, and principal) was designed not only to obtain an idea of the child's functioning as a whole, but also how he functioned in partial areas. Accordingly, our first request of the school was to submit the names of all children they considered not to require a behavior study. (If a child in the public school system seems sufficiently disturbed, machinery is set in motion to obtain a behavior study from the Bureau of Child Study, which is under the Board of Education.) Next, we asked the school personnel to designate whether they felt the child was well adjusted or just fairly well adjusted. We added the proviso that they should not automatically select the most conforming or the most scholastically diligent as the best adjusted, but to base their opinion on all-around adjustment. A check list was provided the school personnel so they could indicate in several partial areas how the child was functioning.

These partial areas were (1) adjustment to the general school program (very co-operative, averagely co-operative, stubborn or defiant); (2) co-operation with the teacher (very co-operative, averagely co-operative, stubborn or defiant); (3) relationship to the teacher as a person (seeks attention, friendly, distant); (4) relationship to the group (interferes, mixes well, avoids); (5) role in the group (leads, leads or follows depending upon the situation, usually follows); (6) customary mood (usually carefree, appropriately carefree or serious depending upon the situation, usually serious); (7) nervous habits (some, none); (8) parental complaints regarding child (some, none); (9) tardiness (some, none); and (10) relationship of scholastic achievement to intellectual capacity (working up to capacity, not quite working up to capacity).

The identical questionnaire was sent to the schools four years later. Reports were available on 42 children, those who were still in the Chicago or suburban school system.

Interview with the Mother. We observed the mothers in this study under considerably different circumstances from those in which we observe mothers who come to the clinic for help. Many clinic mothers are in a stress situation inasmuch as their child is having problems which are beyond the capacity of the mother or the family to manage. Their presenting emotional tone can be quite varied: anxious or confused about how to deal with the child, annoyed or punitive because the child is giving them so much trouble, or on the defensive, blaming the school if the school has suggested that the mother seek help from the clinic. The mothers in the normal study came to us with a different tone. In order to secure their co-operation in this study, we had told them that because their child had been designated as well adjusted, they could help us on our research on normality. Thus many mothers had some feeling of pride regarding their success with their children. This different emotional setting is mentioned as a warning that the data collected from these "normal" mothers are not strictly comparable with data selected from "clinic" mothers.

Both the psychiatrist and the social worker interviewed the mother separately, with the division of labor between the two interviewers being that the psychiatrist would dwell mostly on the mother as a woman, whereas the social worker would be occupied mostly with the mother as a mother. There was, of course, some overlapping of inquiry and observation.

The psychiatric interview, for example, proceeded differently from the way it would in the case of a clinic mother. In the latter situation, the presenting problem of the child would be gone into, an idea of the family tensions would be obtained, and some inquiry regarding an evaluation of mother as a participant in a treatment plan would be made, etc. But with the normal mothers, since there was no pressing problem a different interview procedure was deemed necessary. Accordingly, the interview began with a few remarks and questions regarding their reactions to their children being selected as well adjusted. The mother was then asked to describe the child as she saw him.

After this preamble concerning the child, the mother was asked about her own childhood and background. Questions were asked to elicit feelings and facts as to whether mother had a happy or unhappy childhood, and if unhappy, why so; the number of siblings and mother's ordinal position in the family; whether or when the home was broken by death or divorce; how she felt about her mother and father; how her mother and father got along; how she felt about her siblings, and was there any preference shown by her parents toward the children; mother's educational and occupational history. Most significant, it developed later, were the questions concerning the way mother felt towards her parents, the way her parents got along, and a comparison of the way her own mother had handled her and the way she handled her own children.

After going into mother's background, the psychiatrist explored mother's current emotional adjustment. Questions were asked to ascertain the state of mother's health, her "nervousness," her handling of her anger, her tendencies to be orderly and worrisome, her moods, and her dream life.

Finally the questioning went on to mother's marital adjustment, which was investigated from two angles: her feelings toward her husband and her sexual adjustment. The sexual adjustment was gone into routinely with the explanatory statement that all this information was necessary for our research. Most of the mothers, when asked regarding their sexual satisfaction, took the question in their stride and seemed to answer honestly. A few obviously felt embarrassed and threatened.

The social worker's interview with the mother, after a preliminary establishing of rapport, more or less followed certain regular lines. This was possible, as was said earlier, because these mothers were usually not anxious or under pressure. The current family situation was explored (e.g., how did the child get along with his siblings), and then the early development was gone into (e.g., did he show difficulties in feeding or in toilet training).

In both the interviews, the examiners utilized the feeling-tone which accompanied mother's statements and answers in order to evaluate the mother. The social worker, in particular, made an evaluation of the mother as a mother and the mother as an adult woman. This evaluation was based as much on the feeling-tone and other nuances forthcoming from the mother as on her actual statements.

CONCERNING THE CRITERIA
FOR RATING.

SCHOOL AREA *very well adjusted:* Children designated as well adjusted and who did not receive check marks indicating "stubborn with authority" or "interferes with the children," or "not working up to mental capacity." *Well adjusted:* Children designated as well adjusted but who received one or more check marks. *Fairly well adjusted:* Children designated "fairly well adjusted."

PSYCHIATRIC INTERVIEW *very well adjusted:* Children who showed no impairment in the following four areas: ability to communicate, ability to come into rapport, quickness in coming into rapport, appropriate affect and zest in the interchange with the psychiatrist. *Well adjusted:* Children who showed impairment in one or two of the areas. *Fairly well adjusted:* Children showing impairment in three or four of these four areas.

FAMILY LIFE *very well adjusted:* Children described by their mothers as showing no present problems and being better adjusted than their siblings. *Well adjusted:* Children described by their mothers as having no present problems but not as well adjusted as their siblings. *Fairly well adjusted:* Children described by their mothers as having a definite current problem.

In separating out the four groups discussed in the chapter "Types of adjustment," we used the following method. For adjusting well within the family, we took mother's statement that either the child had no present problem, or that if he had one he was better adjusted than his siblings, who themselves were not undue problems to mother. Included in fair adjustment within the family were all those children who had problems and were adjusting no better or they were adjusting worse than the other siblings. For adjusting well outside the family, we used our evaluation of "very well adjusted" in the combined social rating. For adjusting fairly well outside the family, we used our evaluation of fairly well adjusted on the combined social rating (omitted were children in the middle combined social rating of well adjusted).

2. OTHER SAMPLE BEHAVIORS OF CHILDREN AND MOTHERS

EARLY DEVELOPMENT

Example 1

Allen had been a planned baby. During pregnancy mother was not actually sick, but she had not felt good physically and had always been tired. She had had some nausea during the pregnancy with Allen, but not as much as with another child. She was satisfied with the medical care she had received. Delivery had been easy with no injury to Allen or to herself. When she first had seen him she had thought he was adorable. During his first year he had been a very good baby, ate and slept well. Allen had not cried much, but he was picked up if he did cry. He had not seemed to require much, but had just wanted to be held, and they had played with him. Mother had not followed any of the rules as she had with an older daughter. As an infant, Allen had gone to strangers readily, but as he grew older, he became more reluctant to go away from home. He has always been an active child. He had been nursed for nine months on a demand schedule. Weaning Allen had not been a problem. It seemed automatic and had been done gradually. He had been on a bottle for only a short time and had given this up easily, too. He had sucked his thumb for about a year, but had stopped this by himself. He was never a feeding problem. Toilet training had been started at about eight months. Bowel control had been established at about one year, and wetting stopped at two. Mother used to put Allen on the pot after meals or at his regular time for a bowel movement, but she said he seemed to have learned his toilet habits without much fuss on her part. There have been no problems in this area.

Example 2

Samuel had been a wanted baby, at least by his mother, but his father had not been ready for him. He had been born one year after his parents' marriage. Mother had felt wonderful during pregnancy. She had been nauseated for the first two months, although she had not been nauseated with her second son. Mother was very satisfied with her doctor and with her medical care. Mother had had a very unpleasant experience during the delivery of Samuel, and she had not felt well after the baby had been born. People had not believed there had been anything the matter with her and had suspected that she was only depressed. Her nurse had said that her complaints were only in her head. Mother had felt as if she were in a jail. Some trouble was discovered: some packing had been left inside of her and that had caused mother a lot of pain and discomfort. After the packing had been removed she was all right. Instruments had been used for delivery, and when Samuel was born he had looked rather beaten up. Mother first thought he was ugly, others said she had a beautiful baby, but she had not agreed at first. During his first year Samuel had cried a lot before he would fall asleep. Mother had not always picked him up when he cried, and if he had stopped crying when she had picked him up she would put him down again. She said she knew there was nothing wrong with him. She would go into the bathroom to read a book so she could not hear Samuel cry. She found the solution to this problem when he was three months old. Her solution had been to prop him up in a sitting position so that he had been able to see what was going on. Also she gave him a bottle at night to stop his crying. He never had liked to be picked up. He had never rested comfortably in anyone's arms, because he would hold himself so erect. He was an active baby in his first weeks and has continued to be that way. Mother had tried to nurse Samuel, but she had not had enough milk. He had been bottle-fed on a four-hour schedule. Mother explained that this had been the new psychology at the time, but she feels everyone has to use her own judgment about these things. Samuel had done a lot of vomiting and still had been doing this at two years. Mother had become very angry with him and at such times had handled him harshly. She had held him for awhile during the bottle feedings, but she said her back had not been too strong and that although she had known she should have held him, she could not, or she had not. He was weaned at one year and there were some minor difficulties. He had never liked milk much from the bottle, but had seemed to enjoy just having the nipple in his mouth. Mother had started toilet training Samuel at six months, which was when he had begun to sit up. She would put him on the toilet every half hour. She remarked that she had considered the bottle and the toilet the most important things for a baby. He had been trained for his day-time toilet habits at sixteen months, but he had wet his bed until he was four years old. After the age of four, mother had no further difficulty with him.

HANDLING OF DISCIPLINE

Example 1

In discussing the disciplining of her daughter, Karen, mother said she does not believe in hitting a child. Mother herself had never been spanked and her father had always kept them in line. She said her parents had been easy going and had let many things ride that other parents would not for fear that they would turn out to be too severe with them. Mother thinks that too severe punishments or punishments for every little thing makes a child afraid. She loved her father because he never hit her. If Karen has been disrespectful she has been reprimanded by having something taken away from her. Mother feels she has been able to talk to Karen. She gives Karen credit for being more adult than most parents she knows do with their children.

Mother has handled any discipline as the occasion has demanded. Father has sometimes said that she has not been strict enough but she, in turn, has felt the same has been true of him. Karen has been quite obedient and has not gone against what mother has said, very much. Mother said that she thinks before she does anything in the matter of discipline, and when she does a thing, she thinks it is the thing to do and she carries it through.

Example 2

The disciplining of Gail rests mainly on her mother. Most things have not bothered father and it has been mother who has had to get after the kids to keep them in line. Father has thought that mother has taken things too seriously. Mother has felt that he should take more responsibility and help her more. Father has contended that he would run his business and she would run the house, but mother thinks that there is more to living than that. They usually discipline Gail by depriving her of things she likes to have, but mother thinks there is too much threatening without enough action—actual taking away. She is afraid Gail will not respect father because he is so easy going. Sometimes mother has really to get mad at Gail. Gail likes father more and always has. Mother thinks this is because of what father does for Gail. He has always pampered her, doing more for her than mother. Mother thinks she was too strict with Gail earlier in instituting bowel and bladder control and she thinks a lot of Gail's present contrariness started along this time. Mother would make her sit on the pot and Gail would still get up and do it on the floor. Mother would then scold and spank Gail. Now she feels that she should not have spanked the child.

HANDLING OF SEXUAL CURIOSITY

Example 1

Mother said Ronald was told about his sister's coming into the world and he felt mother's stomach when she was carrying the baby. He did not ask questions before and he had not noticed other women who were pregnant. He was four when mother had a miscarriage, and he knew about this and was told that mother had lost the baby. When he asked questions during her pregnancy with his sister, mother told him that when people love each other they marry and have a baby and that the baby grows inside of mother. She did not think that Ronald knew about the father's role and was not sure if he really knew how the baby was delivered. She said she talked to Ronald as though he were an adult. She said she had done most of the explaining about sex and she thought she could do it better than his father.

Ronald knew about sexual differences before his sister was born, although his parents had not dressed or undressed in front of him. Although Ronald wants mother to leave the bathroom when he uses it, he and his father take showers together. He says that father is different—that father is a man and he is still a little boy. He never lets anyone but his parents see him undressed, although he got along all right at day camp where boys all undressed together when they went in swimming. Mother has not noticed any masturbation since Ronald was little, at which time he used to play with his penis when he sat on the toilet. Last year, however, he had a sore on the tip of his penis, and the doctor told him not to scratch it because that was causing the sore. Mother knows children do masturbate, but she does not think that Ronald would let her see him if he did. Mother said she would not make an issue of his masturbating because she thought that would only make Ronald continue to do it.

Example 2

Harold has only asked rare questions about sex. When mother was pregnant with his younger sister, he only told mother she was getting fat, which she handled by saying that she was eating more. She said she had not given any deep explanation. She is not sure what he knows, but feels she will wait until he asks her before she tells him anything. Mother acknowledges that she dreads talking to Harold about sex; her mother had never believed in telling her about it. Mother knows there are books she can get to help her out. Harold had asked, when his sister was born, why she had no penis, and mother explained very briefly just the difference in the way they were built. She has noticed no masturbation and said if she had she would have gotten father to talk to Harold. She would have been bothered by this because raising children is a new experience, and she does not know what to expect.

RELATIONSHIP TO SIBLINGS

Example 1

Margaret was prepared for her little sister's birth and helped mother get the things ready. She stayed with her grandmother when her sister was born, and was very happy to see her parents again. She loved her baby sister. Mother says Margaret has always liked children. Mother feels that Margaret gets along with all the children and never shows any rivalry with them, or complains that they get more than she. Whereas Margaret loved little brother Tim, the younger sister had not, and wanted mother to take him back to the hospital.

Example 2

Although Allen's older brother accepted him very nicely when he was born, Allen was different with his younger brother. He frequently says that his younger brother is better liked and that he (Allen) is always blamed for things his younger brother does, and he says his parents do not like him. Sometimes he asks why they have to have a baby and complains that the baby spoils his fun. He does not like to have his younger brother tag after him, but mother does not think they get along too badly or in a way out of proportion to what might be expected.

MOTHER'S ABILITY TO RELATE

Example 1

Mother is short and plump. She related well, although there was some nervousness shown in the frequently opening and shutting of her purse, and she commented twice on how long and how much she was talking. She tended to be serious, appeared to have a great deal of warmth, and was very much at ease about her own feelings and the discussion of them. She impressed the social worker as extremely understanding in her family relationships and of her daughter's reactions. Although there may be some tendency for mother to want things just so, yet her desire for achievement seems to be amply compensated for and controlled by mother's understanding.

Example 2

Mother is very tall and of large build. Her speech is difficult to understand because she seems to have a lisp or uses baby talk. She spoke mainly in terse, abrupt phrases or sentences with much vernacular. Social worker did not feel that mother related well to her. She often answered questions with material other than that asked for, but never said she did not understand the question. With the psychiatrist she was at first irritable about having to wait. She frequently flew off on her own tangent, and would misinterpret what was asked of her. She seemed to be on the laconic or passive side.

MOTHER'S BACKGROUND

Example 1

Mother opened her talk about her childhood by saying that it was a very happy one. She thinks she had more fun than children do now-a-days. Her father was very wonderful and kind. Everybody liked him, and he helped everybody out. They had an open house at home. Her father owned a business, worked hard, and provided well for them. Father favored her older brother slightly, but not to the point of discomfort for the rest. When asked about her mother, she said she was determined and always was very well. "We could do anything we wanted. We had a dog, played in the yard, and were a very happy family." "My parents never quarreled outright among themselves, and they never had much to quarrel about inwardly. My mother's favorite was my second brother, but I'm not showing any favoritism with my own children." Mother thinks her father and mother got along very well. Neither one tried to dominate the other and they were both reasonable. Mother patterns her present household after her original one—mostly about the fun they have and the openness of the home. She does avoid any favoritism among the children.

Example 2

Mother said, "Well, I was not raised under ideal conditions, on account of my parents' conflict, my parents bickered and argued. My mother was not at home much. She worked. So that is why I try to be at home with my kids. My mother had to work, but she was also very possessive. I try to be the opposite. I give my child more chance for freedom, even if I have qualms about it." Her father was a happy-go-lucky, kind-hearted, easy-going man, very nice to mother. However, her mother was the nagging, dominating type and mother did not get along well with her. Her mother constantly nagged her father, who couldn't take it very well.

MOTHER'S CURRENT PERSONALITY

Example 1

Mother said her health is very good. Concerning nervousness, mother said: "Although all of us have nervousness at times. I'm about average. I get tense and angry when the kids fight too much, and I tell them off. But in a quiet situation I am very easy-going." Mother said she becomes just averagely angry with her husband. He is a very easy-going guy and not the type to make her angry. She is rarely angry at other people. Usually when angry she releases it and feels better. Mother said she is not fanatically orderly; she likes order, but is just about average. She said she doesn't worry too much. She worries at times, but they are not the kind of worries that make her unhappy—mostly they are realistic worries. She sleeps very well and dreams seldom. Regarding her moods, she said she is pretty happy if things go right. The only thing that would really throw her, would be that her husband would not be able to earn a living for his family. She gets the blues occasionally for a day or so pre-menstrually, but doesn't get very elated or enthusiastic. "I'm not too much depressed —more on an even keel." For recreation she likes to read or knit and likes to read all types of books. About friends, she doesn't need them all the time, but she likes to be with them sometimes.

Example 2

Mother said about her health that she is not too well. She is anemic and gets tired easily and can't keep up. She has been this way for the past five years since the birth of her second baby. Nine months after the baby was born, she had a nervous breakdown. She was very nervous, jittery, crying: "As if there was something wrong with my head." This lasted for a year. She has always been nervous about such things as meeting new situations, new people, and responsibilities. When she is confronted by these things she gets palpitation and picks at her hands. She becomes angry with her husband occasionally when they have a difference of opinion as to how to spend money, or if her plans have to be discarded for his plans. She holds in her anger against her husband more than she releases it. With people in general she holds it in. If she lets it out, it doesn't come out all the way and she gets choked up. Of this she said: "The result is that I hold myself aloof, away from people. Then I can't get all my feelings out." With the kids she lets it out rather than holds it in. Mother thinks she likes neatness and orderliness, but that she is not too fussy. She is, however, quite a bit of a worrier. Her moods are changeable. Sometimes she is happy, sometimes she is "down in the dumps." The longest period of depression was when she was quite nervous. It lasted for about six months. Now she only gets depressed before menstruation. Mother said they don't go out much except to visit relatives. They have company off and on. She has friends, but doesn't feel badly if she doesn't see them very often.

MOTHER'S MARRIAGE

Example 1

Mother said that her husband is very good natured, very thorough, very punctual. "He has accepted me as I am throughout the years. I'm not so punctual because I do like to get the chores done. Then I have to get the kids off the street." When asked about faults in her husband, she said that he liked to do one thing only—he likes to go his way. "He is quite helpful when I show what I want, and we get along very well. One thing we haven't done lately is to have a vacation by ourselves." Mother thinks that their marriage is, in general, quite successful. She admitted having a good many dates before her marriage and was seriously interested in a few men, but her marriage went right from the beginning. Her mother had not prepared her for sex or menstruation, she picked it up by herself. Mother thinks her sexual adjustment is very good. There is complete satisfaction when she is in the mood, and her husband has been very considerate of her. The frequency is two or three times a week, and mother said they have always been very much in love.

Example 2

Mother said in a rather flat tone that their marriage was OK. She said, "I think one person has to give up more than the other in marriage and I have had to do that in order to get along more easily." But as to drawbacks, mother said: "My husband manages to get out more than I do, and I am stuck with the kids. My husband doesn't share the responsibility of taking care of them. He doesn't spend enough time with them." When asked if she had discussed this matter with her husband, she said, "No." And then with resentment, "He isn't the kind you can discuss things with." Mother thinks her sexual adjustment is just so-so. "Well, maybe I'm not the warm type, but we get by." Mother was embarrassed while talking about the sexual adjustment. She revealed that her mother hadn't prepared the girls for sex or for menstruation. She was ignorant of all sex until she was married. Her husband has not been too considerate of her in sexual relations. Some of his actions remind of her own father, who used to drink a lot.

3. CONTINUITY IN CHILDREN'S PROBLEMS.

The child manifested his continuity even in his problems. We could see that the problems mentioned by mothers as having occurred in the preschool period had a very strong resemblance to the problems mentioned by mother as occurring currently. This resemblance may indicate a continuity in the child's personality and/or a continuity in mother as to what she is sensitive to in the child.

Some examples may be helpful in illustrating this continuity. An example of strict continuity was observed in one girl whose mother said that in the preschool period her daughter had been reluctant to be separated from her and that the same difficulty still was present. The problem, in other words, continued unchanged. One could think of either or both of two possibilities. (1) The girl has a deep-seated anxiety about being separated from her mother; or she wishes to re-assure herself that her mother is still alive in spite of her death wishes; or she wishes to control or annoy her mother. (2) The mother is particularly sensitive to any clinging behavior, from guilt over having not done enough for the child and/or anger at having her independence encroached on.

Another example of continuity, but less strict, is the following one in which two of the previous problem manifestations dropped out but one remained unchanged. One of our mothers reported that in the preschool period the difficulties she had encountered with her son were that he bit people, was mean, and resented his brother. However, at the present time biting and meanness had disappeared, leaving only his resentment of his brother as a problem.

From the standpoint of continuity, the largest group was the one in which, although the surface manifestations changed, the inner core remained the same. For example, in one boy the preschool problem was lying; the present problem was that he had become a show-off. Superficially, of course, these problems are not identical. However, from the viewpoint of the child, both behaviors could serve the pur-pose of bolstering up his damaged self-esteem; lying, to ward off punitive criticism, the showing off to exaggerate his accomplishments and prowess. From the viewpoint of the mother, the continuity may take the form of an intolerance to masculine surgency by which she would pounce on any beginning show of strength or expansion in the boy. (The mother in this case happened to be one of those who in-tensely disliked her domineering father.)

There are other examples of problems superficially different, but basically the same: a girl who had the preschool problem of diffi-culty in being trained for bowel movement had a current problem of being slow in doing things. Again we see the continuity of balkiness and contrariness in the girl, and a continuity of controlingness in the mother. A boy went from the preschool problem of stealing and fire-setting to the current problem of temper reactions—the continuation of explosive aggressiveness being quite obvious. A girl with a problem in first-grade of "poor" marks had a current problem of "slow in learning manners." In this case the continuity was more apparent in the mother than in the child. The mother had had a psychotic breakdown and, although recovered, described her life-long inferiority feelings and a particular sensitivity to what people thought of her. According to the school, and according to the psychiatrist, the child socialized and performed well, but her mother, through her identification with the child, was over-anxious regarding her daughter's adequacy.

A very small group of children had current problems that did not have an immediately recognizable resemblance to their past problems. One of these was a boy whose preschool problem was "worried, difficulty sleeping, easily startled," and whose current problem was "asthma." Although the previous problem adds up essentially to an anxiety state, the connection between the anxiety state and the asthma is not clear on gross inspection. If, however we utilize the concept gained from research into psychosomatic conditions (as was done in the instance of asthma by French and Alexander), we could say that the anxiety state was due to a basic fear of being separated from the mother and that this anxiety state is replaced by a somatic anxiety equivalent, the asthma attack.

Thus we have seen that the problem of the child complained of by the mother speaks of a characteristic continuity in the child and/or the mother. By virtue of constitutional and hereditary tendencies (about which we have no data), and by virtue of certain interaction with the particular mother, the child develops a characteristic "favorite" or familiar way of discharging his growth tensions. Though the surface manifestations may change, this character structure contains his favorite way, be it aggressiveness, passive resistance, ego inflation, etc. The mother by virtue of her own personality and her own past also has developed set sensitivities which continue and which are characteristic for her.

4. WORK OF OTHERS ON CONTINUITY.

The systematic development of the generational continuity concept was not carried out by Freud but was left to his successors. Particularly, those of his successors who worked with children and mothers (Freud worked with adults only) saw vividly the continuity influence of mother on child, and so they developed more systematically this concept. One of the former was Anna Freud, who recognized at least two types of emotionally disturbed children, one type in which personal continuity was more marked and was characterized by somewhat inflexible, neurotic structure, not too remediable by changing the environment, but yielding to psychoanalytic treatment; the other type, which emphasized more the continuity between child and mother, was characterized by a plastic, open personality structure, highly responsive to environmental stresses and remediable by changing the environment for the better. A host of other psychoanalytic workers both in the adult and child areas wrote on the intimate and significant connection between the mother's character structure and her conscious and unconscious feelings on the one hand, and the child's emotional growth on the other. Included in this group are such analysts as Sandor Ferenczi, Michael and Alice Balint, Therese Benedek, Josephine Hilgard, Stanislaus Szurek, and Adelaide Johnson.

Hilgard has described the so-called "anniversary" reaction, which consists essentially of the parent becoming emotionally upset when her child reaches any particular age, if, at that particular age the parent, as a child, experienced some emotional trauma. This reaction illustrates the reverse direction of the generational continuity, the parents being affected by the child rather than the child by the parents. Szurek and Johnson drew many of their insights about the influence of mother on child from their use of collaborative therapy, which consists essentially of mother and child undergoing therapy simultaneously with two therapists. Johnson in her later work has emphasized the origins of delinquent and anti-social behavior of the child as being due to unconscious or dimly conscious anti-social impulses in the mother who incites, in subtle ways, the child to act out her unconscious. This sequence of events is very similar to repercussions on the children when mothers are of the rebellious type.

5. ON SEXUAL CURIOSITY.

We found that one group we studied was somewhat paradoxical inasmuch as the matrix was supportive (mother liked her father) yet the impulse was not lively (no sexual curiosity). In other words, although there was an apparently favorable matrix, the child did not, or was not permitted to, take advantage of it. To make it further puzzling, these mothers were rather dependable and understanding of the child's individuality. The maladjustment showed by the children was not striking or considerable; the adjustment at eight and nine was at least average, but the puberty reports were quite on the unfavorable side.

The only clue that emerged concerning this group was the high frequency of mothers seeing themselves in their child. This conscious identification by mother with the child seemed to have a uniquely significant relationship to the absence of lively impulse behavior. Thus, in children who showed neither sexual curiosity nor sibling rivalry, 70 per cent of the mothers saw themselves in their children; of the children who showed either sexual curiosity or sibling rivalry, 42 per cent of the mothers identified themselves with their children; whereas in children who showed both sexual curiosity and sibling rivalry, only 27 per cent of the mothers saw themselves in their children.

Although we are not satisfied that we know completely what this trend signifies, we shall offer our conjectures. Whatever the previous sequence of psychic events in the child and mother is, the final effect would seem to be that the shadow of mother's personality has fallen over the child. The loyalty bond to mother appears to operate in such a manner that the child has difficulty in differentiating or individuating himself from the mother. While this phenomenon will have some detrimental effect upon growth at the age of eight or nine, it would have a much greater hampering effect at twelve or thirteen when the child is faced with the task of seeking his own destiny and identity in the world.

In terms of our concepts of the integration of inner impulse with an outer matrix, we might say that this self-realization impulse in the child cannot be integrated into the maternal matrix because the mother is more interested in the child's realizing the mother than in the child's realizing himself. As would be expected, we found that this identification by the mother was more seriously hampering to the boy in puberty than to the girl. The intrusion of a feminine component into the boy's personality would bind him on some level to a complicating feminine orientation, whereas the girl would only suffer from an intrusion by a personality of the same sex.

6. *EGOCENTRISM.*

The "I" or "me" emphasis in the mother who consciously recognizes herself in the child may have several psychoanalytic correlates. Out of fear of personal death, out of intense need for generational continuity, the mother may be saying, "I shall not die because here I am in the growing child." Another aspect, which may arise from the intense rivalry or power needs, gives rise to the dim thought, "It is not true that there is any you or he; there is only I.' " In either case the over-evaluation of self is contained in Freud's description of secondary narcissism. He ascribed the origin of this kind of narcissism to a sequence of events in which the affectionate erotic feelings of the child, having gone out to another person and then having been rebuffed, are withdrawn and centered on the child himself. Not only does he love himself (which in mild degrees promotes healthy self-esteem) but also he is quite resentful at being slighted by other people. The net result is a touchy egocentric person who is consciously or unconsciously quite rivalrous with all those who might "steal his thunder," is afraid of mortal retaliation because of his own hostile impulses toward rivals and non-appreciators, and is also afraid of personal death because, since most of his love is centered on himself, every meaningful thing in the world will die with him, his only continuity being with himself.

Thus the "I" or "me" secondary narcissism represents in mild degree a common, almost normal phenomenon, but in greater degree a defect in psychosexual maturation. One cannot go on to love fully the opposite sexed parent if the major part of one's love goes to one's self. Even though a person has matured relatively beyond this point in childhood, he is always susceptible in later years to a revival of secondary narcissism when his affectionate or hopeful ties to other people and goals are disrupted. Freud described, in his book on group psychology and the ego, how the different members of the group keep their individual egocentric motivations in check so long as they feel loved and furthered by the leader of the group. But once the leader meets a failure or shows partiality, the group solidarity disintegrates and the group members become rivalrous, egocentric, and individualistic.

The "I" or "me" secondary narcissistic component as related to the loyalty bond has not received much systematic attention in psychoanalytic theorizing, although it is implicit in many of its concepts. The boy's hostile rivalry with the father has been much more often considered to be his fight with father over who should possess the mother. Rather neglected is the aspect that he might also be fighting the father because the mother unconsciously hates domineering father figures. Similarly with the girl. Her masculine protest, penis envy, and antagonism to men has been more frequently attributed to her feeling of inadequacy about having no penis. This feeling can be exacerbated by a rebuff by a man, an experience which robs the girl of confidence in her feminine appeal, that leads to her falling back to an ever available masculine role, and that makes her competitive with men. Or the feeling can be exacerbated by a rebuff and rejection by her mother who prefers penis-endowed men, a situation that leads the girl to be antagonistic to males who deprive her of her mother's affection. Comparatively neglected is the additional part played by the loyalty demanded of the girl by the mother, a loyalty that compels the girl to feel the hate that her murderous, narcissistic mother has toward males.

The loyalty bond is mentioned by Freud in his work on group psychology. Also, it is mentioned by many writers in the field of sociology, politics, and history. One kind of leader of the group in effect, could, be saying, "I have labored to bring you the good things of life, and I have suffered for you. You then should be loyally grateful. You should love me and each other because I am for you, and I regard you as me and mine. It is disloyal to hate me no matter what the provocation. Furthermore it is not I who frustrates you. It is the outsider. You should welcome to the group all who are for me, and hate all who attack me." Thus the separate, egocentricisms of the individual group members are lost and merged or identified with the great narcissism and egoism of the leader. The parallels in political and religious movements are obvious and include the divine right of kings, political bosses, demagogues, militant churches, and religious messiahs. More homely examples of the transmission of hate by loyalty bonds are such vendettas and feuds as the Hatfield-McCoy feud in which succeeding generations of each family try to kill off the other family.

7. CASE EXAMPLE OF HOSTILITY TOWARD FATHER.

A case example taken from private practice is of interest because it illustrates a long-term repercussion of a mother's hatred of her father. Instead of viewing the effects on children at eight and nine or twelve or thirteen, in this case we may see the repercussions of this father hate when such children are in their thirties or forties. Although the central character in this case is the son, the effects on the daughters are also in evidence.

At the age of thirty-three, this forty-year-old man had gone into psychoanalysis because of sexual impotence. He had been in psychoanalysis for three years, which had been followed by a two-year interval before he resumed with a new analyst (the writer). He was the second of three children, his younger sister had been born when he was five. His father and mother had gotten along very well and his mother had often instructed him to be like his father, who was a very admirable person in her eyes. However, the patient had expressed a chronic hostility to his father and had attempted to rid himself of any similarity which existed between them. The puzzling aspect in this case was that in spite of the harmonious marriage between his parents, not only was this patient so very dependent, unconfident of his masculinity, and still rather impotent with women, but his two sisters also showed signs of marked emotional disturbance. One sister had a chronic ulcerative colitis and extreme nervousness which required her to be hospitalized two or three times. The other sister had made three suicidal attempts. Both these sisters were married to men described by the patient as being insensitive and inconsiderate toward them. As previously stated, the puzzle was: Why should three children have such marked personality disturbances when they came from parents who were so devoted and happily married?

The clue emerged from questioning the patient about his mother's relationship to her own father. It then was revealed that his mother had hated her own father and had felt only a little less hatred for her brothers. The basis for the hatred was that her father was so inconsiderate and selfish toward her mother. However, her husband (the patient's father) was a very different sort of person who made her mother's life (grandmother) very comfortable by his extreme considerateness. The patient felt that his mother had revealed her depreciation of her own father in her responses to an incident which occurred when he had been nine years old. The patient had accidentally spilled milk on the table, to which his mother had said, "Oh, you are just like your grandfather."

Although at the beginning of the second analysis, the patient described his father in depreciating terms and his mother in admiring ones, very gradually and with some discomfort he began to give a more realistic view of her. He revealed that she was quite touchy, and that she would withdraw into a cold silence if her opinions or motives were questioned. She was also never satisfied with the manner in which a *man* behaved. Although generally positive about her husband's considerateness to herself and to her mother, at other times she would be highly critical of his passivity, claiming that he had no backbone because he let customers walk all over him. Undoubtedly the patient could not be sure which type of man it was safe for him to be, "damned if he were strong, and damned if he were weak."

8. WORK BY OTHERS ON STRESS.

Many workers have been particularly interested in the subject of stress. Thus Roy Grinker and John Spiegel viewed the effects of combat stress in soldiers from the psychoanalytic viewpoint; Karl Menninger has described a system of psychic defenses (first, second, and third order) used to cope with increasing stress; Jules Masserman has been deeply interested in the subject and has conducted experiments on animals to learn what happens to them under a variety of stresses and what can be done about bringing these experimentally produced neurotic animals back to normal functioning. Those workers in animal psychology beginning with Ivan Pavlov have contributed greatly to our understanding of the subject. In the field of physiology Walter Cannon, with his account of homeostasis, has shown how the body readjusts itself after external or internal stresses and Hans Selye, with his work on cortisone, has enlightened us further in this area. In historical theorizing, Arnold Toynbee has used stress and inflexibility concepts, e.g., in accounting for the survival of a civilization such as the Esquimaux, a civilization that is largely shaped by one severe stress—the Arctic cold. Lastly, in evolution, certain species like the dinosaurs did not survive because, among other things, thier particular structure, although inflexibly well suited to a particular environment, could not adapt to a new and rigorous environment.

9. INFLEXIBILITY.

An example of unfavorable inflexibility was seen in some data that yet we have not described. We saw evidences of beginning stereotyped repetitiveness in the group of our study children who later had unfavorable puberty reports. In the psychiatric interview at the age of eight or nine, these children showed clusters of phenomena that could be interpreted as premature consolidation of the personality toward one way of handling life's problems. One example was what might be called the regressive cluster. Some children, when they were asked what age they preferred to be, said that they would like to be younger, others said older, and still others said the same age. Then, in regard to pleasant dreams, many children had them but others did not. Now if we consider the wish to be younger and the dreaming of a pleasant wish dream as indicators of a solution of life problems by regressive escape, then these children who have both indicators are likely to be predominantly oriented to this particular adaptive solution. We did find that children with both indicators did less well in puberty than those who had only one. We surmise that while regression is a rather normal adaptive mechanism to be used at times of undue pressure, the double regressive responses point to an infiltrative development of regressive pleasure escape as the main adaptation of the personality. We found similar double response involving social anxiety and aversion to pleasure which were also associated with maladjustment at puberty.

10. SLEEP DISTURBANCES.

Several findings concern sleep disturbances suggested to us that sleep itself might be regarded as an internal supportive matrix, serving the same supportive function as the external mother does. One finding was that occasional sleep disturbances were more frequently reported in children whose mothers were understanding of the child's impulses. From this finding we conjectured that perhaps the child was more ready to face anxieties in sleep because he had with him during sleep, as it were, an understanding mother. Just as a small child makes himself secure by taking a Teddy Bear to bed with him, so he is made safe in sleep by his knowledge that his mother is understanding of his impulses. He will then allow some of these impulses to get near consciousness as in a dream because his mother is allowing of them. Conversely, children whose mothers were not understanding could be afraid to dream in sleep. Since the mother did not allow these impulses in waking life, the mother is not "with" the child when he attempts to discharge these impulses through dreams.

Another clue consisted of findings very similar to those we had noted earlier in the interaction of the child's lively impulse and maternal matrix. Just as we found that sexual curiosity in a matrix milieu of maternal sexual maturation (positive feelings for her father) was highly related to good adjustment, so we found that sexual curiosity when associated with occasional sleep disturbances was also significantly related to good adjustment. Contrarywise, just as we found inability to work up to mental capacity in children having sexual curiosity whose mothers disliked their own fathers, similar inability was found in those children having sexual curiosity without sleep disturbances. In other words, it seemed to us possible that, without a sleep disturbance, i.e., without a sleep-dream attempt to discharge and integrate sexual excitation, the sexual curiosity impulse floats around loosely, distracting the child from persistent, goal-directed activity. Thus we were led strongly to the hypothesis that the sleep state represents an internal matrix which is supportive enough to permit the child to face the anxiety necessary for him to master and integrate occasional overdoses of excitatory stimuli.

11. TYPICAL ANXIETY DREAMS.

About 95 per cent of the actual anxiety dreams reported by the children when they were asked to tell the nature of their scary dreams fell into three categories. (1) A dream of falling from some height ("I fell off a mountain.") was designated the falling dream. (2) A dream of being in danger from some external object from which the dreamer had difficulty in escaping ("A lion was chasing me and had me cornered.") was designated the attacked dream. (3) The dream of some person other than the dreamer, but to whom the dreamer felt close, being in some danger, dying, hurt, or dead was ("My little brother was run over.") designated the object-in-danger dream.

After the children had spontaneously reported one or more of these three types of anxiety dreams, they were questioned directly about the occurrence of any type of dream they had failed to mention spontaneously. Thus, if a child had spontaneously reported only a dream of the attacked type, he was asked directly if he had ever had a dream in which he was falling, or a dream in which someone close to him was in danger or had died. Finally, the children were asked which of all the dreams they had reported spontaneously or admitted on questioning was the most unpleasant. Results of such questioning revealed that the children differed as to the type of dream they reported spontaneously or on questioning, and as to the type of dream they considered most unpleasant. The same type of questioning had revealed similar individual variations in the parents of these children, in children and parents seeking help at the Institute for Juvenile Research, and in military inductees and military psychiatric patients whom the writer had examined some years earlier. Because of the wide-spread prevalence and distribution of these anxiety-dream types, both in healthy and in unhealthy population samples, it was thought that they should be reckoned with in trying to understand general personality growth. Because they were so common, it was thought that they did not reflect any specific psychopathology, but rather a universal type of experience. In the following discussion, we shall attempt to indicate the lines of thought that suggest some universal characteristic inherent in these dream types.

First, we might state that the particular type of dream most frequently reported spontaneously by the children and even more frequently designated as most unpleasant was the attacked dream. This trend was so marked that it was not possible to compare the children as to whether they did or did not have this type of dream. What the children did differ on was the spontaneous reporting of the falling dream and the object-in-danger dream. In comparing the children on this basis, it was found that these two types of dreams were much more often spontaneously reported by children showing lively, erotic theme impulses in their behavior. Conversely, practically the only dream spontaneously reported by children with a quiescent and inhibited impulse life, was the attacked dream.

Our impression from this was that the falling dream and the object-in-danger dream were indicators that the child was encountering some situation of conflict or overstimulation and was trying to discharge and master these tensions through dreaming. Furthermore, it was thought that the children not experiencing these dreams were either unusually protected or insulated from the external stimuli, or were preoccupied with mastering whatever situation the attacked dream represented. As to what psychic situation each of the three types of anxiety dream might signify, our evidence is rather spotty and inconclusive. However, because it is believed that the universality of these dream types must have some basic significance, for the sake of completeness we shall offer our evidence and hypotheses.

Let us first take up the object-in-danger dream. Evidence from several sources, our study children, their mothers, clinic children and mothers, and adult psychiatric patients, indicates that this dream may be an indicator of an attempt to integrate the conflict posed by a hostile, aggressive impulse toward a person for whom the dreamer has also positive affectionate feelings. This is confirmatory of Freud's thinking about the dream which, incidentally, he used to derive his theory of the oedipal complex. A personality trait frequently seen in combination with the reporting of this dream type is that of altruism, concern for the rights and feelings of other people. Our impression, then, is that this dream represents an attempt at socialization, an effort to balance one's egoistic needs with the other person's' egoistic needs. Sometimes this attempt leads to a harmonious vital interaction with others, but, if carried too far, it can lead to a disabling over-concern for the needs of others.

One indicator in our study children supporting this explanation is that children who manifested only sibling rivalry (not sexual curiosity) did not report this dream spontaneously. Our feeling is that the absence of the spontaneous report may signify that the sibling rivalry is not being worked through and mastered intrapsychically, but is remaining primitive and in open behavior. Another indicator was in our study mothers to the effect that this type of dream was much more frequently reported and designated as most unpleasant by the study mothers than it was by the clinic mothers. This trend, we feel, reflected a greater interest in the needs of their children on the part of the study mothers. Furthermore, the children of study mothers who had this dream, much more frequently had favorable puberty reports than did children of study mothers who did not have the dream. We were thus led further to the impression that mother's socialization, acting as an influence and pattern for the child, may derive from her working through her own rivalry via this type of dream.

The falling dream represents a greater puzzle. Several lines of evidence lead at most to an informed guess. We will guess that it represents erotic impulse in discontinuity with a supporting matrix. That erotic excitement is represented is not only indicated from the investigations of Freud and later analytic writers (Freud connected it with the exhilaration that small children exhibit when thrown up into the air, and also with the moral downfall following a sexual transgression) but also from certain of our findings. For example, it is most often reported spontaneously (33 per cent) in children whose mothers liked their own fathers and have orgasms, less frequently (21 per cent) by those whose mothers either liked their fathers or had orgasms, and not at all by children whose mothers disliked their fathers and did not have orgasms. We gathered from this that a certain degree of eroticism must be in the maternal atmosphere in order to stimulate this dream. Also, that there is lively impulses associated with this dream is indicated by the fact that it was not reported spontaneously by children of traditional mothers, nor by children who were no problem to their mothers, but were inhibited outside the family.

That discontinuity with a supportive matrix is represented by the falling dream is more difficult to demonstrate. The first hint in this direction is that in the group with much erotic stimulation from the mothers (mother likes her father and has orgasms), the falling dream is most often spontaneously reported by those children whose mothers show evidences of matrix discontinuity themselves. These mothers, more frequently than the others, had lost their own mothers before the age of twelve, and none of them were traditional and emulating their living or dead mothers. It is possible that the dislocation and discontinuity of these mothers from their own mothers has something to do with the subtle discontinuity of these mothers from their own children.

Supportive of this concept of discontinuity and dislocation are the writer's findings in a large number of military inductees, to the effect that the falling dream was reported much more often as the most unpleasant dream, by the selectees whose homes had been broken before the age of six than by those whose homes had been broken after the age of six. Even after the age of six, there is a hint of emotional discontinuity with the fathers inasmuch as the falling dream was reported much more frequently by men who had lost their fathers by divorce or separation than by men who had lost them by death. In both these findings a suggestion appears that before the strands of the weblike matrix between child and parents have had a fair chance to grow strong, before the knowable image of the parent has become internalized in the child, there has been a disruption, a discontinuity of the parent-child relationship. The anxiety stimulated by the potential discontinuity is possibly reflected in the falling dream.

We are now left with the attacked dream. Since it was reported so frequently, we shall have to deduce its significance by studying those groups in which it was the only anxiety dream spontaneously reported. The characteristic of these groups is that the lively, erotic theme impulses are quite dampened, the children seem outwardly quiescent or static. In such groups as children of non-understanding traditional mothers and children of non-understanding mothers who see only themselves in their children, the attacked dream is practically the only anxiety dream spontaneously reported. All this suggests that the child is confronted with the problem of a mother who chronically and heavily intrudes her ideas and wishes upon the child, disregarding his own current needs and capacities. Rather than not enough mother, or too much discontinuity, as we speculated regarding the falling dreams, here it is too much mother, too much continuity, and not enough lively individuation.

12. PERMANENCE AND CHANGE.

More direct evidence of this relationship comes from viewing certain personalities in action. In the parents of our study there were several instances of one parent tending toward inhibition and having the attacked dream predominantly, and the other parent tending toward change and impulsivity and having the falling dream predominantly unpleasant. One such instance was that of a mother who was reserved, but eager to cooperate in the psychiatric interview. She had a somewhat sober, conservative attitude toward life. She said she was alternately intrigued and exasperated by the behavior of her husband who was on the go all the time and could not be prevented from rearranging the furniture in the house at least once a month. The father (also interviewed) appeared quite loquatious and animated. As for the predominant anxiety dreams reported, the mother mentioned the attacked dream and the father mentioned the falling dream.

Another type of personality reaction associated with change and the falling dream pertains to fluctuation in identity roles. Some examples of this were seen in private psychiatric practice. The most striking incident was that of a twenty-five-year-old American student who appeared to be very adept in social interaction with persons of different national origins. He was living at a place that had a number of students from various foreign countries and very quickly he picked up and learned a number of the foreign languages. At one group function he was selected as the most typical German; at another function, as the most typical Frenchman. It seemed that his frequent changes of roles were quite similar, and were probably on the same basis as the man just described who rearranged the furniture at least once a month.

A twenty-eight-year-old married woman illustrates very well the eroticism, the susceptibility to discontinuity, and the personal identity confusion connected with the falling dream. Her early childhood was marked with considerable instability, her mother being an alcoholic and promiscuous. In adolescence the thin lid on her crude impulses was lifted and for two years she went through a period of excitement and confusion, including much sexual misbehavior. This excitement came to an end through a conventional marriage to an overly motherly, individuality constricting man. During the marriage she had cycles of depression and elation that prompted her to seek psychiatric help. In the opening interview of her therapy, she told how she never knew what she really thought because an opinion she had one day would be the complete opposite of the opinion she had held the day before. She also spoke of frequent dreams of being suspended in the air and then falling rapidly. Although she began to achieve some integration in the course of therapy, during one period of stress she got lost in downtown Chicago where she had lived for years, forgot her name, and thought she lived in a different section of town.

An example of the turbulence connected with change dynamisms might be seen in the case of an American writer at the turn of the century, John Jay Chapman. Although this example is not related to the falling dreams, since we have no information about Chapman's dreams, yet it does illustrate how emotion and change is related to emotional tempestuousness. A biography of him states that when enraged by a young man who was paying attention to a young lady who was his (Chapman's) sweetheart, Chapman beat the man over the head with a stick. A few remorseful hours later when he returned to his room, he put his hand deep into the fire and held it there for a few minutes. He then went to hospital by foot and the next morning awoke without the hand, but very calm in spirit. Similar intemperatenesses marked his life. He was tempestuously interested in politics and in later life became violently anti-Catholic and anti-semitic. From an essay entitled, "Fatigue and Unrest," the following phrases illustrate the connection between change and emotion. "Their works [writers of humanistic, artistic, or religious matters] reflect the emotional life that was in the air they breathe. Their very vehicles are restful because action, as of waves, is ended. They cradle us with motion; and life is motion, the only rest we can know is to be absorbed and soothed by motion." [Later] "Contraction kills feeling and feeling is a gift that must be spontaneous. Emotion is a fluid which connects all the provinces of our being."

Examples of the permanence-inhibition-attacked dream triad are not so dramatic or easy to cite. The sober, conservative characteristics are readily seen but they present no colorful, vivid incidents. Perhaps one illustration of their quiescence and lack of susceptibility to change is the behavior in psychoanalytic treatment. The "falling" person is active in the treatment room alternately sitting up, lying down, walking around, or turning over on his stomach, whereas the "attacked" person stays flat on his back for months or years, with no strong impulse to sit up. These remarks should not be taken to illustrate that one type is more successful in psychoanalytic therapy than the other. Rather, they illustrate the different attitudes toward change and permanence.

Perhaps an illustration of the permanence personality may be contained in the works of Martin Buber, the theologist. He opens his book, *Between Man and Man,* with a description of a dream he had which influenced his philosophical and theological thinking. In this dream, a piece of flesh is bitten out of his arm by a wild animal. This variety of the attacked dream may have some connection with his writings, a prominent aspect of which is an urging of man to overcome his isolation and inhibition in communicating unreservedly with his fellowmen and God. One receives the impression from Buber that he has struggled to overcome the inhibiting fear of the intrusive, destructive attack coming from without. Certainly Buber's life and his advocacy of closer union is in sharp contrast to Chapman's life and his advocacy of motion.

TABLES

PREFACE

Although the titles and column headings of the tables are rather self-explanatory, a few orientating remarks may be helpful. The data-items are drawn from various interviews and tests: the psychiatric interview with child and mother, the social service interview with mother, the school reports at eight and nine, and at twelve and thirteen, the Rorschach Test, and the Despert Fables Test. An explanation of these items can be derived from the column heading and/or from that part of the text proper pertinent to the table.

Some explanation may be necessary regarding the Rorschach Test and the Despert Fables. In most of the Rorschach items, the scoring is of a comparative nature. For example, when the children of rebellious mothers score high in intellectual originality, this high score is in comparison to the rest of the group of 54 children—not in comparison to some already established norms. The children were divided into three equal groups so that scoring high in intellectual originality means being in the upper third of the entire group. (A few of the children could not be scored in this comparative manner and this accounts for apparent discrepancies beteween the number of cases and the score-breakdown in some of the tables.)

In the Despert Fables Test (see Appendix D, *1 Methods of Study*), Fables 5, 12, and 16 were used to gauge hostility to the mother. Presence of hostility was assumed if, in Fable 5, the responses were along the lines of "The mother got hurt the most"; in Fable 12 "The hunter kills the mother deer"; in Fable 16 "The teacher tells the boy that his mother was hurt." Fables 2 and 6 were used to gauge conformity *vs.* pleasure seeking on the child's part. Some children conform to the mother's wishes to eat grass in both fables, some conformed on one but not on the other, or others had non-conforming, pleasure seeking responses to both.

TABLE I.—Identifying Data on 54 Subjects.

A) Sex:
   Boys—28
   Girls—26

B) Age:
   8 years—30
   9 years—24

C) Siblings:
   1 sibling—30
   2 siblings—19
   3 siblings—5

D) Ordinal position:
   Oldest—30
   Middle—9
   Youngest—15

E) Socio-economic dwelling:
   Lower class homes—9
   Middle class homes—18
   Upper-middle class apartments—18
   Upper-middle class homes—9

TABLE II.—Adjustment Ratings*.

RATING	AREA			
	A. Psychiatric Adjustment	B. School Adjustment	C. Home Adjustment	D. Home Adjustment
Very Well	18	25	17	
Well	17	15	22	31
Fair	19	14	15	23
No. of cases:	**54**	**54**	**54**	**54**

* "C" represents the three point method of rating the home adjustment as described in Appendix D.1. In order to set up the groups described in Chapter XIV, "The Types of Adjustment," it seemed more feasible to have a two-point rating as in "D." "Well adjusted" refers to those children having no present problem or, if having one, were better adjusted than the siblings. "Fair" refers to all of the remaining children.

TABLE III.—Comparison of Adjustment Ratings.

	Equal	1 Step Discrepancy	2 Step Discrepancy	Total
A) Psychiatric to school	24	17	13	54
B) Psychiatric to mother	11	29	14	54
C) School to mother	12	29	13	54

TABLE IV.—Combined Social Adjustment Ratings*.

Degree of Adjustment	No.
Very well	25
Well	11
Fair	18
Total	**54**

* The combined social adjustment represents the combined rating of school personnel and psychiatrist. Children who were evaluated as very well adjusted in one of the two ratings and at least well adjusted in the other rating were designated as "very well adjusted" in the combined social scale. At the other extreme and designated "fairly well adjusted" were those children who were evaluated as "fairly well adjusted" in one of the two ratings, and no better than "well adjusted" in the other rating.

TABLE V.—Continuities in Adjustment from Ages 8 and 9 to 12 and 13.

Progression	No.
From very well to very well	11
From well or fair to very well	12
From very well to well or fair	13
From well or fair to well or fair	6
Total no. of cases:	**42**

TABLE VI.—Phenomena Crucial to Social Adjustment.

	Total No. Displaying Phenomena	Combined Social Adj., Very Good	Combined Social Adj., Good	Combined Social Adj., Fair
No difficulty in weaning	41	17	8	16
No sibling rivalry	28	10	6	12
Eats grass	23	7	4	12
Dog hurts self	25	9	5	11
Sadness, non social	18	6	4	8
Hostile play	10	3	2	5
No. of cases		**25**	**11**	**18**

TABLE VII.—Relation of Sex Curiosity and Sibling Rivalry to Puberty Adjustment.

SEX CURIOSITY AND SIBLING RIVALRY	PUBERTY SCHOOL REPORT		
	Very Good	Good or Fair	Total
Both present	9	3	12
Both absent	3	7	10
Sex curiosity only present	8	6	14
Sib. rivalry only present	3	3	6

TABLE VIII.—Relation of Maternal Qualities to Child's Adjustment.

COMBINED SOCIAL
ADJUSTMENT   MATERNAL QUALITIES

	Depend-able, Under-standing	Depend-able, Not Under-standing	Undepend-able, Under-standing	Undepend-able, Not Under-standing	No.
Very good	10	3	6	6	25
Good	2	2	2	5	11
Fair	2	3	4	9	18
No. of cases	14	8	12	20	54

TABLE IX.—Effect of Emphasis on Maternal Dependability or Understanding on the Child.

	Mother Is Dependable Not Understanding	Mother Is Understanding and Not Dependable
Hurt feelings causes anger toward parents	0	6
Restriction causes anger toward parents	5	3
Denies anger toward parents	4	3
Child would prefer to be older	6	4
Child would prefer to be younger	2	3
Child would prefer to be either older or younger	1	3
Child prefers his own age	0	2
Child has oral problems	3	8
Child has sleep disturbances	3	9
No. of cases	9	12

TABLE X.—Continuities of Children's Problems from Preschool to Present.

CURRENT SITUATION   PRESCHOOL SITUATION

	Without Problem	With Problem
With problem	17	19
Without problem	8	10
Total No. of cases: 54		

TABLE XI.—Effect of Types of Mothering on First-borns.

CHILD'S ORDINAL POSITION	COMBINED SOCIAL ADJUSTMENT			
First	Very Good	Good	Fair	No.
With mother:				
Dependable and Understanding—	5	1	1	7
Dependable or Understanding—	6	1	5	12
Neither—	4	1	7	12
Not First				
With mother:				
Dependable and Understanding—	4	2	1	7
Dependable or Understanding—	3	3	2	8
Neither—	3	2	2	7

TABLE XII.—Relation of Mother's Ordinal Position to Her Mothering Qualities.

MATERNAL QUALITIES	MOTHER'S ORDINAL POSITION				
	First	Middle	Youngest	Only	Total
Dependable and Understanding	1	7	6	0	14
Dependable or Understanding	4	8	7	1	20
Neither	8	7	3	2	20
No. of cases	13	22	16	3	54

TABLE XIII.—Relation of Mother's Adequacy to Child's Adjustment.

DESIGNATION OF MOTHER	COMBINED SOCIAL				PUBERTY SCHOOL REPORTS		
	Very Good	Good	Fair	Total No.	Good	Fair	Total No.
Adequate							
Traditional and Understanding—	3	2	1	6	4	1	5
Rebellious and Understanding—	8	0	1	9	4	4	8
Dependent and Dependable—	6	2	0	8	4	3	7
Total	17	4	2	23	12	8	20
Inadequate							
Traditional and Not Understanding—	2	1	5	8	3	3	6
Rebellious and Not Understanding—	3	1	4	8	1	3	4
Dependent and Not Understanding—	1	2	3	6	3	1	4
Total	6	4	12	22	7	7	14

TABLE XIV.—Relation of Mother's Aspirations to Her Mothering Qualities.

MATERNAL QUALITIES	MATERNAL ASPIRATION THEME			
	Traditional	Rebellious	Dependent	Uncertain
Dependable	7	4	8	3
Undependable	7	13	6	6
Understanding	6	9	5	6
Not understanding	8	8	9	3
No. of cases	14	17	14	9

TABLE XV.—Relation of Mother's Aspirations to Child's Adjustment.

CHILD'S ADJUSTMENT	MOTHER'S ASPIRATION THEME		
	Traditional	Rebellious	Dependent
Combined Social Adjustment:			
Very good	4	11	7
Good	4	1	4
Fair	6	5	3
No. of cases	14	17	14
Puberty School Adjustment Reports:			
Very good	7	5	8
Good or fair	4	7	4
No. of reports	11	12	12

TABLE XVI.—Characteristic Effects of Traditional Mothers on Their Children.

	MOTHER'S ASPIRATION		
	Traditional	Rebellious	Dependent
Psychiatric interview adjustment:			
Very good	3	6	6
Good	5	7	4
Fair	6	4	4
Mystery stories:			
Likes	10	3	6
Equivocal	3	2	3
Dislikes	1	12	5
Rorschach neurotic shock indicators:			
0-1	8	3	4
2	5	8	6
3+	1	6	4

TABLE XVI. (Continued)

	MOTHER'S ASPIRATION		
	Traditional	Rebellious	Dependent
Report of falling dream:	0	5	4
Hostility to Mother on Despert fables:			
None	8	5	5
Some	6	12	9
Grass-milk response on Despert fables:			
G/G	7	7	3
G/M or M/G	4	5	8
M/M	3	5	3
No. of cases	14	17	14

TABLE XVII.—Characteristic Effects of Adequate Traditional Mothers on Their Children.

CHARACTERISTICS	ACHIEVEMENT ASPIRATION	
	Adequate/Traditional	All Others
Rorschach: M>C	5	14
C>M	1	32
Mother asks questions regarding child	0	27
No. of cases	6	48
Puberty School Adjustment: Very good	4	19
Good or fair	1	18
No. of puberty records	5	37

TABLE XVIII.—Characteristic Effects of Inadequate Traditional Mothers on Their Children.

	Achievement Aspiration, Inadequate, Traditional	All Others
Anti-pleasure clusters*	5	5
Confidante: Mother	3	20
Mother and Father	0	12
Father	0	6
a sibling	1	1
self	4	7
DESPERT. Hostility to mother: none	5	16
some	3	30
Rorschach reality test result: low	3	13
middle	4	15
high	1	16
No. of cases	8	46

* Anti-pleasures consist of two or more responses indicative of avoidance of pleasure. Examples of such responses are "I would not spend the thousand dollars, I would save it." "I can't think of what to do with three wishes." "I can't remember any pleasant dreams."

TABLE XIX.—Characteristic Effects of Rebellious Mothers on Their Children.

CHARACTERISTIC EFFECTS		ASPIRATION THEME	
	Rebellious	Dependent	Traditional
Sex curiosity: none	2	6	6
at pre-school	1	0	2
at present	8	6	4
pre-school and now	6	2	2
Oedipal phenomena: none	6	9	10
prefers opposite sex parent	3	3	2
fears same sex parent	3	0	0
prefers and fears same sex parent	5	2	2
No sphincter disturbance	4	7	8
Delay in sphincter action	5	0	2
Break down in sphincter action	6	3	2
Delay and break down in sphincter action	2	4	2
Intellectual originality on Rorschach: low	2	6	6
medium	7	4	4
high	6	4	3
Emotional stability on Rorschach: low	7	2	6
medium	7	4	2
high	1	8	5
DESPERT. Host to mother: none	5	5	8
some	12	9	6
Mother has depressions	9	5	2
No. of cases:	**17**	**14**	**14**

TABLE XX.—Characteristic Effects of Adequate Rebellious Mothers on Their Children.

CHARACTERISTIC EFFECTS	ACHIEVEMENT ASPIRATION	
	Adequate, Rebellious	All Others
Leader at School	4	4
Leader or follower at School	4	24
Follower at School	1	17
Open jealousy at sibling's birth	4	8
Indirect jealousy at sibling's birth	1	10
No jealousy at sibling's birth	0	17
Uncertain	4	10
Excess sibling rivalry	4	6
Moderate sibling rivalry	2	13
No sibling rivalry	3	26

TABLE XX. (Continued)

CHARACTERISTIC EFFECTS	ACHIEVEMENT ASPIRATION	
	Adequate, Rebellious	All Others
School mood: carefree	0	7
carefree and serious	8	27
serious	1	11
Rorschach reality test result: low	5	11
medium	3	15
high	1	16
Rorschach accepting group codes test result: low	5	11
medium	3	17
high	1	14
No. of cases	**9**	**45**

TABLE XXI.—Characteristic Effects of Inadequate Rebellious Mothers on Their Children.

	ACHIEVEMENT ASPIRATION	
	Inadequate Rebellious	All Others
Misbehavior of child: active opposition	1	16
passive opposition	4	12
Rorschach—F+: Below 65%	1	13
65%-79%	3	17
80% & above	4	16
No. of cases	**8**	**46**

TABLE XXII.—Characteristic Effects of Dependent Mothers on Their Children.

CHARACTERISTIC EFFECTS	ASPIRATION THEME		
	Dependent	Rebellious	Traditional
Has pleasant wish dreams	13	12	7
Does not have pleasant wish dreams	1	5	7
Grass-milk on Despert: G/G	3	7	8
G/M and M/G	8	5	4
M/M	3	5	2
Rorschach frustration tolerance: low	6	2	2
medium	5	7	6
high	3	6	5
Respond to Rorschach color test	14	13	10
Do not respond to Rorschach color test	0	4	4
No. of cases	**14**	**17**	**14**

TABLE XXIII.—Characteristic Effects of Adequate Dependent Mothers on Their Children.

CHARACTERISTIC EFFECTS	ACHIEVEMENT ASPIRATION	
	Adequate, Dependent	All Others
Affect in Psychiatric interview: exuberant	4	7
adequate	3	14
inadequate	1	25
Sad feeling: social	7	12
non-social	1	14
Content in infancy	7	32
Fretful in infancy	1	14
Mother relates: very well	4	15
well	4	17
fairly	0	14
Mother has question re. child	7	20
No. of cases	**8**	**46**

TABLE XXIV.—Characteristic Effects of Inadequate Dependent Mothers on Their Children.

CHARACTERISTIC EFFECTS	ACHIEVEMENT ASPIRATION	
	Inadequate, Dependent	All Others
DESPERT. Fly to mother's tree	0	22
RORSCHACH. Frustration tolerance: low	4	9
medium	1	22
high	1	14
RORSCHACH. Intellectual vigor: low	4	12
medium	1	16
high	1	17
Content in infancy	2	37
Fretful in infancy	4	11
Mother worries excessively	4	6
No. of cases	**6**	**48**

TABLE XXV.—Relationship Between Mother's Feelings Toward Her Father and the Adjustment of the Child.

	MOTHER-GRANDFATHER RELATIONSHIP	
	Positive	Negative
Combined Social Adjustment: very good	18	7
good	5	6
fair	5	13
No. of cases	**28**	**26**
Puberty School Adjustment: very good	16	7
good or fair	5	13
No. of puberty reports	**21**	**20**

TABLE XXVI.—Relation of Mother's Adequacy and Feelings Toward Her Father to the Child's Adjustment.

	POSITIVE MO.— GRF. REL.		NOT POSITIVE MO.— GRF. REL.	
	Adeq.	Inadeq.	Adeq.	Inadeq.
Combined social adjustment:				
very good	9	5	6	1
good	3	2	2	3
fair	0	3	3	8
No. of cases	12	10	11	12
Puberty adjustment:				
very good	8	6	4	3
good or fair	2	1	6	6
No. or puberty reports	10	7	10	9

TABLE XXVII.—Effects of Child's Sex Curiosity at Ages 8 and 9 and Mother's Feelings Toward Her Father.

	Sex Curiosity, Present; Mother— Grf. Rel., Positive	Sex Curiosity, Absent; Mother— Grf. Rel., Positive	Sex Curiosity, Present; Mother— Grf. Rel., Not Positive	Sex Curiosity, Absent; Mother— Grf. Rel., Not Positive
Psychiatric adj., very good	7	4	3	3
good	7	3	5	3
fair	4	3	6	6
School adj., very good	13	5	2	5
good	3	4	6	2
fair	2	1	6	5
Total School Problems	5	5	12	7
Combined social adj., very good	11	6	4	4
good	4	2	3	2
fair	3	2	7	6
No. of cases	18	10	14	12
Puberty adj., very good	12	4	5	2
good or fair	2	3	6	7
No. of reports	14	7	11	9

TABLE XXVIII.—Relation of Mother's Sexuality to Child's Adjustment.

	MOTHER HAS ORGASMS		MOTHER DOES NOT HAVE ORGASMS	
	Positive Mo.— Grf. Rel.	Not Positive Mo.— Grf. Rel.	Positive Mo.— Grf. Rel.	Not Positive Mo.— Grf. Rel.
Combined Social Adjustment:				
very good	14	4	4	4
good	3	1	2	4
fair	2	9	3	4
Total School problem:	4	11	5	8
No. of cases	**19**	**14**	**9**	**12**
Puberty Adjustment:				
very good	11	2	5	5
good or fair	5	7	0	6
No. of reports	**16**	**9**	**5**	**11**

TABLE XXIX.—Interrelationship of Mother's Sexuality and Child's Sexual Curiosity.

Mo.—Grf. rel.:	Pos.	Pos.	Pos.	Pos.	Not Pos.	Not Pos.	Not Pos.	Not Pos.
Mo. achieves orgasm:	Yes	Yes	No	No	Yes	Yes	No	No
Child's sex curiosity:	Pres.	Abs.	Pres.	Abs.	Pres.	Abs.	Pres.	Abs.
Psychiatric adj.:								
very good	5	3	2	1	2	1	1	2
good	3	3	4	0	2	0	3	3
fair	3	2	1	1	3	6	3	0
School adj.:								
very good	10	4	3	1	1	2	1	3
good	1	4	2	0	2	1	4	1
fair	0	0	2	1	4	4	2	1
Total School Problems	1	4	4	1	6	5	6	2
Combined Social Adj.:								
very good	8	5	3	1	3	1	1	3
good	2	2	2	0	0	1	3	1
fair	1	1	2	1	4	5	3	1
No. of cases:	**11**	**8**	**7**	**2**	**7**	**7**	**7**	**5**
Puberty adj.:								
very good	8	3	4	1	1	1	4	1
good or fair	2	3	0	0	3	4	3	3
No. of puberty reports:	**10**	**6**	**4**	**1**	**4**	**5**	**7**	**4**

TABLE XXX.—Effects of Mother's Feelings Toward Her Father.

EFFECTS ON MOTHER	MOTHER-GRANDFATHER RELATIONSHIP	
	Positive	Not Positive
Positive feelings toward husband	20	12
Not positive feelings toward husband	8	14
Mother experiences orgasms	19	14
Mother does not experience orgasms	9	12
Child confides mainly in father	6	0
No. of cases	**28**	**26**

TABLE XXXI.—Characteristics of One-to-One Relators and Group Relators.

	Adj. Psych., Very Well / Adj. School, Fair	Adj. Psych., Fair / Adj. School, Very Well
Parents agree on discipline	2	6
Parents disagree on discipline	4	1
Mother releases anger	5	2
Mother holds back anger	1	5
Mother is not orderly	4	2
Mother is moderately orderly	2	3
Mother is excessively orderly	0	2
No sibling rivalry	1	4
Moderate sibling rivalry	1	3
Excess sibling rivalry	4	0
No. of cases	**6**	**7**

TABLE XXXII.—Effect of Grandparents' Compatibility on Mother's Feelings to Her Father.

GRM.-GRF. REL.	Mo.-Grf. Positive No.	Mo.-Grf. Not Positive No.	No.
Compatible	17	11	28
Not compatible	6	12	18

TABLE XXXIII.—Relation Between Mother's Feelings Toward Her Father and Child's Fantasy About His Father According to Despert Fable.

PERSON SENT AWAY	MOTHER-GRF. RELATIONSHIP AND MOTHER-FATHER RELATIONSHIP			
	Both Positive	Both Negative	GF Positive	F Positive
Father	9	5	4	9
Mother and Father	2	1	1	0
Mother	2	3	1	0
Child	6	5	3	3
Total Fathers	11	6	5	9
Total Mothers	4	4	2	0
No. of cases	19	14	9	12

TABLE XXXIV.—Relation of Gun-playing in Daughter to Mother's Feelings Toward Men.

MOTHER-FATHER RELATIONSHIP	PLAYS WITH GUNS		
	Yes	No	Total
Positive			
Mo.-grf. rel. positive	1	9	10
Mo.-grf. rel. not positive	3	2	5
Not Positive			
Mo.-grf. rel. positive	0	6	6
Mo.-grf. rel. not positive	1	4	5

TABLE XXXV.—Relation of Mother's Egocentricity to Complaints of Suffering.

	Mother Sees Self In Child	Mother Does Not See Self in Child
Nausea in pregnancy: no	5	13
medium	9	12
excess	9	6
Mother injured in childbirth	12	9
Present health: good	13	23
fair	6	6
neutral	4	2
No areas of complaint	1	9
One area of complaint	8	12
Two or three areas of complaint	14	10
No. of cases	23	31

TABLE XXXVI.—Four Types of Adjustment.

	DESIGNATION			
	Generally Adjusted	Socially Adjusted	Family Adjusted	Generally Unadjusted
Combined Social Adjustment	Very well	Very well	Fair	Fair
Adjustment to Family	Well	Fair	Well	Fair
No. of cases	12	13	9	9

TABLE XXXVII.—Characteristics of the Generally Adjusted Children and Mothers.

CHARACTERISTICS	Generally Adjusted Group	Other Three Groups
Mother has orgasms	9	18
Mother does not have orgasms	3	13
Parents agree on discipline	11	21
Parents disagree on discipline	1	10
Mother-grandfather relationship: positive	8	14
not positive	4	17
Mother-grandmother relationship: positive	1	11
not positive	11	20
Maternal qualities: dependable	8	8
undependable	4	23
understanding	7	15
not understanding	5	16
Mother sees self in child	3	16
Mother does not see self in child	9	15
Mother relates: very well	6	10
well	5	11
fairly well	1	10
Aspiration adequacy: yes	8	10
no	3	17
Weaning difficulties	4	6
Open jealousy at birth	5	4
Indirect jealousy at birth	3	6
No jealousy at birth	2	12
Unsure of jealousy at birth	2	9
Misbehavior: active opposition	6	5
passive	2	13
Leads at school	5	3
Follows at school	3	12
Leads and follows at school	4	16
School mood: carefree	0	5
carefree and serious	11	16
serious	1	10

TABLE XXXVII. (Continued)

CHARACTERISTICS	Generally Adjusted Group	Other Three Groups
Mother is confidante	6	7
Mother and father are confidantes	3	10
Father is confidante	2	3
Sibling is confidante	1	1
Child confides in himself	0	10
Sad feelings are expressed: socially	8	8
non-socially	2	10
Worry feelings are expressed: socially	4	6
non-socially	2	8
No. of cases:	**12**	**31**

TABLE XXXVIII.—Characteristics of Socially Adjusted Children and Their Mothers.

CHARACTERISTICS	Socially Adjusted Group	Other Three Groups
Mother's feelings to her parents: Excessive	10	13
Moderate	3	17
Maternal qualities: Dependable	3	13
Undependable	10	17
Understanding	9	13
Not understanding	4	17
Mother sees self in child	7	12
Mother does not see self in child	6	18
Mother sees self in child and is understanding	5	5
Mother is confidante to child	2	11
Mother and Father are confidantes to child	4	8
Father is confidante to child	3	3
Sibling is confidante	0	2
Child confides in himself only	4	6
Denies anger to mother and father	1	12
No. of cases	**13**	**30**

TABLE XXXIX.—Characteristics of the Family Adjusted Children and Mothers.

CHARACTERISTICS	Family Adjusted Group	Other Three Groups
Mother-grandmother relationship: Positive	5	7
Not positive	4	27
Mother-grandfather relationship: Positive	3	19
Not positive	6	15
Aspirations: Traditional	4	5
Rebellious	1	15
Dependent	2	8
Maternal qualities: Dependable	5	11
Undependable	4	23
Understanding	3	19
Not understanding	6	15
Feelings toward grandmother and grandfather: Excessive	2	21
Moderate	7	13
Mother sees self in child	5	14
Mother does not see self in child	4	20
Feeding difficulties: None	6	12
Eating	2	12
Weaning	1	5
Both	0	5
Sphincter difficulties: None	3	16
Completing	0	7
Breakdown	5	8
Both	1	3
Jealousy at sibling's birth: Open	1	8
Indirect	1	8
None	5	9
Uncertain	2	9
Sibling rivalry: Excessive	1	8
Moderate	2	13
None	6	13
Child denies anger to parents	5	8
School mood: Carefree	2	3
Serious	4	7
Both	3	24
Falling dream spontaneously reported	0	10
No. of cases	**9**	**34**

TABLE XL.—Characteristics of the Generally Unadjusted Children and Mothers.

CHARACTERISTICS	Generally Unadjusted Group	Other Three Groups
Mother-grandmother relationship: Positive	1	11
Not positive	8	23
Mother-grandfather relationship: Positive	2	20
Not positive	7	14
Mother and father agree on discipline	4	28
Mother and father disagree on discipline	5	6
Mother sees father in child	0	18
Mother relates: very well	1	15
well	4	12
fair	4	7
Maternal qualities: dependable	1	15
undependable	8	19
understanding	3	19
not understanding	6	15
Achievement: adequate	2	16
inadequate	5	15
none	4	15
Sphincter difficulties: Completing	4	3
Breakdown	1	12
Both	0	4
Feeding-sphincter disturbance: Neither	1	6
Oral only	3	13
Sphincter only	1	8
Both	4	7
Would prefer to be older	2	18
Would prefer to be younger	3	5
Would prefer to be either older or younger	3	4
Prefers same age	1	7
Prefer younger age and experience sphincter delay	4	1
Total prefer younger age	6	9
No. of cases	**9**	**34**

TABLE XLI.—Relation of Sleep Disturbances to Adjustment.

SLEEP DISTURBANCE	COMBINED SOCIAL			Tot No.
	Very Well	Well	Fair	
Preschool and postschool	4	1	4	9
Preschool or postschool	13	3	6	22
Neither	8	7	8	23

TABLE XLII.—Relation of Change and Permanence to Dreams*.

| | CHILD'S SPONTANEOUS ANXIETY DREAMS | | |
	Tot No.	Attacked	Falling
Lively children	12	9	7
Equivocal children	32	19	4
Unlively children	10	8	0
Change mothers	15	13	8
Equivocal mothers	26	13	3
Permanence mothers	13	10	0

* "Lively" children refers to those children who showed adequate zest during the psychiatric interview and who were reported by mother as showing some sibling rivalry and sexual curiosity. "Unlively" children were those lacking zest in the psychiatric interview and reported as not showing any sibling rivalry or sexual curiosity. The equivocal children formed the mid-group of admixtures.

"Change" mothers were those who were more understanding than dependable, rebellious rather than traditional and did not see themselves in their children. "Permanence" mothers were more dependable than understanding, traditional rather than rebellious, and saw themselves in their children. The equivocal mothers formed the mid-group of admixtures.

AUTHOR INDEX

285